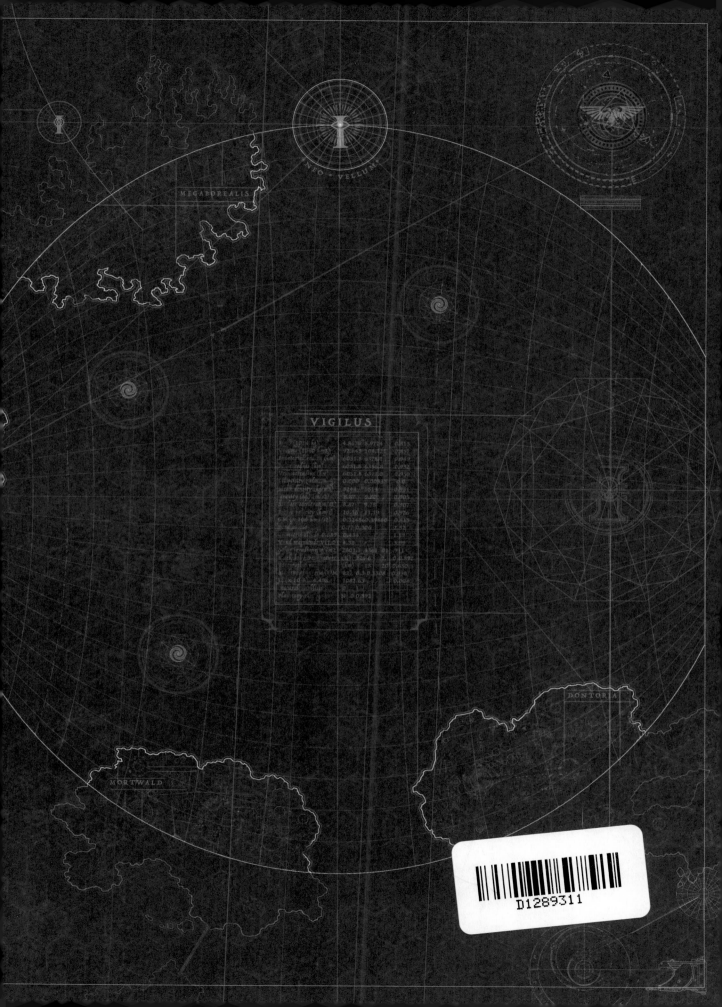

VIGILUS

MEGABOREALIS

NEO-VELLUM

DONTORIA

MORTWALD

VIGILUS DEFIANT

WAR OF BEASTS

CONTENTS

A New Kind of Battleground 4

War on All Fronts 6
At Boiling Point 8
The Great Rift Yawns Wide 11
The Speedwaaagh! 12
The Rise of the Pauper Princes 14
Hidden Agendas, Selfish Souls 16
Doom From Within 18
Defence of Megaborealis 20
The Counter-Attacks Begin.................................22
A Sickness in Dontoria 24
To Summon the Angels of Death 26
Calgar's Journey 28
The Tendrils Run Deep 30
Blood Vendetta 32
Dontoria Firewall 34
Hope Yet 36
A Charge into Legend 38
Aqua Meteoris...40
Assault on the Scrap Cities..................................42
A New Doom 44
The Rise of Chaos 46

War Zones 48
Hyperia Hivesprawl...50
Megaborealis 52
Mortwald 54
Oteck Hivesprawl 56
Kaelac's Bane 58
Scrap Cities 60
Neo-vellum 62
The Wastes 64
The Vhulian Swirl...65
Dirkden Hivesprawl...66
Dontoria Hivesprawl..67
Storvhal 68
The Omnissian Hoist 69

Forces of War 70
Forces of the Imperium 72
Forces of the Ultramarines 76
Forces of the Dark Angels 78
Forces of the White Scars 80
Forces of the Imperial Fists 82
Forces of the Crimson Fists 84
The Chapters Primaris 86
Forces of the Adeptus Mechanicus..........................90
Forces of the Astra Militarum 92
Forces of the Militarum Tempestus 93
Forces of the Adepta Sororitas...............................94
The Knights of Vigilus 96
Forces of the Orks...98
Speed Freek Races 100
Forces of Warlord Krooldakka,
Speedlord Supreme.. 102
Forces of Mad Goff Murk 104
Forces of Big Mek Zogbag 106
Stompa Mobs 108
Forces of the Genestealer Cults 110
Forces of the Asuryani 114
Forces of the Drukhari.....................................115

Campaign Rules 116
Vigilus Campaigns 118
First Phase of the War of Beasts 120
Second Phase of the War of Beasts........................ 122
Third Phase of the War of Beasts........................... 124
Campaigns in the Dark Imperium 126
Nihilus Events Table.. 127

Narrative Play Missions................. 128
Crucible of War: Convoy.......................... 130
Crucible of War: Hold Your Gains 132
Crucible of War: Storm the Lines........................... 134
Crucible of War: Extraction 136
Crucible of War: Running Battle 138
Crucible of War: Data Recovery 140
Echoes of War: The Delta Aflame........................... 142
Echoes of War: The Angels of Death Descend 144
Echoes of War: Forlorn Charge 146
Echoes of War: Behead the Viper.......................... 148
Echoes of War: Breach of Quarantine.................... 150
Echoes of War: Carnage in the Spires 152

Battlezones 154
Battlezone: Wasteland Dust Storm........................ 154
Battlezone: Tundric Blizzard............................... 155
Battlezone: Warquake 156
Battlezone: Geothermal Eruption 157
Battlezone: Spirescape...................................... 158
Battlezone: Genestealer Infestation....................... 159

War Zone Rules 160
Hyperia Hivesprawl..................... 161
Megaborealis 162
The Wastes 163
Oteck Hivesprawl 164
Mortwald 165

Faction Rules 166
Specialist Detachments................ 168
Marneus Calgar 170
Datasheet: Marneus Calgar in
Armour of Heraclus 171
Datasheet: Victrix Honour Guard.......... 171
Haarken Worldclaimer 172
Datasheet: Haarken Worldclaimer 173
Indomitus Crusaders 174
Ultramarines Victrix Guard 176
Imperial Fists Siegebreaker Cohort......... 179
Crimson Fists Liberator Strike Force.......... 180
Black Templars Sword Brethren 181
Ravenwing Attack Squadron................ 182
Space Wolves Stalker Pack....................... 183
Cybernetica Cohort........................ 184
Servitor Maniple 185
Anointed Throng 186
Deliverance Broodsurge 187
Windrider Host.............................. 188

Wraith Host.................................... 189
Emperor's Blade Assault Company 190
Emperor's Wrath Artillery Company.......... 191
Emperor's Conclave Infantry Company............ 192
Emperor's Fist Tank Company 193
Tempestus Drop Force 194
Stompa Mob 195
Kult of Speed 197
Dread Waaagh! 198
Blitz Brigade 200

PRODUCED BY GAMES WORKSHOP IN NOTTINGHAM

With thanks to the Mournival and the Infinity Circuit for their additional playtesting services

Games Workshop Ltd, Willow Rd, Lenton, Nottingham, NG7 2WS

games-workshop.com

A NEW KIND OF BATTLEGROUND

In the period that led up to the War for Vigilus, the planet was poised on the edge of destiny. Its proximity to the Eye of Terror had long put it on a war footing, but with the dawn of the Cicatrix Maledictum, Vigilus became incalculable in value to the Imperium, and a tempting target for xenos and Chaos invaders alike.

The planet Vigilus was always famed as a linchpin of the Segmentum Obscurus. When the Great Rift opened, its status escalated from important to indispensable.

So vital was Vigilus to the Imperium that when a teeming Waaagh! of Orks burst from the Great Rift, the system's defenders responded with terrific force. The Astra Militarum and Adepta Sororitas stationed there contained the Ork invasion and kept it from wrecking the densely populated hivesprawls, while several Space Marine Chapters sent reinforcements from the Stygius sector and beyond. The latter waves were led by none other than Marneus Augustus Calgar, Chapter Master of the Ultramarines, and with him came some of the finest minds in the Adeptus Astartes.

These counter-assaults pulled Vigilus back from the brink. The psychic apocalypse of the Great Rift had disabled the planet's defences and made it vulnerable, allowing the Orks to raid from the wastelands, barging through each defence perimeter to wage war in the city sprawls. In conjunction, a great uprising of Genestealer Cults was triggered, revealing an infestation that had festered upon Vigilus for hundreds of years.

As the races of the galaxy desperately tried to prosper in the horror-filled reality of the Imperium Nihilus, millions of eyes turned towards Vigilus. Were it to fall, so would the hopes of all trapped in the Dark Imperium. With the Cadian Gate broken to the west and War Zone Stygius raging to the east, Vigilus was wide open to invasion by the forces of Chaos.

IN THIS BOOK

This book is the first of a two-part series set in the Vigilus System. It contains an account of the opening stages of the War for Vigilus, then builds to a nerve-shredding climax as the xenos invasion is revealed to be a precursor of dooms to come – amongst them the schemes of the Warmaster of Chaos, Abaddon the Despoiler.

Inside you will find:
- The history of the War of Beasts on Vigilus.
- Rules for playing an epic campaign set on Vigilus, or another planet in the Imperium Nihilus.
- Battlezone and war zone rules that represent the perilous environs of this planet.
- Detachments, special rules and Stratagems for the main armed forces of this great struggle.

AT THE THRESHOLD OF DAMNATION

With the opening of the Cicatrix Maledictum and the passing of the Noctis Aeterna, Vigilus found itself in that dark region of space known as the Imperium Nihilus, upon the threshold of the Nachmund Gauntlet. As one of the two relatively stable paths between the half of the Imperium that contained Holy Terra, known as the Imperium Sanctus, and the far-flung Imperium Nihilus on the other side of the Great Rift, the Nachmund Gauntlet was of immense value to Mankind. It allowed the Imperium to continue the movement of its forces across the interstellar gulf of the Great Rift, and also to maintain a line of astropathic communication – albeit an unstable and dangerous one – with the worlds stranded in the Dark Imperium. Should the Imperium ever truly be divided it would likely fall apart entirely. Hence the importance of Vigilus; it acted as a vital beachhead that kept the Imperium Nihilus under a semblance of Holy Terra's control.

None truly knew how or why the Great Rift formed – but the fight to gain passage across it quickly became intense. Vigilus had always boasted a vast amount of manpower, and had inherited a great number of Imperial Guard regiments since the clearing of the Cadian Gate – an event the Ministorum referred to as the Pre-tempestine Exodus – but it soon became evident that the threats facing the planet would test its defenders to their limit.

The planet was traditionally ruled over by a loose confederation of elders and nobles called the Aquilarian Council, known to the Adeptus Mechanicus as the Council of Cogs. The fact that the different delegates could not even agree on a name demonstrates how divided they were; the palatial areas of Saint's Haven were riven by political wars for decades. Only the spectre of complete annihilation saw Vigilus' rulers united.

VIGILUS

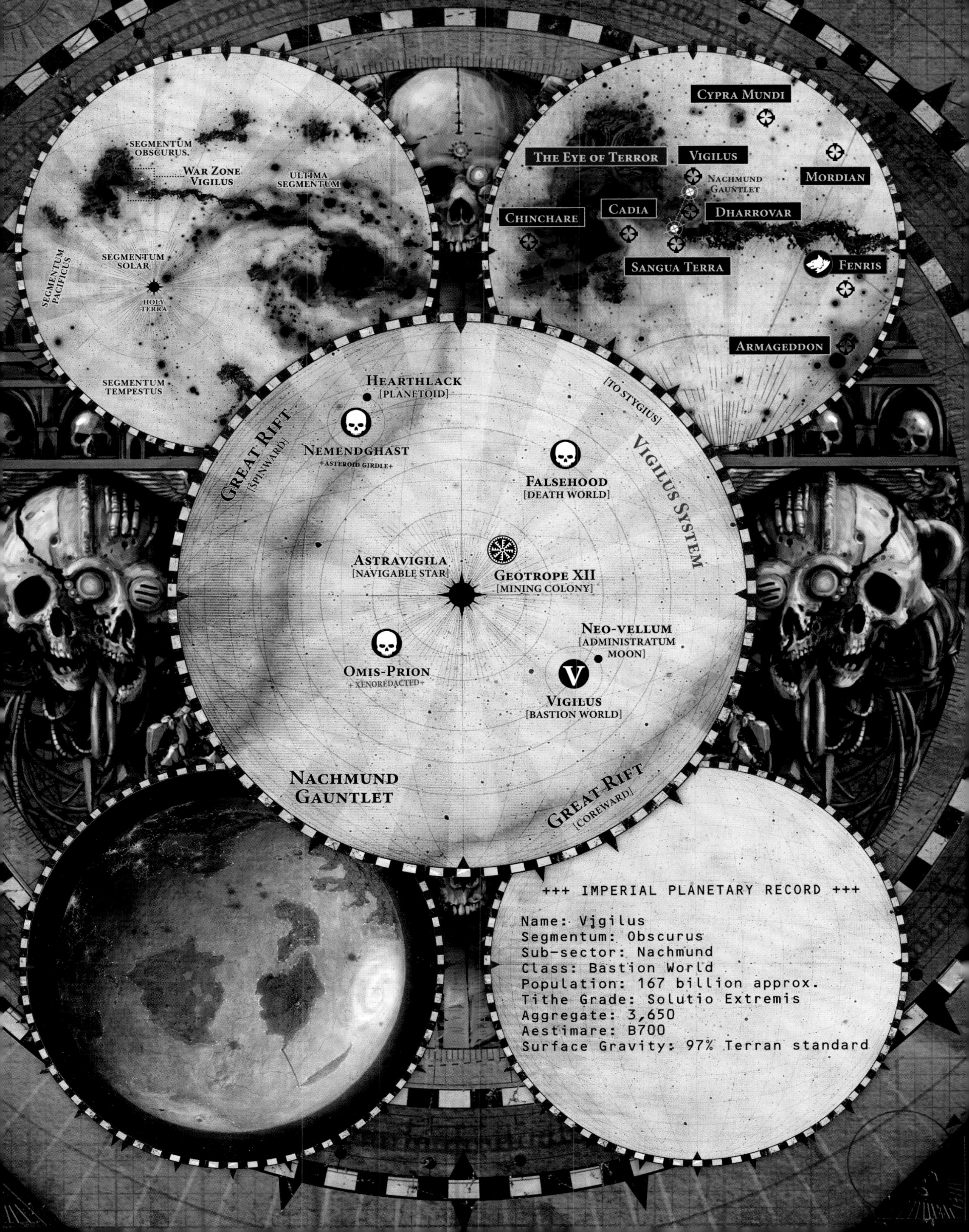

SEGMENTUM
OBSCURUS

WAR ZONE
VIGILUS

ULTIMA
SEGMENTUM

SEGMENTUM
SOLAR

SEGMENTUM
PACIFICUS

HOLY
TERRA

SEGMENTUM
TEMPESTUS

CYPRA MUNDI

THE EYE OF TERROR   VIGILUS

NACHMUND
GAUNTLET   MORDIAN

CHINCHARE   CADIA

DHARROVAR

SANGUA TERRA   FENRIS

ARMAGEDDON

[TO STYGIUS]

HEARTHLACK
[PLANETOID]

VIGILUS SYSTEM

NEMENDGHAST
+ASTEROID GIRDLE+

FALSEHOOD
[DEATH WORLD]

GREAT RIFT
[SPINWARD]

ASTRAVIGILA
[NAVIGABLE STAR]

GEOTROPE XII
[MINING COLONY]

NEO-VELLUM
[ADMINISTRATUM
MOON]

OMIS-PRION
+XENOREDACTED+

VIGILUS
[BASTION WORLD]

NACHMUND
GAUNTLET

GREAT RIFT
[COREWARD]

+++ IMPERIAL PLANETARY RECORD +++

Name: Vigilus
Segmentum: Obscurus
Sub-sector: Nachmund
Class: Bastion World
Population: 167 billion approx.
Tithe Grade: Solutio Extremis
Aggregate: 3,650
Aestimare: B700
Surface Gravity: 97% Terran standard

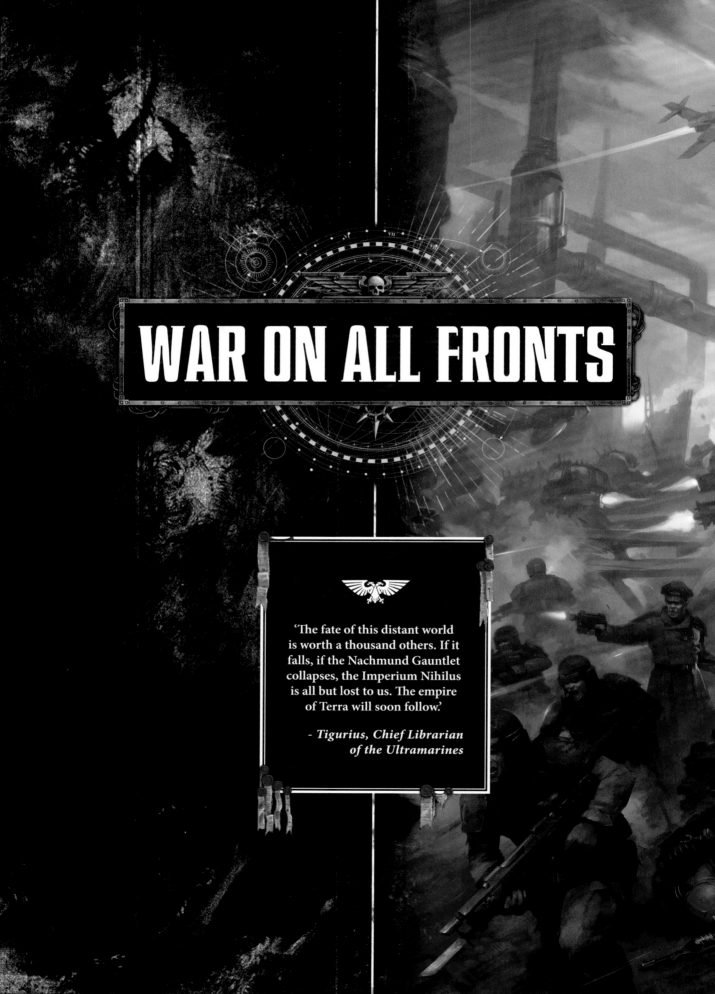

WAR ON ALL FRONTS

'The fate of this distant world is worth a thousand others. If it falls, if the Nachmund Gauntlet collapses, the Imperium Nihilus is all but lost to us. The empire of Terra will soon follow.'

- Tigurius, Chief Librarian of the Ultramarines

AT BOILING POINT

Roboute Guilliman himself designated Vigilus invaluable. The planet was something between a sentinel bastion and a staging post for further conquest, and its many Astra Militarum regiments and Adeptus Mechanicus macroclades formed a second line of defence against Chaos incursions from outside the Cadian Gate.

At the onset of the xenos invasion, Vigilus' vast and contiguous landmasses were broken only by a series of fortified reservoirs. The dust-bowl wastelands between each city-sprawl were analogous to oceans, and just as difficult to cross. They were not only arid and barren, but also hydrophagic – in places the chemical composition of their dust dunes was so saline it could desiccate bare flesh in a matter of hours. In theory, simply wearing enough protective clothing could have assuaged this. Unfortunately, the dust storms and twisters that were spun out from the giant tempest in the east – known as the Vhulian Swirl – caused this desiccant to creep into every chink of a traveller's armour. The dunes were hence populated only by tough-skinned or shell-armoured predators that preyed upon the unwary.

The planet's rare areas of productive land were highly sought after, but rampant industrialisation saw most of them developed into urban metropolises called hivesprawls. These were so large they formed entire continents.

The world was formally ruled by its Planetary Governor, Lucienne Agamemnus IX. That dynasty had overseen the planet's affairs from the spires of the capital, Saint's Haven, for millennia. Yet the planet was famous for being a stronghold of the Adeptus Mechanicus.

Vigilus' relative proximity to War Zone Stygius saw it serve as a way-station for incoming Imperial forces, including the Space Wolves and various Skitarii Legions. Its placement in the cosmos alone made it a valuable asset, but its exports too were vital for the Imperial war machine.

Vigilus was once one amongst a hundred Imperial worlds in the Segmentum Obscurus considered important primarily for the war materiel and manpower it exported. The planet's principal export was its exceptional defensive technology. The Adeptus Mechanicus of Vigilus were blessed with the Standard Template Construct for psy-tech force fields, and were sanctioned by Mars to put them into production. As well as being shipped out to aid the defences of countless other worlds, these Bastion-class

THE WATERS OF VIGILUS

Water was scarce on Vigilus, for the planet had a very low water table, and, aside from the wide-scale recyc operations, there were few ways to replenish used stores. In addition, plant growth and arable farming were a rarity. The planet's food production came from various inventive sources, amongst them cactus farms, vermin abattoirs and subterranean nutri-vats. These latter methods recycled the fat-rich run-off and nutrient-rich sweat that dripped from the grates of the planet's grossly overpopulated manufactorum habs.

On Vigilus, the kind of water a person drank was a powerful

status symbol, indicative of their wealth and position. The majority of people in the under-classes and working populations drank water from deep underground, known as aqua subterra. This was dirty, foul-tasting and yellowish, but affordable. The rich and powerful drank aqua glacius, mined in vast cuboid icebergs on the polar continent of Kaelac's Bane. The faithful flock of the Ministorum in Hyperia Hivesprawl drank recyc water purified with holy oils – aqua sanctus – whereas the Adeptus Mechanicus drank aqua meteoris, which was mined from frozen asteroids they harnessed with the Greater Omnissian Hoist.

force fields were installed around the perimeter of every Vigilant continent as part of a treaty that had been agreed between the Tech-Priests and the Agamemnus Dynasty. Until the opening of the Great Rift and the xenos invasions that followed, these defences kept the planet's industry and populace safe from outside invasion.

In exchange, the Adeptus Mechanicus were largely left to their own devices on the forge continent of Megaborealis – one of the 'false continent' cityscapes that covered Vigilus' crust – but as time went on this proved a high price. Much of Megaborealis was given over to the unearthing of a strange black mineral that ran like veins through its crust, which the Tech-Priests obtained through vast and destructive mining operations. For the most part, these excavations were powered by energy produced in the volatile volcanic region of Storvhal to the south.

The deep drilling of the Adeptus Mechanicus' bore-hives caused such violent earthquakes across the planet that many a hive was toppled,

many a ruler's statue cast down, and the water table disrupted to the point that potable water became extremely scarce. Still, the Machine Cult of Stygies VIII delved ever deeper in their search to unravel the mysteries of the universe – no matter their provenance, or cost.

Meanwhile, the gradual but undeniable influence of the Ministorum was to see the Agamemnus Dynasty slowly infiltrated by agents of the Ecclesiarchy. None could gainsay their encroachment, for to challenge them was to challenge faith in the Emperor himself. The Ministorum Priests installed amongst the local Vigilant Guard worked ceaselessly to indoctrinate their Astra Militarum charges until they too

became dogmatic soldiers of faith. As the decades slid by, the inner districts of Hyperia Hivesprawl, Vigilus' capital continent, echoed to the march of ever more Adepta Sororitas and their pious Vigilant Guard allies, until some said the Planetary Governor was ruler in name only. Vigilus was becoming host to several distinct power bases, all determined to pursue their own agendas no matter the cost.

The planet's disparate continents came into conflict over resource monopolies many times, but outright war was always avoided due to the efforts of the Aquilarian Council. Unfortunately, as resources were sequestered in ever more blatant power grabs, the grievances of the Aquilarian Council escalated from bickering and infighting to sabre-rattling and threats of violence that saw the planet brought to the brink of deadly civil war.

Then, under the malignant light of the Great Rift that broke across the galaxy, Vigilus and the other planets orbiting the star Astravigila entered a new phase of their tempestuous existence.

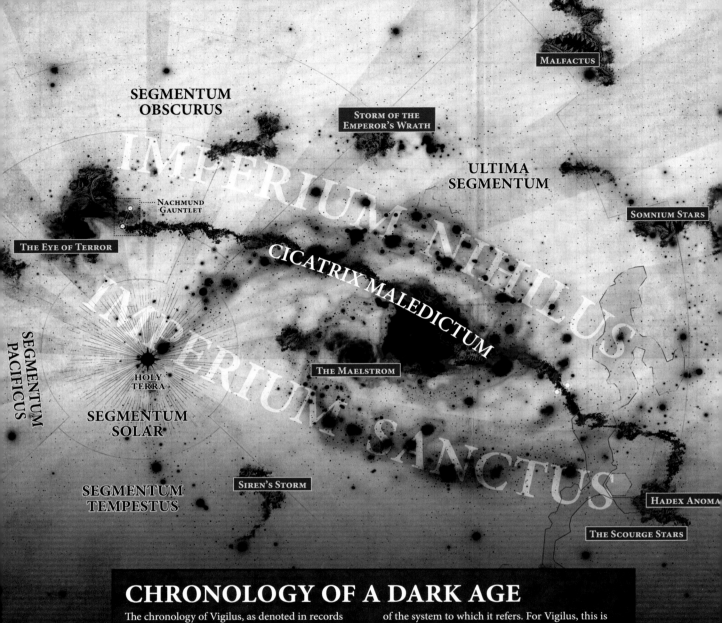

SEGMENTUM
OBSCURUS

MALFACTUS

STORM OF THE
EMPEROR'S WRATH

ULTIMA
SEGMENTUM

IMPERIUM NIHILUS

SOMNIUM STARS

NACHMUND
GAUNTLET

CICATRIX MALEDICTUM

THE EYE OF TERROR

IMPERIUM SANCTUS

HOLY
TERRA

THE MAELSTROM

SEGMENTUM
PACIFICUS

SEGMENTUM
SOLAR

SIREN'S STORM

HADEX ANOMA

SEGMENTUM
TEMPESTUS

THE SCOURGE STARS

CHRONOLOGY OF A DARK AGE

The chronology of Vigilus, as denoted in records
of the War of Beasts, uses as its anchor point the
opening of the Great Rift above the planet. This was
an event of such incredible magnitude it rewired the
planet's temporal logic altogether, much as it did a
thousand other war zones across the Imperium.

The first element of Vigilus' timestamp is the annual
designator. It starts with the number of years either
before or after the rift opened, and then a number
of chronosegments within that year as the second
element. Imperial days are broken down into
chronosegments of eight hours. After this is a third
element – either 'previo' if the events occurred before
the opening of the Great Rift, or 'post' if after it. This
third element is sometimes denoted as a minus sign
or a plus sign.

The fourth element of the Vigilus timestamp is the
system's designator initials; in essence, the initials

of the system to which it refers. For Vigilus, this is
VCM which stands for 'Vigilus Cicatrix Maledictum'.
For its neighbouring planet, Omis-Prion, the
designator initials would be OPCM.

By way of a full example, if the time of an event
in the Vigilus System was three days (nine
chronosegments) before the opening of the Great
Rift, the timestamp would be '0.9 previo VCM.M41',
also expressed as '0.9 previo' or '0.9–'.

This translates as '0 years and 9 chronosegments
(three days) previous to the Vigilus System's
first instance of the Cicatrix Maledictum in the
41st Millennium.'

If it was one year and eight hours after, the
timestamp would be '1.1 post VCM.M41', also
expressed as '1.1 post' or '1.1+'.

THE GREAT RIFT YAWNS WIDE

Before the onset of the conflict known as the War of Beasts, Vigilus witnessed a cataclysm so great it all but split the galaxy in half. The Cicatrix Maledictum ripped from the Eye of Terror in the galactic north-west to the Hadex Anomaly in the south-east. Aside from a few corridors, the rift was all but impassable.

When the skies split around Vigilus, many feared the planet would be consumed forever. Instead, as the swirling nebulae dissipated, it seemed that Vigilus had held the Cicatrix Maledictum at bay. The planet's strange aegis linked it with the Knight world of Dharrovar and the distant planet of Sangua Terra to form the corridor known as the Nachmund Gauntlet.

Whether it was faith, the Emperor's Will, a fluke of quantum entanglement or some other phenomenon that kept this rift passage open, none knew. But the route from the reaches of the still-functional Imperium to the desperate realms of the Imperium Nihilus remained stable. Vigilus became more vital than ever, and not only to the Imperium. Traitor generals and xenos masterminds

looked upon it with covetous eyes, and hatched secret plans to conquer it. Drukhari raids struck from the arctic webway portal on Kaelac's Bane, whilst Craftworld Saim-Hann sent emissaries to warn of a doom to come.

A dark new era dawned across Vigilus' desert wastes and over-populated hives. With the sky rent in twain by a warp rift that bled purple light into the heavens, and civil unrest reaching new heights, draconian laws were put into place by the planet's governing bodies. It was forbidden to look at the night sky on those rare occasions it could be glimpsed through the thick banks of cloud that choked the stratosphere, and a strict curfew was imposed that ensured all citizens would be indoors by nightfall – or flogged for a full hour. The

repression that resulted saw many civilians look to new cults and underground orders for succour. Ironically, it was this heavy-handed lawmaking that sowed the seeds of anarchy.

With the warp rift of the Cicatrix Maledictum scarring the Vigilus sky, the doom that many had feared would consume the planet from outside instead began to take its toll from within. To one extent or another, every citizen of Vigilus found themselves harrowed by dark dreams and recurring nightmares. The sleep deprivation and foul tempers that resulted spilled over into a hundred new conflicts every day, from small skirmishes and beatings in alleyways to industrial strikes, organised uprisings and spates of assassinations that scoured the upper spires.

TO RUN THE GAUNTLET

The Nachmund Gauntlet ran from Vigilus to the planet of Sangua Terra in the Imperium Sanctus. Near the northern end of the warp corridor was the world of Dharrovar, the stronghold of an ancient dynasty of Imperial Knights ruled over by King Kaligius. Once considered cautious, the king's behaviour had become ever more paranoid and erratic, and it was said he protected his holdings with the ferocity of an enraged drake. His defenders claimed he was like that with good reason, for on either side of the Nachmund Gauntlet was a seething tide of Chaos that constantly sought to break its metaphysical bonds and spill into realspace.

At the dawn of the Great Rift, ships that sought safe passage through the gauntlet had no choice other than to pass near Dharrovar. Those who gave the planet a wide berth were allowed to slink past without interception. Those who sought safe haven or attempted to contact the Knight world under a

flag of parley were treated with hostility, suspicion or even violence. A staunch independent, Kaligius was already convinced that no good would come from allowing the Imperium to draw him back into the fold. Instead he turned to tyranny and oppression. Even as the term 'Imperium Nihilus' was coined, he was declared Excommunicate Traitoris.

THE SPEEDWAAAGH!

The Ork invasion of Vigilus was sudden, and its scale caught the Imperial defenders off guard. At first it was contained, though it brought to light threats that had lingered unseen for years.

At the end of the 41st Millennium, the tensions upon Vigilus had risen sky-high, what with the Adeptus Mechanicus triggering ever more frequent earthquakes, and the power struggle between the Planetary Governor's dynasty and the Ministorum developing into covert violence. Then the Great Rift, a new celestial phenomenon appearing like a slowly opening wound in the sky, spat out a hurtling fleet of ramshackle Ork spacecraft into the Vigilus System.

With the rift scrambling the foresight of the planet's sanctioned seers and prophets, there was little warning of the Ork invasion's approach – the fleet punched through Vigilus' naval cordon with sudden, overwhelming force, then crash-landed its ships in the great deserts between the hivesprawls. Those that survived, protected from destruction by bubble-like force fields, formed ready-made fortresses, which became the heart of the Scrap Cities from which the Orks would attack the hivesprawls. What they lacked in organisation and structural integrity they made up for in sheer mass and firepower.

For days the wastelands echoed to the hammering of metal, the thudding of rivet guns, the guttural commands of Ork Mekaniaks and the throaty roar of smoke-spewing engines. Vehicle by vehicle, then swarm by swarm, a hundred mechanised invasion forces emerged at great pace from the dust-bowls. The Speedwaaagh! had begun, and at their head rode the Speedlord Supreme, Krooldakka.

The Orks were stymied, at first, by the Bastion-class force fields that surrounded each hivesprawl. The invaders were forced to content themselves with raiding the convoys and armoured regiments that braved the wastes and deserts, either to escort dignitaries or move materiel from one continent to another. Some Orks took to racing one another around the planet, even skirting the edge of the vast dust storm known as the Vhulian Swirl.

When the Great Rift grew to split the galaxy entire and the Noctis Aeterna dawned, the baleful emanations of the rift's warp storms washed across Vigilus. The eddies of psychic disruption caused a plague of nightmares to intensify in the populace, but worse still, collapsed all of the psy-tech force fields that kept the Orks from Vigilus' cities.

If the Orks had been a rational, right-thinking race, it may have taken them days to capitalise upon the lack of force fields. But with their Speed Freek outriders constantly daring one another to run through the perilous energies – or at least get as close as possible – it was less than an hour before word spread that the defences were down. When the Orks got wise to this they wasted no time, and poured into the outskirts of each city in tremendous numbers. The Adeptus Mechanicus, Astra Militarum and Adepta Sororitas that defended the hivesprawl borders found themselves engaged on all fronts, and within days they were fighting desperately to slow the Orks' momentum. Even the bio-dome sprawl of Mortwald, protected by a network of traditional trenches and bunkers as well as force fields, suffered invasion – as the Ork attack intensified, Mortwald's succulent forests and rejuvenat complexes were ransacked in several districts.

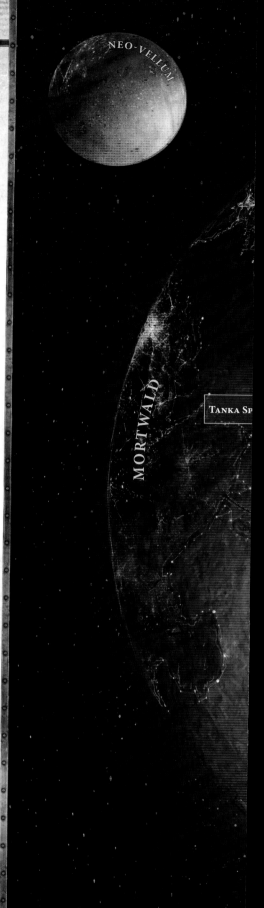

NEO-VELLUM

MORTWALD

TANKA SP

DONTORIA
HIVESPRAWL

MEGABOREALIS

Da Wheel
Hub

Gork's
Landing

Rakkuk's
Mekmaze

Runthive

Skumtown

STORVHAL

Fort Dakka

Drogzot's
Crater

Hurrikane
Rekk

VHULIAN
SWIRL

OTECK
HIVESPRAWL

HYPERIA
HIVESPRAWL

Mekstop
City

DIRKDEN
HIVESPRAWL

KAELAC'S BANE

THE RISE OF THE PAUPER PRINCES

The seeding of the Genestealer Cult of Vigilus began long ago, in silence, and in darkness. With the first successful invasions of the Orks, the cult burst forth in a tumultuous eruption, its members falling upon not only the citizens they had planned to usurp, but the invaders that sought to deny the cult its prize.

In the Vigilant year 210.33 previo, a clutch of Purestrain Genestealers was sent out from the planet of Chancer's Vale by the Genestealer Cult known as the Pauper Princes. Only one managed to make it to Vigilus, but one was enough. Secreting itself in the seismic caverns beneath Megaborealis, it began to spread its insidious creed across the planet. Over the ensuing years, it grew larger and more powerful as it became the dominant father of brood cycle after brood cycle, and ultimately the Patriarch known as Grandsire Wurm.

Centuries later, when the greenskins descended upon Vigilus, they triggered – albeit unwittingly – a premature uprising of the Genestealer Cultists who had long been hidden among the populace. Just as possessive of the planet as were its Imperial authorities, and a good deal less divided, they refused to see their long years of subterfuge and infiltration wasted amidst the anarchy of the Ork onslaught.

They staged insurrections within every hivesprawl on Vigilus and, thanks to the psychic coordination of Grandsire Wurm and his Nexos strategists, they rose with eerie synchronicity to enact ambushes and cunning strategies across the planet. Nowhere was this more evident than in Dirkden Hivesprawl.

Dirkden was under-resourced and underdeveloped. Here, the Pauper Princes had gained such a foothold that in some sub-districts their faithful outnumbered the non-believers. Moreover, the cult had infested the ranks of Dirkden's defence regiments, the Vigilant Guard, like gutworm riddles the innards of a dying ore-miner.

Acting upon secrets pried from the minds of compromised Tech-Magi, the cult leaders gained access to alpha-level data psalms and scriptoral mnemonics that enabled them to temporarily shut down Dirkden's Bastion force fields.

The shields had wreathed Vigilus' hivesprawls for centuries. Had such a failure occurred during more normal times it would have been immediate cause for suspicion and investigation. However, with the

DIRKDEN HIVESPRAWL

GLAIVE POINT

THE GRAND PIT

HYPERIA-DIRKDEN FORTWALL

SUBSKEIN CAVEWAYS

ASHENID NON-HIVE

RESCALID UNDERWORKS

baleful influence of the Great Rift playing havoc with the Adeptus Mechanicus' shield technologies, it was a simple matter for cult-corrupted officers of the Vigilant Guard to convince their fellows that the shut-down was caused by a technical glitch.

Panic ensued, just as the cultists had known it would. The Orks of the Speedwaaagh! were quick to respond to Dirkden's weakness, and dust-trails choked the horizon as the xenos invaders grew near.

It was those same cultist agents who contrived to order elements of the Vigilant 86th, 94th and 313th out into the dusty wastes beyond the shield-line. Each platoon was hand-picked for the duty of defending the hivesprawl, their officers given stern assurances that they would be drawn back within the walls as soon as the Tech-Magi had placated the truculent machine spirits.

Some four thousand soldiers marched into the wastes from

Glaive Point to the Rescalid Underworks. They faced an onrushing horde of over fifteen thousand Orks, but took solace in the knowledge that they would only have to hold until the shields were reactivated. It was then that the cult's undercover agents in Dirkden staged their uprising. Outnumbering the remaining loyalists ten-to-one, they seized control of the sprawl's military assets. Then, as their dismayed former comrades realised the scale of their betrayal, the Pauper Princes raised the force field again, stranding Dirkden's Vigilant Guard on the wrong side of it. The Orks fell upon their horrified victims, who now had no line of retreat. The slaughter was brief and horrific.

Not all of those remaining within the sprawl were xeno-corrupted. Sensing their peril even if they did not fully understand it, thousands of industrial labourers, dust-miners and menials gathered their families and meagre possessions before fleeing over the Hyperia-Dirkden

Fortwall. Yet this, too, worked in the Pauper Princes' favour. Swathing themselves in rags, or donning the workers' coveralls, hundreds of cultists mingled into the refugee tide. Thus was their curse carried to the southern reaches of Hyperia.

At Oteck Hivesprawl, too, the Pauper Princes struck hard. If Dirkden had been chosen for its comparative weakness, Oteck was selected instead for its strategic importance. Its vast reservoirs, known locally as the Hollows, were one of Vigilus' primary water sources. On such a dry and barren world, this made each reservoir as valuable as a lake of liquid adamantium.

The battle to control Oteck was far more bitter than that in Dirkden. Still, thanks to their frightening levels of preparedness and their utter fanaticism, the Pauper Princes were able to seize control of Greigan Hollow and start corrupting the drinking water of billions with their insidious genetic taint.

OTECK HIVESPRAWL

HIDDEN AGENDAS, SELFISH SOULS

The Aquilarian Council had watched pict-thief relays of the Orks being hurled back by their psy-tech force fields with a sense of confident superiority. Now they received reports of a new force rising. To their consternation, the messages told of a threat coming from within, rather than without.

The scattered missives detailing subterranean uprisings were at first attributed to malcontents, criminals and opportunists. The prevailing opinion was that the perpetrators would soon be put down by the local Adeptus Arbites or, failing that, the companies of Astra Militarum despatched to destroy such rebellions before they could gain too much ground. These forces of law and righteous oppression were sent to deal with uprisings and demagoguery wherever they were reported. Then the Hyperian leaders and their ilk went back to focusing on how best to capitalise on the industry of war.

The after-action reports that made it back from those violent suppressions revealed signs of something far worse than mere civilian unrest. Strange sigils had been spotted on many walls and archways, depicting a curled and spined creature that some called a 'wyrm-form'. There were rumours of sinister four-armed creatures scuttling in the darkness, and the word 'xenos' was being whispered more and more amongst the common folk.

It was enough to cause those who held power to shore up their defences – it was their instinct to look to their own safety above all other concerns. The Ministorum ensured those armed forces over whom they held the most sway – the resident orders of the Adepta Sororitas and the ever-faithful Vigilant Guard – stayed close at hand within Saint's Haven, even though the nearest xenos sighting was some hundreds of miles away. The Adeptus Mechanicus withdrew many of its glacier claimants and aqua-prospectors from Kaelac's Bane, though a skeleton crew remained to quarry for water.

As the industry of Vigilus broke down, the frequency of the convoys that were crossing the wastelands on export missions or trade delegations slowed to a crawl. To make matters worse, the Speed Freeks that used those desolate reaches as their hunting grounds were merciless. The leadership of Vigilus launched tentative counter-attacks, but prioritised their own safety, putting aside alliances and pacts in favour of self-preservation.

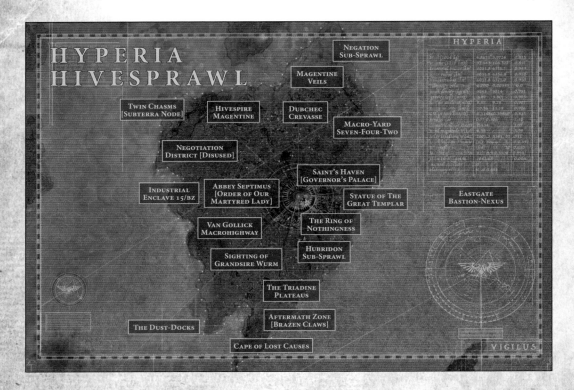

HYPERIA HIVESPRAWL

NEGATION SUB-SPRAWL

MAGENTINE VEILS

TWIN CHASMS [SUBTERRA NODE]

HIVESPIRE MAGENTINE

DUBCHEC CREVASSE

MACRO-YARD SEVEN-FOUR-TWO

NEGOTIATION DISTRICT [DISUSED]

SAINT'S HAVEN [GOVERNOR'S PALACE]

INDUSTRIAL ENCLAVE 15/BZ

ABBEY SEPTIMUS [ORDER OF OUR MARTYRED LADY]

STATUE OF THE GREAT TEMPLAR

EASTGATE BASTION-NEXUS

VAN GOLLICK MACROHIGHWAY

THE RING OF NOTHINGNESS

SIGHTING OF GRANDSIRE WURM

HUBRIDON SUB-SPRAWL

THE TRIADINE PLATEAUS

THE DUST-DOCKS

AFTERMATH ZONE [BRAZEN CLAWS]

CAPE OF LOST CAUSES

HYPERIA

VIGILUS

THE SCAR IN THE NIGHT SKY

Though the worlds of the Vigilus System had not been entirely cut off from the rest of the Imperium, it became ever more obvious that a new and darker phase of existence had dawned. The Great Rift was visible only as a purple blur during the daylight, but at night the immensity of the Cicatrix Maledictum glowered across the sky, its curling extremities and swollen central mass seeming to form screaming mouths and deformed faces when glanced at out of the corner of the eye. It stole sleep and distorted rational thought, even affecting the chronoslates and data-webs of the Adeptus Mechanicus with its anarchic emanations.

On Vigilus, the Great Rift became particularly prominent at night, and hence curfews were put in place across all of Vigilus' conurbations. In every hivesprawl it was forbidden to be outside after sunset, lest the Cicatrix Maledictum take that person's attention for so long they become infected by its strangeness and rendered susceptible to psychic phenomena. Even with these precautions, the shape of the Great Rift – a serpentine mass with the channel of the Gauntlet across it – began to appear in the daubings of madmen and the idle scrawlings of those who thought themselves to be concentrating on something else. More disturbing still, it appeared in natural phenomena as well. After-images of the rift manifested behind the eyes of those who had looked upon it too long, but unlike those caused by strong natural light, they did not fade. Parents looked in horror as they found birthmarks on infants born directly under the night sky when the rift glowered bright, each red weal broken by a thin white line of unblemished skin. Mildew growths and water stains on the walls and ceilings of the Hollows water purification plants formed in shapes that were uncannily similar, if not identical, to the rift in the sky above.

The purge-squads of the Ecclesiarchy, operating out of Saint's Haven, tracked down such phenomena with cold efficiency and zealous verve. But soon even they found themselves growing desperate, for as the years went by, these phenomena became more pronounced. Where the planet's earthquakes rent the land, chasms would fall open in shapes that echoed that of the Great Rift, complete with thin land bridges that corresponded to the position of the Nachmund Gauntlet.

IMPERIUM

ADEPTUS MECHANICUS

GENESTEALER CULTS

DRUKHARI RAIDERS

ORKS

CHAOS

DONTORIA HIVESPRAWL

MEGABOREALIS

STORVHAL

MORTWALD

OTECK HIVESPRAWL

HYPERIA HIVESPRAWL

DIRKDEN HIVESPRAWL

VHULIAN SWIRL

KAELAC'S BANE

DOOM FROM WITHIN

The first Space Marines to make planetfall on Vigilus were the Iron Hands and their successor Chapter, the Brazen Claws. Their intent was to drive back the Orks assaulting the hivesprawls, but they soon found themselves fighting for their lives against an unexpected foe.

The Iron Hands and their allies in Battlegroup Gauntlet translated into the Vigilus System without interception. They had calculated their approach through the beleaguered star systems of the Imperium Nihilus with great care; it is a testament to their metamathic skill and attention to detail that they arrived on target despite the massive disruption the Great Rift had caused to the star systems nearby.

The vast mechanical cathedrums of the Iron Hands fleet plunged out of the warp-nebulae like red-hot javelins through a veil of cobwebs, bursting into realspace in an eddying cloud of stardust. Within minutes of translation from the empyrean, they had

targeting solutions for each of the Ork vessels that still hung in orbit between them and the planet. Those were few and far between, for the vast majority of xenos had made haste planetside, leaving little behind to guard their rear. The Orks had, in all likelihood, assumed their conquest would be over quickly, but the Bastion-class force fields had frustrated them. Now, they were over-committed and their prey had been able to summon reinforcements. It was an elementary mistake, and the Chapter Master of the Iron Hands, Kardan Stronos, resolved to make the Orks pay dearly for it.

The battle barges and strike cruisers of the Space Marine fleet quickly made orbit above each of the major

hivesprawls, the Adeptus Astartes within filling the Drop Pod launch bays before hurtling through the atmosphere towards the battles below. Many more were to descend to the planet via Thunderhawk or bulk lander. They made for the most war-torn areas, usually around the fringes of each metropolitan zone, where the Orks were attacking in force. But in many of these areas they encountered no Ork presence whatsoever. In Megaborealis, they found themselves beset by a different breed of xenos altogether.

Since the uprising of the Pauper Princes, the planet's defenders had found themselves fighting two wars. The Aquilarian Council had despatched what resources it could spare from Hyperia, hoping

to swiftly restore order within Megaborealis – where a hive spire had been toppled by long-range fire and fallen across the force field border, making a bridge into the hive's interior for opportunist Ork attacks. Meanwhile, Adeptus Arbites and Adepta Sororitas patrols that ventured into territory claimed by the Genestealer Cult were swiftly ambushed. Those in transports were stranded amongst a maze of tank traps and barbed wire choked with the corpses of those who had gone before. On three separate occasions Astra Militarum armoured columns, bullying their way through the rubble of the streets with dozer blades and spade-shovels, took alternative routes when the going got too tough. They toppled into sink-holes and hidden subterranean chasms as the ground gave way beneath their cumulative weight. Those that managed to survive the fall were hunted by the horrible, half-glimpsed mutants that haunted the lower levels.

Refugee convoys made for zones as yet untouched by the Ork assault, thinking themselves safe. Much of Vigilus' air support was focusing on the movements of the greenskin tribes, and confining them where necessary with punitive strafing runs. The Ork Speed Freek formations were easily discerned, for they left long trails of dust in the wastelands – many were heading straight for the landing sites of the Space Marine drop forces, where the fighting was fiercest. By avoiding these tell-tale trails, Imperial strike forces were able to evacuate high-level personnel from those areas of the city where law and order still reigned. However, the Genestealer presence was much harder to identify, and attempting to perform relief and evacuation operations in regions infested by the xenos insurgents was akin to diving head first into a nest of vipers. In the space of a few days, the dual threat of Ork and Genestealer Cult had torn apart the Vigilus command structure.

BATTLE FOR THE SEEPING DELTA

The mid-western fringe of the continent Megaborealis came under siege within hours of the force fields going down. Its westernmost point, known as the Seeping Delta due to the rivers of industrial runoff that had burned across its reaches, became a killing ground. There were few built-up areas here, for the ground itself had been poisoned. Though the hyper-acidic soil was of little consequence to the metal-legged Skitarii and tough-skinned Orks that fought over it, the quagmires and sudden subsidence meant that vehicles could swiftly get bogged down or vanish without trace. The death toll spiralled into the millions as both forces poured ever more infantry into the fight.

With the pragmatism of one who has long forgotten notions such as honour, Fabricator Vosch of Megaborealis ordered the Seeping Delta set alight. Just as the Orks mustered an overwhelming force against the city's defenders, six hundred flamer-armed Kataphron Breachers trundled into place and set the entire Delta aflame. The Fabricator had ordered refined promethium to be funnelled into the area, so the entire landmass was consumed in liquid flame as if a match had been dropped into a petrochemical spill. The Orks were consumed by the fire, turning into flailing, living torches in their tens of thousands. The Skitarii burned with them – all save the Ruststalkers equipped with anti-incendiary ablative armour for the subsequent clean-up operation. These specialised, stilt-legged killers were tasked with running down any Orks that survived and preventing their leaders from escaping into the city. It was a victory, but it was won at an insanely high cost.

CONFLAGRATION OF THE SEEPING DELTA

ORK ATTACK · SKITARII GARRISON ZONE · PROMETHIUM FIRESPREAD

CHRONOLOGICA POST CICATRIX

After the opening of the Great Rift, near every active Imperial war zone had to devise and reinforce its own chronological system. Even had the Imperium of Man not been split in half, the sheer interstellar distances it covered prohibited any accurate reflection of time and space. Despite the flexibility of the 'check number' system of old, where the first digit of each timestamp indicated its veracity, it became easy for dates and times to lose all meaning between star systems.

It was Guilliman, Lord Commander of the Imperium, who made steps to resolve this after a long conference with his Historitors and the mysterious organisation of the Ordo Chronos. He decreed that a single logic could no longer be applied to time and space within the Imperium.

Through the High Lords of Terra he made his theory and resultant process into law. There could be no unified calendar with so much temporal distortion occurring. Even though the rift's warping effects might not have reached the furthest spinward planets at the galaxy's fringes, its psychic echoes – and the lack of the Astronomican that resulted – were still felt profoundly on those worlds.

Therefore, each sub-section of the Imperium would have to look to its own chronology, and use the coming of the Great Rift in that sector as its reference point. The Cicatrix Maledictum became the defining point of the new era.

DEFENCE OF MEGABOREALIS

The continent of Megaborealis was unlike any other on Vigilus. Punctured, wounded, torn up and left as a landscape of chasms, pits and sink-holes, its tumbled cities provided a million places to hide.

Though the entire continent of Megaborealis felt the sting of war at times, during the early stages of the conflict the fighting was thickest around Bore-hive Scelerus. Situated to the south of that ravaged sprawl, the hive provided over half of the energy that kept Megaborealis' countless manufactorums running, for it had been built atop a massive thermal stack that yielded endless geothermic power. In many ways it was the key to power in the sprawl.

When the Orks first attacked the planet Vigilus the lord of Hive Scelerus, the Tech-Priest Dominus Ipluvius XIV, spent over eighty nights with his internal cogitators running hot as he attempted to categorise the war in the wastelands. During this time he also gazed in awe at the giant cosmic aberration that was appearing in the night sky, doing his level best to rationalise what was happening to his planet. Content that his holdings were well-defended by the force field network on the ground, Ipluvius XIV coordinated a flak net of Onager Dunecrawlers to destroy the Ork aircraft that sought to hurtle over the defences. Though the fringes of the false continent were being bombarded – and in places, demolished – by the artillery of the Ork strongholds in the wastes, he contented himself that Megaborealis' key installations were safe. He went back to his studies of the rift.

When the backlash of the warp cataclysm bathed Vigilus in its strange energies, the disruption to the Bastion-class force field networks was quickly discovered by the roving Ork Kommandos probing the frontier for weak points. A terrible storm of dust and pollution was raised by the esoteric forces roiling across Megaborealis, and the Orks were quick to capitalise. The Speed Freeks in the wastes scrambled from their camps and hurtled towards Megaborealis without a second thought, their headlong charge obscured by the tempest of pollution and dust that rolled across its borders.

With speed and recklessness as their prime weapons, the Orks made exceptional progress through the hivesprawl, for the continent's defenders could not bring their big guns to bear in time. Bursting through the outskirts came smoke-belching swarms of Ork vehicles, so ramshackle and careless in their construction it sickened the faithful of the Machine God just to look upon them. Across the refineries of Kraxxon, the slag fields and the south reaches of Grisport, they proved nigh impossible to stop.

Upon realising the full extent of their predicament, Ipluvius XIV froze, caught in a mental feedback loop that robbed his Skitarii and Cult Mechanicus troops of any directions other than squad-level leadership. Perhaps his cogitator mechanisms had been damaged by the Great Rift, perhaps he had been a victim of some midnight hypnosis at the hands of an agent of the Pauper Princes, perhaps he was simply paralyzed by fear. Whatever the reason, his forces found themselves without orders and unsupported by the Imperial Knights that stood ready to defend the hive, and the God-Machines of the Legion Ferroxus that languished dormant in Scelerus' war hangars.

The continent's defenders fought the sudden Ork assault as best they could, but in a hundred places and more they were overwhelmed. When the Genestealer Cultists of Megaborealis rose up, their day of ascension triggered prematurely by the Ork invasion, Hive Scelerus' defences swiftly came apart. All the perfectly calculated kill zones and flak solutions put in place against invasion from without were rendered obsolete by the attack from within.

The gene-sect of the Writhing Wyrm – a sub-faction of the Pauper Princes under Slygaxx the Prophet – aimed to immediately orchestrate the most devastating assault they could. They had captured a vortex missile at great cost in lives, and now took that terrible payload deep into the hivesprawl's heart, using stolen access codes and the torn-out eyeballs and severed fingers of slain authority figures to confound each hangar's biomantic checkpoints. The vortex missile was detonated beneath the slumbering Warlord Titan *Dominus Rex*. The megatonnage of its explosion was so potent it set off a string of detonations that destroyed not only the *Rex* but also triggered a chain reaction that spread to all the Titans alongside it. At a stroke, the most powerful assets in the entire continent were destroyed.

Only when Archmagos Nesium Caldrike seized the malfunctioning Ipluvius XIV, had him placed in cryostorage and took his place, did the Adeptus Mechanicus manage to put together something approaching a coordinated war effort. Caldrike proved a canny and decisive war leader. Uniting his efforts with Clan Company Kaargul of the Iron Hands, recently despatched by Kardan Stronos to reinforce Megaborealis, he stopped the insurgencies of the Genestealer Cultists from attaining critical momentum, forcing the war into a grinding stalemate where every city district and manufactorum was the site of bitter fighting.

'Get yer engines revvin'! This is wot we been waitin' for, ladz. The Meks say all that zoggin' force field gubbins ain't working no more. Get inta that dust storm, boyz, and keep goin', fast as you can. You'll hit da humies on the other side. Now what you waitin' for, eh? Last one ta get his blade red is a runty little git!'

- Rukfang, Ork war leader

THE COUNTER-ATTACKS BEGIN

Many Imperial Commanders of Vigilus saw the Ork junk forts blighting the horizon as a call to arms. They mustered their mechanised regiments and artillery, sending them out into the wastes with the express intention of hammering the Orks into the sand before they could consolidate their positions.

After the Orks made planetfall, Astra Militarum armoured columns rolled out of city gates across the planet to the blare of fanfare klaxons and the cheers of the citizenry. Into the wastes they went, so numerous that the dust kicked up by their passage could be seen from low orbit. Valkyries and Vendetta Gunships hurtled overhead, their holds packed with veteran soldiers and elite Militarum Tempestus Scions eager to take the fight to the foe.

Some of the armoured convoys, sent on missions of reconnoitre or resupply, made it to their destination with minimal damage. The Padrillus Pan'te fuel column allowed Storvhal to reinforce Fort Kaphinus with vital war materiel mere hours before it was assailed by Ork Kommandos. The Valkyrie squadron known as the Winged Grail carried several demolition squads through a network of Ork flakka-dakka wagons, braving intense fire to land near the Kan Factory of Runthive – and before dawn that site was reduced to smoking scrap. The Aquario Column reached Dontoria Hivesprawl virtually intact, its water tankers holed by Ork bullets but plugged up once more with the fingers of the

many conscripts sent to guard it, until the steel of each cylinder could hardly be seen for human bodies. A great many of their fellow convoys, however, did not return.

Already the Ork speedsters were scouring the wastes, driving pell-mell in search of things to kill. Here and there an ambull colony or sandrat nest was riddled with bullets for target practice, but the nascent Waaagh! was yet to get truly stuck in. Red eyes scanned the horizon for signs of life, barked commands directed outriders ever further, and pointed ears pricked up for the tell-tale crump and boom of distant battle.

At the sight of the blocky silhouettes of Chimeras and Leman Russ battle tanks on the horizon, a great whooping shout went up from each Speed mob, and the Orks closed in from all sides. The resultant desert warfare was typified by the shriek of heavy lasfire, the ping of bullets ricocheting from reinforced armour, and the thunder of detonating battle cannon shells.

Huge losses mounted on both sides. At first the convoys of the Imperial Guard reaped a heavy toll, blasting

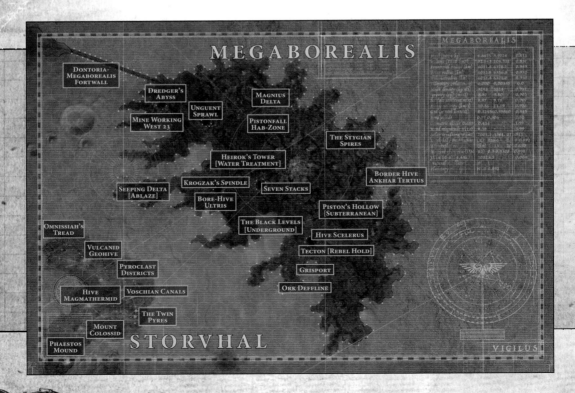

dozens of Ork contraptions into scrap with each passing minute, for in long-range engagements their artillery and ordnance gave them a definite edge over the ramshackle vehicles of the Orks.

But the Imperial forces could not kill them all, and in announcing their presence in so spectacular a fashion, they had sealed their fate. Attracted by the signs of battle from miles around, the Ork Speed Freeks swarmed ever thicker. At first a few isolated warbikers and buggies got through the cordon of gunfire with cunning and reckless abandon, only to be cut down by volleys of lasfire and sheets of flame. But every time a squadron was occupied in killing one target, another got closer, and at breakneck pace. Before too long the Orks had reached close quarters, where their heedless fury could truly make its mark – and once that tipping point had been reached, there was no coming back.

BATTLE OF MOURNING GORGE

On the southern outskirts of Megaborealis, the 121st Goliath Armoured Battle Group was destroyed by the actions of a single maniacal Ork. Fragbad Squigbiter intended to watch the Speedwaaagh! race through the miles-deep Mourning Gorge from a commanding vantage point. He and his mob scaled the cliff edge ahead of time, only to see an Astra Militarum blockade move to the end of the canyon and a Vigilite artillery company take position on the precipice.

As the Speedwaaagh! drove headlong into the trap, Squigbiter hurled so many stikkbombs at the nearest artillery piece – a Deathstrike Missile Launcher – that the cliff itself gave way, toppling the giant warhead into the valley below. The resultant explosion annihilated the blockade and much of the Speedwaaagh! warband before the rest bullied its way through the flames, completing the encirclement of nearby Storvhal and cutting off a vital supply route for the Imperium.

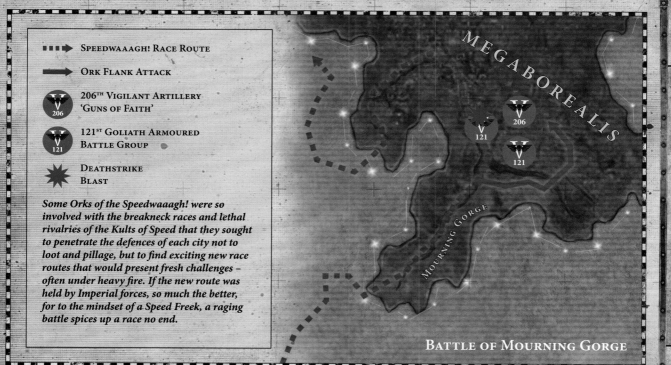

SPEEDWAAAGH! RACE ROUTE

ORK FLANK ATTACK

206TH VIGILANT ARTILLERY 'GUNS OF FAITH'

121ST GOLIATH ARMOURED BATTLE GROUP

DEATHSTRIKE BLAST

Some Orks of the Speedwaaagh! were so involved with the breakneck races and lethal rivalries of the Kults of Speed that they sought to penetrate the defences of each city not to loot and pillage, but to find exciting new race routes that would present fresh challenges – often under heavy fire. If the new route was held by Imperial forces, so much the better, for to the mindset of a Speed Freek, a raging battle spices up a race no end.

MEGABOREALIS

MOURNING GORGE

BATTLE OF MOURNING GORGE

A SICKNESS IN DONTORIA

Dontoria Hivesprawl was the largest of all the planet Vigilus' inhabited regions. It was noted for one thing above all else – its overpopulation. As a result, when one of Mankind's darkest and most ancient enemies decided to make Dontoria its playground, the consequences were devastating.

The bustle and mayhem of Dontoria's streets was bewildering, even before the coming of the Cicatrix Maledictum. The black market barons and czars in control of that hivesprawl knew well enough that building tall was a waste of resources. Unlike many of their peers, who were too hidebound, unimaginative or afraid of bucking the rules to stop building upward, they had instead opted to spread as wide as possible – even if that meant narrowing the streets to the point that entire regions became one vast contiguous hab-block.

As a result of this land grab, the buildings were packed in close together, every available space capitalised upon so much so that people had to rub shoulders and share humid air if they wished to proceed above ground. To enter the subterranean levels brought its own risks. Down there, power cuts were common, and those stranded in the darkness did not always come back out.

Such a rich, teeming source of life attracted predators and other baleful influences, just as shoals of vexenkrill attract the leviathans of the ocean deeps. The Drukhari of Kaelac's Bane had raided the hivesprawl more than once, taking a rich haul of slaves back to their base. The Cult of the Pauper Princes, seeing in the sprawl a great many converts-to-be, spread from Megaborealis to infest its lower levels and began the slow, insidious life cycle of their Patriarch all over again. But the false continent's doom was to come from another source entirely.

In the year 2.230 post, Dontoria's principal spaceport – Litmus Dock – received reports of an unknown vessel inbound. It was a pattern of vessel that even the Tech-Adepts seconded from Megaborealis considered ancient, encrusted with the filth of millennia and some manner of strange caulk that made its shape seem as much organic as mechanical. A rain of filth drizzled from its hatchways

THE GELLERPOX INFECTION

Sickness and disease in Dontoria was commonplace, a natural by-product of having such a high population density. By and large the hivesprawl had become inured to it; even when hundreds of thousands of lives were claimed by affluenza, dry lung or red smog fever. However, rumours of a strange supernatural plague were emanating from the districts around Litmus Dock, a disease that melded flesh with metal to form hideous blends of man, machine and daemonic anatomy.

With each day the reports became more prevalent until the entire area was on the verge of panic. Only the Rogue Trader Delarique du Languille, operating out of Litmus' highest spire on her quest to chart the Nachmund Gauntlet, recognised the disease for what it was – the Gellerpox. It was a sickness contracted on long warp journeys where the ship's Geller field had glitched long enough for baleful empyric energies to enter the vessel, and it mingled the paranormal maladies of the Plaguefather Nurgle with the flesh and metal hybridisation so common to the ranks of the Imperium – especially those of the Adeptus Mechanicus.

Du Languille theorised that the disease had been deliberately carried to the hivesprawl by the Death Guard, who then released it amongst the population before going to ground. It spread like wildfire. Already the citizenry were up in arms, burning the infected wherever they were uncovered – but in doing so, driving the rest into hiding. In the slums and shanty towns of the Pravdus and Grodholev Subsprawls, the creatures known as Twisted Lords rose to prominence, each the monarch of his own ever-growing band of mutants and nightmarish, hulking terrors. The streets thronged with giant vermin, twisted beyond biological limits into monstrosities, gutters were thick with sludge-grubs, and eyestinger swarms flitted through the skies in search of fresh prey. The blessings of Father Nurgle were well and truly upon Dontoria, and it would take a herculean effort to banish them.

Using her own ship and high status to travel from Litmus Dock to Saint's Haven, du Languille requested extensive quarantine measures of the Aquilarian Council – though privately, she feared her revelation was already too late.

DONTORIA

and airlocks as it came down, its crew ignoring the increasingly insistent calls for its animus codes. When the dock's garrison opened fire upon the vessel with their Icarus autocannon emplacements, some manner of shield repelled the shots. Even lascannons proved unable to pierce the unaccountably strong barrier. The ship docked, by now surrounded by Arbitrators and garrison troops. Its hatches clunked open, and stumbling out came a crowd of distended, bloated mutants – the ambulatory corpses known as Gellerpox Infected. Their assault on the garrison was easily put down by disciplined lasfire, but that which followed was all but impervious – a detachment of Death Guard. Their bulbous and horned silhouettes identified them as the same Heretic Astartes that had assailed Ultramar not long before. A fierce close-range firefight broke out, but the Death Guard shrugged off all but the most dire injuries. They used the Infected as fleshy shields, quickly going to ground via the underway dry docks of Litmus' lower levels.

With coordination at an all-time low due to the Noctis Aeterna and the myriad other threats upon Vigilus, the hunt for the invaders was not reinforced. No armed force was keen on rooting out entrenched Heretic Astartes, but many of the elite Guardsmen and those Arbitrators with a keen sense of duty braced themselves and went into the depths. Most found nothing. Others found painful death. When Tempestor Naiod ordered the lower levels firebombed within a two-mile radius, the Imperial forces considered the matter closed. Naiod withdrew the 98th Lamdic Oxen from the operation, and the hunt slowly ground to a halt. Only when a strange plague started to manifest across the district did it become clear that the scions of Nurgle had been diligent indeed.

'The magnitude of this infection cannot be underestimated. This is no natural plague, no malady that the human body can fight and overcome. This is the Gellerpox. It is fully capable of causing flesh to run like wax, to swell and burst, even to blend with augmetics, wargear and those machineries close at hand whilst the sufferer sleeps. The resultant hybrids are as tough as Ogryns and singularly focused on bringing their blight to as many uninfected as they can find. In the name of the Astra Cartographica, I implore you – quarantine Dontoria, effective immediately, or lose your planet to an enemy you cannot fight.'

- *Delarique du Languille*

Hyperia Hivesprawl, long defended by the Vigilant Guard and the Adepta Sororitas of Our Martyred Lady, had succeeded in holding the Orks at bay for over a year by the time the Brazen Claws arrived. Using the vast structures of each building as ready-made keeps and conceding the ground floors to the Ork menace when necessary, the allied forces used stairwells, alleyways and crypt entrances as choke points to hold back the green tide. Yet their orders from the Aquilarian Council were explicit, and oft repeated – they were to defend, to hold their position in case of any surprise assault or assassination attempt that might threaten their masters.

Because of this, they were robbed of the ability to counter-attack – to land a killing blow upon the reeling foe. As it was, even when beaten soundly, the greenskins regrouped and always came back for more within a matter of days. It was only when the striking red-and-blue heraldry of the Brazen Claws appeared in the streets that Orks were trapped, caught between the hammer of the Space Marine armoured assault on the outskirts and the anvil of the Imperial troops in the city proper. From that point on, the south of Hyperia Hivesprawl remained under Imperial control.

TO SUMMON THE ANGELS OF DEATH

With the Noctis Aeterna stealing away the guiding light of the Astronomican, most Space Marine forces had arrived piecemeal, or not at all. Those that made planetfall hit home with punitive force.

The elements of the Adeptus Astartes that reached Vigilus first had already been en route from the Stygius System when the Great Rift appeared. They had therefore made it to the system with but a single warp transition. This had been fraught and violent, but in comparison to the suffering of the other Space Marine Chapters that headed for Vigilus, it was a relatively short ordeal to endure, like swimming across a fast river full of sharp rocks. The true odyssey was undertaken by those Chapters that would come later.

The first Space Marines to make landfall were far from numerous – small but potent strike forces that were less than Chapter strength even when counted as one single military unit. They were engaged in battle within seconds of setting foot upon the planet, for it is in the nature of Space Marines to attack from above with speed and surety. In Hyperia, the Brazen Claws set about slaughtering the Ork menace in as efficient and merciless a fashion as possible, hoping to stem the tide of greenskins that encroached upon the richest of the false continents – and its seat of governance. The Iron Hands took the fight to Megaborealis, recognising the macro-structures of their Adeptus Mechanicus allies. The Space Wolves concentrated their attacks upon Oteck Hivesprawl, for they had received word of a xenos infestation there that would test their hunting skills.

The strike forces hit hard, but so disparate were their attacks they failed to make any global impact – indeed, the Space Wolves hardly communicated at all with Kardan Stronos of the Iron Hands, and did not coordinate their assault in any real way. After briefly communicating their intent to the Planetary Governor's council, a process that in itself proved frustrating and counter-intuitive, none of the Space Marine Chapters sent representatives to the war councils of Saint's Haven. They were made to fight, and to kill, and spending hours in debate with bureaucrats was not their way. Instead they focused their efforts on communicating with their Chapter brothers, no matter how distant they might be.

As they made their way from the Vigilus System's Mandeville point to orbit the planet itself, the ships of the Space Wolves, Iron Hands and Brazen Claws had passed several worlds that appeared to be under heavy Chaos attack. The Librarians of the respective strike forces sent psychic missives as best they could to their Chapter Masters, hoping more reinforcements would be sent in time.

No mental communion could be attempted without risking dire consequences now that the Great

Rift split the Imperium, rendering even the most stable astropathic duct volatile. Even a planet-to-planet communiqué could cause a sender's mind to be rent apart. Nonetheless, all knew that the situation was dire, and the notion of duty was so thoroughly ingrained in the Adeptus Astartes that not one Librarian shirked from the task of communicating with their Chapter to call for reinforcements. From the relative sanctity of the Terran side of the rift, word spread of Vigilus' plight and newfound importance, and fleets were mustered from a dozen Chapter home worlds to head out for the mouth of the Nachmund Gauntlet.

In the dead of night, whilst en route to Vanantis IX, Marneus Calgar of the Ultramarines had been visited by a vision of his old friend Tigurius. He was glad to see that ghostly apparition, at first, for he knew that this was not simply some insubstantial dream – the Chief Librarian was reaching out to him in his astral form, and evidently he had a message of great import to convey. Tigurius pressed his spectral index fingers against Calgar's temples. In that moment the terrible knowledge gleaned by the Chief Librarian was imparted, a collage of mental images and powerful symbolism that seared itself into Calgar's mind.

That link might have driven a lesser man to madness, but despite the recent ordeal of his surgical enhancement to Primaris status, Calgar withstood the mental blitz, parsing and compartmentalising the flood of images almost as fast as they entered his mind. The high council of Macragge had need of him as their sword and shield in the Imperium Nihilus; the Primarch himself had ordered that Vigilus could not be allowed to fall. Then the image of Tigurius faded, tears of blood streaking his cheeks, and was gone. But the deed was done, and soon a new host of angels took flight.

Master Magus,

The council has of late received three traditional Adeptus Astartes hails, two of which I obfuscated as best I could, sending contradictory information in return without straying into lies that might expose my position. The third somehow reached Lucienne herself without passing through the correct channels. I have faith that the self-serving witch will attempt to harness the Space Marines to her own private concerns, and hence alienate them entirely when they see the gambit for what it is. Nonetheless, I urge you and Grandfather to keep Oteck Hivesprawl in your thoughts; a force of the infamous Fenrisians is abroad there.

Yours in eternity,
Brother Theronvid

CALGAR'S JOURNEY

Though the Ultramarines had a long and harrowing journey to reach Vigilus, Lord Calgar arrived to lead a full four companies into battle. He aimed to command the fight on every level, from the calculations of the strategic long game to the brutal onslaught of adrenalin-pounding melee.

After recovering from Tigurius' strange visitation, Marneus Calgar hastened to gather a relief force of every Adeptus Astartes asset he could requisition, convince or command to his side. Though all forces were already engaged in the active protection of the Imperium and the destruction of its foes, Calgar's sharp analytical mind allowed him to pare off resources from stable fronts wherever possible, repurpose war fleets that had become stranded or misplaced, and enlist several new Primaris Chapters from the Indomitus Crusade. He had ordered his captains and fellow Chapter Masters to brief their Navigators as to what was at stake, and made haste for the Vigilus System.

To make the necessary warp jumps in time to reach the planet before it fell would have been next to impossible were it not for the astropathic link Tigurius had forged with Lord Calgar. Surrounded by his finest Librarian disciples in the depths of the Fortress of Hera, the Chief Librarian mentally guided the Ultramarines fleet – and by extension their allies – through the madness of the Imperium Nihilus.

Doing so had a terrible cost. Several Epistolaries died clawing out their own eyes, slowly consumed from the inside by the empyric ritual, just as the psykers that fuel the Astronomican are consumed by the Emperor's psychic might. Others were executed point blank by their

attendant Chaplains when the tell-tale signs of daemonic corruption appeared upon their bodies. Tigurius himself withered and burned under the strain, but did not falter. He collapsed, at the end, his mortal form aged by decades – but only after Calgar's relief fleet had made translation into realspace and established an orbit around Vigilus.

The Ultramarines armada had not reached Vigilus without suffering heavy casualties. Several battle barges and strike cruisers, each with a storied history of its own, had fallen in battle en route or been swallowed by the roiling tides of a warp vortex. The admirals, commodores and captains of the remaining ships gritted their teeth,

squared their jaws and kept going. When the armada finally neared the Vigilus System, Calgar despatched Vanguard strike forces to the system's other besieged planets, while his main force pressed on through the remnants of the Ork flotilla to Vigilus itself.

Calgar issued communiqués to the Space Marines already on the planet below, though he did not inform the Planetary Governor of his approach – there was no time for formality, and he did not wish to become embroiled in protocol and politicking. He had but one thing on his mind: swiftly and efficiently restoring order to Vigilus.

The skies blazed as the Space Marines launched their planetstrike, tight formations of Drop Pods hurtling down to the critical locations Calgar had outlined. In every false continent the Adeptus Astartes united their efforts with the local forces, restoring hope with their sheer presence and beginning the long work of stitching the tattered patchwork of Vigilus' defences into a coherent whole.

The Lord Macragge himself made straight for the tallest and grandest building of Saint's Haven, for he knew the Planetary Governor would be there in state. Whilst his battle-brothers fortified the palace, at times having to pacify its defenders, Calgar made haste to the chambers of the Aquilarian Council.

When Calgar flung open the doors to the sumptuous, richly appointed debating hall of the Council of Cogs and demanded an explanation for the war effort thus far, he found evidence not of glory, but of rot and corruption. Ostensibly, the council was a collection of Vigilus' finest, the great and the good – but all Calgar saw was a room full of feckless incompetents. As soon as the initial shock of such an Imperial luminary arriving in the flesh wore off, the council devolved into back-biting, sniping and blame-slinging.

Pointing a finger of accusation at the members of the council he believed to be traitors to the war effort, Calgar bade his shield-brothers round up and remove those he found wanting. One of these malcontents, roughly seized, was exposed to have purplish, knobbled skin under his collar, well-concealed by greasepaint but stark when revealed. Another cultist was uncovered soon after, coming to the aid of his fellow with a knife drawn from the flesh of his forearm.

It was then that the council hall erupted into a cacophony. The resultant explosion of violence was swift, terminal and definite. Bolters boomed, Space Marine blades flashed red, cultists were executed, council members were bound in chains and exiled, and within the hour a new form of governance was declared.

At the head of this new order was Calgar himself, grim but purposeful. He had suspected that the Genestealer Cult uprising might have reached the highest echelons of society, and he had no intention of allowing such a thing to ever happen again. His fellow Adeptus Astartes commanders took their places with a collection of hand-picked advisors from what remained of the Aquilarian Council. The corruption of Saint's Haven had finally been excised, and a new body of governance – the Vigilus Senate – installed in its place.

THE INSIGHT OF A MASTERMIND

Marneus Calgar was well known as a strategic genius, a true successor to the Primarch Roboute Guilliman. Guided by the advice of his mentor, Ortan Cassius, the Chapter Master defended the empire of Ultramar from countless foes. It was Calgar's strategic acumen that broke Hive Fleet Behemoth as it ventured hungrily across the Eastern Fringe, defended the Imperium against Heretic Astartes, and devastated the Necrons of Damnos. Much of this he achieved in close collaboration with his old friend, Varro Tigurius.

In recent years, Calgar had found his Chief Librarian to be distant, haunted even, prone to staring into nothingness for minutes at a time unless spoken to directly. Some said he had glimpsed the true vastness of the void beyond the known limits of the galaxy. Others maintained that in psychically duelling the synapse creatures of the Tyranid race, and even prying into the minds of their fallen, he had touched something that had left an indelible mark on his soul.

Perhaps it was that latter connection that had alerted Tigurius to the swarming dangers of the Genestealer Cult boiling up from beneath Vigilus' crust; perhaps it was his greater perspective of the shape of the galaxy, and its fate should he fail, that gave him the insight he imparted to his Chapter Master. The Chief Librarian did not say, and never would.

THE TENDRILS RUN DEEP

The Cult of the Pauper Princes, having spread their influence throughout Vigilus for generations, had inveigled themselves into the water processing industry of Oteck Hivesprawl. So well hidden were they, so deeply embedded, that only the Space Wolves had senses sharp enough to hunt them down.

The Space Wolves, under the Primaris Battle Leader Haldor Icepelt, were amongst the first wave of Adeptus Astartes to answer Vigilus' distress calls, making planetfall only a few months after the Iron Hands and their successors. Upon reaching the planet, the Fenrisians swiftly observed that the scarcity of water made it a critical resource, and that any who wished to conquer the planet would attempt to gain a monopoly upon it. They sent word to the Aquilarian Council that the Blackmanes were inbound, and then made haste to the great reservoirs of Oteck Hivesprawl, known as the Hollows. There they set about rooting out the insidious foes beneath the streets, determined not to let the planet's water supply fall into enemy hands.

During the fierce early battles against the uprisings in the streets – waged alongside the 14th Vigilant 'Mourning Stars' artillery regiment – the Space Wolves believed they had found their true quarry lurking beneath the cityscape around Greigan Hollow. The Mourning Stars shelled the whole region, which had been deemed infested beyond recovery, before the Space Wolves charged in. In return, the cult triggered demolitions charges that toppled buildings on their foes and then sent out waves of hulking, mutated assailants. Close behind came skittering Genestealers to tear apart those who dared trespass on the cult's domain. The Space Wolves were trapped, and many of their number were slain, but they were not yet defeated.

Fighting their way through the alien hordes with blade, tooth and fist, Haldor Icepelt's hunters ventured

deep underneath Greigan Hollow even as the city above seethed in open war. Expert trackers, their senses were so preternaturally sharp they could detect the scent of the xenos leaders amongst the subterranean reek of mould, wet rock, stale urine, hyperchlorin and rotten animal carcasses. The oddly mingled scent implied a riot of out-of-control biologies – they were tracking the Claw of the Thirsting Wyrm, a splinter faction that boasted some of the most disturbing lifeforms on the planet.

Using Fenrisian fieldcraft, the Space Wolves tracked the hybrids through a dank labyrinth of pipes and passageways that would have confounded even other Space Marines. They had to negotiate many traps and false trails in the under-tunnels of Greigan Hollow, and fight their way past countless broods and Neophyte assailants. Their ferocity and firepower saw them through even when the bullets were flying thick. In the depths of the infestation's heartland, they were attacked by the gene-sect's icon bearer, Gilgas Vendella, and his swollen Abominant war leader, Bregg, but even they could not stop the Space Wolves' headlong assault.

The Genestealer Cult excelled at ambush, and they knew every inch of their home territory; they had spread far beneath the hivesprawl using subterfuge and disguise, working out of sight and out of mind to ensure their lairs were as defensible as possible. As Haldor and his kinband progressed, they found themselves hard pressed once more, gradually worn down by traps, deadfalls and ambushes.

A long, gruelling hunt with a fierce battle at its conclusion is a way of life upon Fenris, and the Thirsting Wyrm soon found to their cost that the sons of Russ do not tire easily. As he fought through the main purification plant of Greigan Hollow, Haldor detoured to unite with a towering Redemptor Dreadnought – Asger the Frozen. The war machine's piston-driven strength let him smash a path through rockcrete walls and wrench foot-thick pipes aside whenever the strike force's path was barred.

Learning of a vast amount of rigged explosives planted in caches throughout the city above, Haldor resolved to turn this would-be booby trap to his advantage. He sent word over the company vox to his Blackmane brothers in the wider war zone, telling them to sniff out any caches of explosives they could find and prime them to detonate at a set time. His plan was to trigger a simultaneous detonation above the main macro-duct and collapse a vast chunk of the city into the substrata below. He calculated that this would stop the flow of polluted water through the underground pipes to the other hivesprawls. Even if Oteck could not be saved, there was some hope for the other metropolises' survival.

A NEW POLLUTION

The cultists of the Thirsting Wyrm had spread throughout the Oteck reservoirs' infrastructure, and had been spiking the waters with chemicals and foul elixirs. Some of these were brewed from their own blood – solutions that rendered the populace more susceptible to the hypnosis and mental suggestion of their masters – whilst others were corrupted by the corpses of those who had died in the cult's service. Successive generations polluted the water still further until it had a faint purplish hue at times, or a wan yellow at others. Then, at the beginning of the uprising in 1.823 post, hundreds of pipe-worker teams and filtration crews had revealed themselves as mutant cultists. Those traitors had swiftly seized the artillery emplacements and flak batteries around each reservoir, killing those still loyal to the Emperor before taking over the water purification plants one by one. For all their cunning, however, they met their match in the Space Wolves of Ragnar Blackmane's Great Company.

The cult boiled from the shadows in ever greater numbers, and still the Space Wolves refused to give up. In the ensuing battles the cult troops were cut apart by power axe, piston-driven claw and hypersteel knife, or else blasted to steaming cadavers by tight volleys of mass-reactive shells. Under the direction of Gilgas Vendella, the Thirsting Wyrm fell back in a series of deliberate retreats to lure the Space Wolves into a killing field where the long-hidden explosives could be brought to bear – but in doing so, they conceded the ground that Haldor sought to demolish. It was Haldor himself that set off the last in a circular chain of demolition caches that ringed the city in fire, shaking that district of the metropolis to its core. A half-mile wide section of Greigan Hollow collapsed into the under-levels below – and in doing so blocked off the macro-duct. The remnants of the district were reclaimed by Imperial troops soon afterwards.

That saga-worthy deed was not in vain, for it stopped much of the corruption in Vigilus' veins from flowing any further. A subsequent cleanse-and-purge operation launched by the Deathwatch deemed the water too polluted to recover. Two of the five Hollows – Greigan and Agamemnus – were pronounced Condemnatus, and the others were put under vigil extremis. The planet's resources were in dire peril.

BLOOD VENDETTA

The Aeldari of Craftworld Saim-Hann had divined that Vigilus was of paramount importance in the battle against the Great Enemy. During the first phase of the War of Beasts, they sent some of their fiercest clan warriors to tip the scales of fate against the Chaos uprising that was gathering pace on the planet.

The Seer Council of Saim-Hann, at the insistence of Farseer Anvirr Keltoc, petitioned the clan chieftains to head through the webway towards Vigilus. The Aeldari were hard-pressed defending their own territory from Chaos incursion, but nonetheless sent a small force into the labyrinth dimension, for they knew the Farseer would not send them on such an errand unless it would further the craftworld's own agenda. At the head of the webway force was the Autarch Rhyloor of Clan Moirec. Alongside him was his close relative, the Spiritseer Qelanaris.

Farseer Keltoc had determined that the critical point of Vigilus' fate could be shifted by the assassination of a single individual – Vannadan the Firebrand. Originally of Storvhal stock, this demagogue had roused the populace of that volcanic region, converting them to the worship of a fiery god that he alone knew as Tzeentch, the Changer of the Ways. With the seeds of rebellion sown in the fertile ground of Storvhal, he had moved on the poorer districts of Hyperia, seeking to convert the people there to his chaotic creed. Should he be allowed to succeed, Keltoc had foreseen that an industrial magma eruption would be triggered in Storvhal, causing a chain reaction that would stretch to the Martyr's Pyre district of Saint's Haven. This would kill many of the continent's leaders, and destroy the planet's war council.

The Aeldari force emerged from the webway gate in the west of Kaelac's Bane, the spirit divinations of Qelanaris enabling them to avoid the Drukhari that raided from the blizzards. Making haste upon sleek jetbikes or riding within Wave Serpent transports, the Aeldari sped through the clouds towards their target. They found Vannadan preaching his rhetoric exactly where Keltoc had said he would be. Eschewing coordination with Imperial forces, their killing strike was swift – after a brief and bloody battle, Vannadan's lacerated body was pitched into the street.

The flashing blurs of Saim-Hann's jetbikes had not gone unnoticed, and the Aeldari's sudden

appearance in Hyperia had been reported to the Aquilarian Council. The planet's rulers, upon hearing that a force of Aeldari was engaged in the slaughter of citizens, assumed them to be the same breed as the Drukhari that had been reported raiding Oteck and Dirkden Hivesprawls. The council sent orders for a retributive strike, and within minutes an airborne team of Militarum Tempestus descended from the skies. Dropping into the fray on grav-chutes, the 47th Antrell Lions surrounded the Aeldari even as the xenos killed the last of Vannadan's tainted rebels. Qelanaris attempted a parley, explaining that they had excised a canker at the heart of the realm.

His words were met with a barrage of firepower. Autarch Rhyloor was gunned down, and most of the Windriders of his kinband were slain alongside him in that first bloody act. Qelanaris and the survivors withdrew, vowing a bloody revenge.

Qelanaris made haste for the webway gate, taking the spirit stones of his slain comrades with him. Upon returning to Saim-Hann he used all his arts as a Spiritseer to install the souls of his kindred in wraithbone shells. He sought not the sanction of the Seer Council, and did not heed the warnings of the other clans. He and his kindred would have their vengeance, even if it meant raising the dead to do so.

Years later, when Qelanaris returned to Vigilus in the third phase of the war, he sought revenge not only against the thuggish infantry that had gunned his people down, but the commanders that had orchestrated the strike. He did not know that by this point the Aquilarian Council had been replaced. Moving fast, the strike force of the living and the dead brought their vendetta against the seat of governance itself – the Aquilarian Palace. There he was to meet his match against the Ultramarines of Marneus Calgar.

A TRAGIC MISTAKE

Lieutenant Eothrus of the Ultramarines 2nd Company had been entrusted with the defence of the Aquilarian Palace. When he and his Extremis Guard moved to intercept the Aeldari that had slaughtered the Antrell Lions at the eastern gates, he became embroiled in a battle of distractions, feints and false flights. Whilst the bulk of his force took on the jetbikers that moved like lightning through the plazas and gatehouses of the palace, he moved to cut off any thrust aimed for the palace's most vital chambers. It was an insightful move, and sure enough, Eothrus found Qelanaris making for the Senate Hall.

Eothrus approached with the intention of forming a truce, perhaps even an alliance. He had heard from Haldor Icepelt, who had fought alongside the red-armoured Aeldari in the Stygius war zone, that the warrior codes of Saim-Hann were honourable. That day, however, Qelanaris' code was one of revenge. A bitter struggle broke out, Aeldari slain by plasma and bolt even as the Primaris Marines were torn apart by wraithcannon fire. The Saim-Hann warband pushed through the Ultramarines cordon, pinning them with a storm of shuriken and blasting at the doors of the Senate Hall. They were within striking distance of their goal when the doors opened of their own accord – and a quartet of Chapter Masters stormed out, their honour guard close behind. Qelanaris was forced to flee for his life, robbed of his final revenge.

DONTORIA FIREWALL

When it became known that two entire subsprawls and a city-sized spaceport had been lost to the Gellerpox Infected, the Space Marines quickly established a quarantine zone and a military cordon.

The Aquilarian Council had been slow to respond to du Languille's missive; to them Dontoria was of secondary importance. The Vigilus Senate instead summoned the Rogue Trader to hear what she had to say. Within scant minutes of her testimony, the lords of the senate arrived at a consensus. Chapter Master Raquilon Zandtus would lead his Primaris Chapter, the Necropolis Hawks, against the Gellerpox Infected, for his companies were expert in the arts of city-fighting. Meanwhile, the Crimson Fists of Brother-Captain Jhermandes would work with the calculating minds of the Iron Hands to effect the most rigorous cordon imaginable to contain the spread of the plague.

What the Necropolis Hawks found in the decommissioned Litmus Dock was horrific. Peg-legged mutants with skulls distended and melded with steel lurched from alleyways and choke points, vermin leapt from windows to stab at armour joints with proboscis and forelimb, and lumbering flesh-hulks belched flame from their mouths. At close confines, the powerful claws and improvised weapons of these monsters made them lethal opponents, and many a Necropolis Hawk was lain low in ambush. But the warriors of that Chapter were used to employing their guns to full effect even when their targets were but a hand's breadth away. Their Intercessors blasted their foes back in overlapping fields of bolt fire, whilst Hellblasters incinerated the larger mutants. With fury, discipline and self-sacrifice, they corralled the milling Gellerpox mutants, hunting down their leaders as the Crimson Fists drew the cordon tight.

By mustering the Land Raider Redeemers of the Crimson Fists with the Hellhounds of the Vigilant Guard, and setting fire to selected sections of the hivesprawl's promethium pipelines, a literal firewall was established around the infected zone. Calgar and his Senate could see no other choice. Though it meant consigning hundreds of thousands of healthy civilians to a hideous death, the quarantine was established and the area brought largely under control. Yet that too was not to last. For the scions of Nurgle are tenacious foes…

RACE FOR THE MANDEVILLE POINT

Upon her return to Dontoria Hivesprawl, Delarique du Languille met with her contacts in the Vigilant Guard. Her psyker adjutant, the talented Morghalian, had experienced harrowing nightmares of a doom spilling out from Dontoria towards Terra itself. It came in the form of a flesh-plague that turned men into cyborg Daemons.

Du Languille knew better than to dismiss this notion as mere imagination or paranoia, for she took her psyker's advice very seriously. Convincing her Tech-Priest Enginseer contacts of the urgency of her request, the Rogue Trader communicated with the scribes of Neo-vellum via a tight-beam noospheric data tether. She requested the shipping manifests for Litmus Dock with high clearance, and in response received a message tube back. Her worst fears were confirmed. The quarantine had been breached.

The export of goods from the hivesprawl had ceased as soon as the Space Marines had put their quarantine into practice. Few, if any, civilian refugees had managed to flee the area by circumventing the Adeptus Arbites' control of the planet's egress routes. Unfortunately, the blanket prohibition on space travel from the docks had been too late to stop the bulk freighter *Illustrious Cargo* from leaving. It had left the planet three days hence, after the Gellerpox had been detected but before the quarantine had been put in place. If it carried Infected, it was a biological time bomb. Already, it was bound for the planet's Mandeville Point, that zone where a craft could slide into the warp without the gravity of either the planet or its star influencing its navigation calculations.

Should the *Cargo* safely translate into the empyrean, it would be out of their reach forever. With interstellar communication all but impossible, the craft would likely make haste for the Dharrovar System unhindered. From there, it could make the journey all the way across the Nachmund Gauntlet and into the Imperium Sanctus. If there were infected mutants inside, and they carried their hideous warp affliction towards Terra, it could consign an entire swathe of space to damnation.

This was a fate that du Languille could not allow. When she consulted with the war council of Saint's Haven, it became clear that their warships, built for raw might instead of speed, could not catch the freighter before it made warp translation. The only ship fast enough to catch the *Cargo* was in her personal fleet, a sleek corvette she had named simply the *Messenger*. Unfortunately, the craft was for pleasure only, and had next to nothing in the way of guns – certainly nothing that could trouble a bulk freighter.

The Rogue Trader did not shirk. Within the hour, the *Messenger* was streaking through space towards the coordinates supplied by the Neo-vellum augurators.

Within sixty hours the green-grey dot of the *Illustrious Cargo* grew larger on the ship's bridge triptych until its lumpen, ungainly form filled the screens. With grim efficiency, du Languille mustered her team, taking a handful of her finest agents with her in the craft's single transition pod, and boarded the suspect vessel.

What the team found in that hellish interior will remain the burden of du Languille and the Lord Macragge alone. Only she made it back to the surface of Vigilus, and she did not speak a word about it after her quarantine and subsequent debrief with Calgar. What is known is that the *Illustrious Cargo* was destroyed just before it could translate into the warp, the energy signature of the explosion indicating that its engine decks had been sabotaged from the inside.

Only at the conclusion of Calgar's debrief did Dontoria reveal its last, awful secret. The scribes of Neo-vellum had despatched a second message tube, handed over in cordial ceremony to du Languille and the Lord Macragge. It spoke of three other bulk freighters that had left the same Dontorian dock, a day earlier than the *Illustrious Cargo*, but with the same shipping idents and the same destination.

Du Languille had likely saved an entire system from becoming a plague site by destroying the *Cargo*. Yet for all her efforts, for all the sacrifice of those that had fought their way to the heart of the infected craft, the Gellerpox Infection was crossing the stars towards Terra.

HOPE YET

Though the Orks were running wild across much of the planet, there was one false continent where order and efficiency had managed to overcome the anarchy of the xenos threat. Mortwald would not fall – and when reinforcements arrived, the region was able to turn its defence footing to one of aggression.

Since the fall of the Oteck Hollows, water was becoming ever scarcer upon Vigilus, and the convoys for its transference less and less common. With Grodholev Subsprawl falling to the Gellerpox, Dontoria was in danger of losing its own main source of water – Lake Dontor, which was now under daily vigil in case of disease. The Vigilus Senate had still not located the Death Guard forces that had brought the Gellerpox to the planet, and suspected that if the traitors found a way through the firewall they would move against the lake with yet more contaminants.

Water was not the only resource that was hard to come by. The false continent of Mortwald was the producer of most of the planet's

food and medicine, but with the Ork menace threatening its outskirts, and the Cult of the Pauper Princes rising within its southern reaches, production was drying up, and the common people were paying the price.

Some of the original members of the Aquilarian Council implied that Mortwald's rulers, the planetary governor's militant brother Deinos Agamemnus amongst them, would be content to see to their own defence at the exclusion of all else. The question hung in the air – even should Vigilus' defenders throw back the xenos, would they starve to death in the process?

Mortwald did not lack for experienced soldiery, for over the

centuries since Deinos had taken rulership of that prefecture it had been reinforced by regiments from the Indigan Praefects, Loquhar Prime Sandsmen, Ventrillian Nobles, Vostroyan Firstborn, and lately even dispossessed Cadian Shock Troops. They would gladly fight actions against the Orks, whether the force fields were active or not. Many of them had been engaged at the Cadian Gate. A land war where they defended heavily entrenched positions against a foe that would fight in a brutal but traditional fashion seemed far more straightforward than the nightmare of fighting the forces of Chaos.

When the planet's Bastion force fields went down en masse, the Orks of Tanka Spill made a

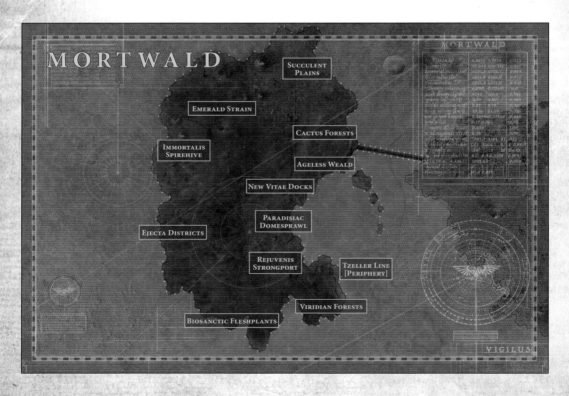

MORTWALD

- SUCCULENT PLAINS
- EMERALD STRAIN
- CACTUS FORESTS
- IMMORTALIS SPIREHIVE
- AGELESS WEALD
- NEW VITAE DOCKS
- PARADISIAC DOMESPRAWL
- EJECTA DISTRICTS
- REJUVENIS STRONGPORT
- TZELLER LINE [PERIPHERY]
- VIRIDIAN FORESTS
- BIOSANCTIC FLESHPLANTS

VIGILUS

headlong assault against the Deinos Trench Network to the north of Mortwald. The Astra Militarum held fast, gunning down the Orks with heavy bolters, autocannons and lasguns as the greenskins raced across the killing grounds. Where the Orks came on in armoured hosts too numerous to stop, the Astra Militarum would fall back, conceding a line or two, forcing the xenos vehicles to flounder in the deep trenches. Slowed to a crawl, they were easy prey for the lascannon beams and krak missiles of the weapon teams in the bunkers behind. Once the push was blunted, Ogryn work teams would be sent in to clear the wreckage and shore up the defences, using anything from slabs of metal to corpses.

For weeks, the Orks made one push after another, even attacking through the forests of barbed wire that typified the Tzeller Line to the south. Still the Astra Militarum held fast, not only against the greenskins, but also the cult uprisings of the Ejecta Districts,

Biosanctic Fleshplants and worker habs. Lord Deinos Agamemnus preached a mantra, compulsorily reinforced via the command echelons and repeated among the troops thousands of times a day – Mortwald would not fall.

When the bulk landers and gunships of the Imperial reinforcements made it through the Ork blockades to New Vitae Docks, the stubborn resolve of the Mortwald defenders turned to outright zeal. The sight of hundreds of Imperial Fists striding to the front line in bright heraldic yellow, unafraid of any enemy weapon, put fire into the souls of all that witnessed them. Within days Captain Fane, the laconic and battle-scarred leader of the Imperial Fists 5th Company, had assessed the plans of the Deinos Trench Network and the Tzeller Line. He put into place an overlapping defence pattern of impressive efficiency, moving his warriors to any site where the Orks attacked with heavy assets. When

it came to enemy infantry and even vehicle squadrons, the captain systematically destroyed anything that dared his gunsights. Only the titanic scrap-walkers that strode over the trenches towards Electros Hive had might enough to break the eastern cordon; so large and numerous were the Stompas that the Imperial forces had no choice but to concede the entire district and retreat to higher ground to muster a counter-attack.

When the vast, fat-bellied hangar ships that transported Imperial Knights lowered through the clouds at New Vitae Docks, Captain Fane was amongst the delegation that greeted the occupants. The ground shook as the massive war engines strode out of their hangars to defend Mortwald. Amongst the adamantium lances bearing the heraldry of the Knightly households came Freeblades from Dharrovar, crusading from the rift corridor to ensure its gatehouse did not fall. On that day, Captain Fane muttered praise to the Emperor.

A CHARGE INTO LEGEND

Many of the Imperial Knights that had landed at Mortwald were keen to sally forth against the monstrous Ork walkers emerging from the Scrap Cities. Some put this down to youthful bravado – though as the weeks of battle slid by, Captain Fane of the Imperial Fists began to think there was something else at play.

The Knights of House Terryn made haste to attack the Stompas that had invaded Mortwald, engaging them at range and methodically taking them out, one by one. In contrast, the Imperial Knights that had arrived from Dharrovar petitioned to drive their adamantium lances deep into enemy territory. They maintained that fighting the footsoldiers of the xenos races amongst the trenches would win them little glory, for to the nobles who piloted the giant heraldic walkers, mere infantry posed little threat. But there was something in the Knights' insistence that they form the vanguard that raised eyebrows amongst their allies in the Imperial Fists, Fane in particular.

Even for headstrong young nobles, these Freeblades seemed too eager for a frontal assault. There was a shadow behind the eyes of these young warriors – and especially their leader, the red-bearded young noble Joren Vanaklimptas – that Fane recognised. Speaking to his trusted aides in low tones, Fane revealed that he saw something of himself in that look. Since his company of Imperial Fists had concluded their war against the Mindclaw Coven of Tzeentch, he had been haunted by waking dreams of such potency he sometimes wished for death just to put an end to them. Could it be that these Freeblades had faced a similar ordeal, but did not have the

mental conditioning of the Adeptus Astartes to cope with it? Could their insistence upon recklessness be connected to the fact they had obscured their traditional heraldic insignia and taken new identities?

To Deinos Agamemnus it was irrelevant. He saw the Knights as powerful tools that would help him win his private war. Naturally, he was glad of their coming, but to him they were but cavalier pieces in a game of Regicide. He issued an edict forbidding them from heading out past the trench lines and the Bastion shield network and into the wastes beyond. As a powerful source of artillery that could out-range nearly all the war assets the

Orks could send against them, they were too valuable to risk. Besides which, they had an obligation to the thrones of their elders and betters. For a time, the Freeblade Knights grudgingly agreed to abide by the laws. The princeps of the Reaver Titan *Heresium's Bane*, a long-time ally of Deinos and his traditionalist cronies, reminded the Knights of the duty they had to the people of Mortwald. He pointed out that despite the fact that his Warhound maniple, the Hyperian Hounds, wished for nothing more than to be on the hunt, they too held fast.

Chastened, the Knights deployed alongside Captain Fane in a series of staggered defences that saw several Ork attacks blunted and scattered to the winds. For long days, however, the Freeblades and their towering Titan allies stood motionless and silent, awaiting a foe that was slow to come.

Every few days the Orks attacked Mortwald, and each time their forces were ground to a halt before being driven back in disarray. Yet the heavy assets being sent against Captain Fane and his allies were growing larger and more formidable with every passing week. The Ork war machines, far more numerous than the Imperial equivalents, were at first the size of Dreadnoughts – but then swelled into fat-bellied monstrosities the size of Knights, then Warhounds.

When lumbering machines that rivalled *Heresium's Bane* in size appeared on the horizon, Fane made his final decision. The Ork factories had to be shut down. He issued a series of curt orders to Vanaklimptas and his fellow Knights over a closed channel, citing his authority as that of the First Founding and a true son of Rogal Dorn. Within the hour they were striding across the Deinos Trench Line and out into the wastelands, accompanied by the Hyperian Hounds.

It was time to let slip the dogs of war.

BATTLE OF TANKA SPILL

The Freeblade Knights that assaulted the Ork Scrap City to the east of Mortwald, Tanka Spill, approached from the Deinos Trench Network under cover of the dust storm kicked up by an Ork attack wave. Waiting until the greenskins were upwind, they smashed their way eastward through the horde at full charge. Expertly plying their ion shields to deflect fire, the Knights were through the foe's lines and out the other side before the xenos realised what had hit them. The Ork horde was confounded, with half their number wishing to go back, and the others not knowing why the sudden delay had occurred. Milling in disarray, they were easy prey for the Warhound maniple and the Reaver *Heresium's Bane*. As twilight turned to darkness, on charged the Freeblade Knights, their attack upon the now-poorly defended Tanka Spill a devastating lance to the guts of a dormant beast of war. Explosions lit the night as the Freeblades cut apart Ork factories with their melta weapons and blasted half-built Stompas to scrap with their rapid fire battle cannons. Fane, sending a vox over a closed channel, ordered the triumphant Knights to head back to Mortwald to resupply, for he could see the factory city was aflame even from the sprawl's trenches. But the Freeblades pressed on, taking their fight to the next Scrap City. There they charged headlong into the massed battlewagons and gunned-up walkers that had mustered for the next assault, killing thousands of Orks before they were surrounded.

AQUA METEORIS

The sudden xenos conquests of Megaborealis had seen much of the city erupt in fire. Resources were growing ever more precious – and none more so than the water harnessed from orbit by the Adeptus Mechanicus. The leaders of the Pauper Princes knew of this weak point, and exploited it mercilessly.

The ongoing war for Megaborealis had seen the ordered mind of Archmagos Nesium Caldrike joined with the merciless pragmatism of Fabricator Vosch and the clinical, cold-hearted logic of the Iron Hands. It had proven a potent combination. Megaborealis was largely coming back under Imperial control, district by district. The Space Marines would break the back of each major incursion, and when the culprits went to ground, the Skitarii and their Tech-Priest masters would exterminate that which was left over.

With the auspicators and omnispexes of the Imperial defenders keyed to xenos bio-signatures, each grid-pattern hunt was methodical and effective. The Cult of the Pauper Princes, having secured brief dominance over a third of the Megaborealis sprawl, had been forced to fall back in a score of different war zones. A month after the arrival of the Iron Hands, the cultists were fighting a guerrilla war once more against the resurgent Skitarii macroclades.

There was one exception, however, and it was a critical one. In the district surrounding the Stygian Spires and the Greater Omnissian Hoist, the icons of the Genestealer Cult were still raised high. A foremost Primus of the cult, Dethru Noan, had designated that region one of paramount importance. Not only was the vast, megalithic hive of the Spires the nexus of all Megaborealis' command structures, it was also the site where water was processed from the meteors caught in orbit and conveyed to the planet's surface via Vosch's towering, counterweighted winch mechanism, the Omnissian Hoist.

Primus Noan was a rationalist more than a fanatic. He knew that without this source of water, and with convoys transporting emergency rations cut off by the Orks all over the planet, the Adeptus Mechanicus could be starved of the vital fluid they needed. He intended to besiege the greater hivesprawl from its own central keep.

To put his plans into motion, Noan entered the vast brood cathedrum in the lower levels of Megaborealis, passing through corpse-strung colonnades and banners propped tall against piles of captured wargear. Waiting for him in the crypt, half-submerged in the semi-liquefied remains of his deceased followers, was Grandsire Wurm. Strange bony growths had risen to form a weird throne of chitin around the hulking Purestrain, and familiars bubbled up from the flesh slurry to stare at Noan with alien intensity. The Grandsire's eyes glittered malevolently as it flexed its claws, for the creature did not relish being disturbed in its bio-psychic communions with the wider cult.

Fortunately for him, Noan had enlisted the aid of the Magus known as Slynte. The psyker made a mind-link with the Grandsire and put across the battle plan on Noan's behalf. A long, tense minute stretched by before the Grandsire shifted from its pool, standing up to its full terrifying height and barging past the petitioners. The Magus announced grandly that the assault upon the Stygian Spires would be led by the Patriarch itself, then hurried from the tomb after his master.

Within a single day of scuttling activity, the undersump of the Stygian Spires was filled with Purestrain Genestealers. They came from all across the continent and beyond, answering the psychic call of their Patriarch without hesitation. There were no hunting howls echoing through the night, no call-and-response or chanting of prayers. The oncoming demise of Megaborealis was silent, but moved with a singular purpose.

The takeover of the Stygian Spires was bloody in the extreme. First came the event that would be known in history books as the Vertical Massacre. Like many Imperial hives, the Spires had under-levels so deep, dank and labyrinthine that none truly knew their full extent. With the war against the Orks taking up so many resources in the city above, the Skitarii patrols that were operating down in the substrata had been drained to almost nothing. It was not only the Purestrains that converged upon the Stygian Spires, summoned by the Patriarch's call, but every cult member in the continent. Long-sealed hatches were broken open, crawlspaces unblocked, and new tunnels dug with rockgrinder and macro-drill. As industrious and focused as termites, the cultists burrowed their way into the lower strata of the Stygian Spires, their kill teams taking down all enemy resistance at a slow but methodical pace. When the warning klaxons sounded, a full fifth of the Spires' tunnels were already under cult control.

The corridors of the Stygian Spires resounded with the metallic crump of thousands of Skitarii feet as the garrison scrambled to intercept the invaders below. A sprawling multi-level battle erupted, with the Skitarii quickly gaining the upper hand. They fought with the determination of zealous men defending their temple, and their Tech-Priest Dominus masters had put into place contingencies and battle plans for every conceivable form of invasion. With the alert protocols triggering these long-honed battle plans, the response was quick, and the corridors were soon littered with the corpses of xenos hybrids. The

one flaw in the Tech-Priests' plans was that they did not factor in the precious water pipelines.

As the vanguard organisms of the Tyranid race, a quirk of Genestealer anatomy allows them to fold their gangling bodies into tight crawlspaces, holes and tubes, the better to exploit vectors of passage from one infection site to another. After Grandsire Wurm's sickle-like claws ripped gaping holes in the water pipes that carried the aqua meteoris, the Purestrains of the cult squeezed inside each pipe, one after another. Tireless, they wriggled and crawled against the high pressure flow for a full day – a feat no man, or even Ork, could have accomplished – until they reached the water farms at the top levels of the spires. Lightly defended, with the bulk of the Skitarii engaged far below, the farms soon looked like abattoirs, strewn with torn flesh and bionic limbs. With their enemies attacking from above and below, the Skitarii were trapped – and after three days of fighting, overcome.

A Strange Stampede

Vigilus' premium water supply industry was slowed to a trickle when the Beastmasters of the Drukhari Wych Cults learned how to control the snow-white ice mantises that hunted through the blizzards of Kaelac's Bane. By modulating their agoniser whips and splinter ammunition to drive the giant insects into a skittering frenzy, they herded hundreds of the creatures across the glaciers and swathes of permafrost – and straight into the canyons of the Kaelac macroquarries. The Drukhari took a great deal of sadistic sustenance from watching the stallion-sized ice mantises scything apart Skitarii and quarrymen in a bloodbath that saw rivulets of gory slush stain the snow of each crater bright red.

KAELAC'S BANE

QUIXOTINE LOOP

TUNDRIC PERIMETER

DEARTHLAND PERMAFROST

QUARANTINE CRYOFERNUS [DRUKHARI PORTAL]

GLACIA BETUS MACROQUARRY

GEOSCRYING INSTILLATION [NON-THETIC]

VENSTRAN IMPACT CRATER

ICE MANTIS DRIFTS

HELIOSTRIKE IMPACT CRATER

GLACIA OMICROID MACROQUARRY

DIVESTRUM BLIZZARD

KAELAC'S BANE

VIGILUS

ASSAULT ON THE SCRAP CITIES

The Space Marines on Vigilus had brought fiery death to the xenos invaders in dozens of hivesprawl districts, and now their leaders were looking further afield. If the Imperial alliance was to win this war, they would have to take on the beast in its own lair.

The charge of the Dharrovar Freeblades, though ultimately doomed to failure, had opened up an unprecedented opportunity for the Space Marine coalition. Perhaps Captain Fane had foreseen this as a consequence of his covert orders to the young Imperial Knights; perhaps the Adeptus Astartes were simply capitalising on the changing face of war. But for a time, in the Ork territory to the east of Mortwald known as the Green Diamond, all eyes were upon the spearhead of Imperial Knights moving in for the kill.

Within seconds of Fane informing his fellow Space Marine Captains of the Knight charge, several strike forces had been despatched via Thunderhawk and Stormtalon Gunship. The bike-mounted assault companies of the White Scars, led by Olujin Khan, and the Ravenwing, led by the taciturn Meneraeus, were not far behind. Seen from the Aeronautica Imperialis bombers that flew in support, the Space Marine assaults were small but lethal, closing upon their Scrap City targets like torpedoes streaking through the void to scuttle a group of bulk cruisers.

The capabilities of the Ork heavy artillery – bristling from the sides of their vessels, and built for ship-to-ship combat in the depths of space – had been felt keenly by the Imperial Guard columns that had strayed within their reach. A single shell could blast apart a tank squadron, and wreak utter havoc on any that approached the Scrap Cities from the wrong angle. Those who attacked the Orks in broad daylight would soon enough be treated to a broadside so powerful that it left a ridge-like chain of craters across the landscape. Olujin Khan, known to some as the Skyhawk for his knack of ensuring air superiority, had mounted enough aerial reconnaissance to spy out where the super-cannons of the Orks were situated, and the areas that they would target. Many of the Ork broadside guns had been dismantled and rebuilt on

ORK SCRAP CITIES
[WESTERN CLUSTER]

RUNTHIVE

FORT DAKKA

TANKA SPILL

DROGZOT'S CRATER

SILTID RIVER

THE GIANTS

mobile carriages, the better to cover every angle of approach. Olujin's squadrons of Stormtalons had reported back that those guns were now targeted on the Knights and Titans that had made their forlorn charges against Runthive, Drogzot's Crater and Fort Dakka. Accessing combat data from previous mechanised assaults, the Khan mapped out routes of approach that capitalised on the blind spots of the Ork guns – a technique he had learned from the harsh lessons of the Damocles war zone. He drove his strike force like a spear into the belly of the xenos settlements.

The initial attack runs saw the biker packs reach the enemy with only a few casualties, for the last of the Freeblade Knights was still holding doggedly on, covering their approach. Every greenskin eye watched hungrily as that proud Knight was finally pulled limb from limb. Thousands of Orks died in that first assault, torn apart by massed bolter fire as the White Scars and Ravenwing swept in. They

jinked through alleys and scrap shanties, attack bikes' heavy weapon firepower thundering into the revving war-wagons and flatbeds that sought to mobilise and join the fight. Wherever the Orks gathered a cogent defence, the Space Marine bikers would peel away, coming back around in a screeching circle to attack from another direction.

Perhaps, if they had made but one strike and then retreated, giving themselves a chance to regroup and return another day, the Space Marines could have worn the Orks down with their shock assaults. But time was running out. They pressed their attack, driving ever further in to engage the Kan Factories at each Scrap City's heart.

Orks do not scare easily from battle, especially not when they have

numbers on their side; if anything, the din of war makes them even more bellicose and aggressive. As such, the greenskins swarmed to meet their Space Marine foes, and with not one but two forces fighting hard against them, the increasing heat of war inflamed their lust for conflict to critical levels.

It was at that point that the entirety of the Ravenwing army broke off from the engagement and made straight for the Vhulian Swirl. They did not communicate their intent to the White Scars they had been fighting alongside – indeed, it seemed to Olujin Khan an act of cowardice, though he was loathe to believe it. With half their strike force gone in a matter of seconds, the White Scars found themselves fighting a growing horde of battle-hungry Orks – including no small number of warbikes that were every bit as fast as their own steeds. Olujin Khan had no option but to order a fighting retreat, hurtling into a dust storm with vows of revenge upon his lips.

A NEW DOOM

The fate of Vigilus was swinging from salvation to damnation with each day the war ground on. For every district reclaimed, another was lost. Citizens prayed for a miracle to tip the balance in their favour – but quite the opposite was to occur.

With the Vigilus Senate making uncompromising strategic decisions and the Space Marines attacking high priority targets in a ceaseless crusade of destruction, the Imperial citizenry had begun to hope they could win back their planet. Then a new threat loomed. Strange vox ghosts and unsettling omens had intensified of late, unsettling all who heard them. The bleeding skies around the Great Rift appeared to blacken at its edges, like the exterior of a gangrenous wound. From those glowering skies came a brief spear of light. Augur rites and hyper-auspex readings were focused upon it, but the source of the anomaly could not be ascertained – and,

amongst the carnage, it was soon forgotten. Only the agents of Tzeentch on Storvhal recognised it for what it truly was – the first sign of a Chaos invasion aimed straight for the Vigilus System's heart.

More unsettling phenomena blossomed, their instances plotted on maps by the Vigilus Senate like spots of mould on a damp wall. Lucienne Agamemnus' psyker-prophets claimed that their readings of the Emperor's Tarot were turning up the same cards over and over again – that of the Daemonblade, crossed with the Herald of Darkness and the Knight of the Abyss. Reports circulated of strange,

bat-winged figures that haunted the tallest spires of the hivesprawls, high above the clouds of industry. Dark rumours of abductions amongst the upper echelons of society spread throughout the populace.

Other tales circulated that the gun nests of the upper hives were strangely empty, and the wildest of the stories spoke of evil-looking dragons circling the tips of the aristocratic citadels. Those of the Astra Militarum that were sent to investigate the anomalies did not return – though reports came back from each hive's spire-seekers that blackened bodies and mangled

DIRKDEN ABANDONED

Recognising that he could not win on every front at once, Marneus Calgar reluctantly withdrew his forces from Dirkden Hivesprawl. That small false continent had been overwhelmed by cultists and surrounded by Krooldakka's Orks. It had to be allowed to fall if the others were to stand, for it was so rotten with xenos corruption that to contest it would have been a waste of manpower that Calgar could ill afford to sacrifice.

Though some on the Vigilus Senate called it callous, and even defeatist, his decision was proven to be a wise one. The evacuation of civilians along the Hyperia-Dirkden Fortwall was stopped altogether, and the guards manning the checkpoints largely withdrawn. Only the military forces leaving Dirkden were granted permission to cross into the capital city. These were able to bolster the Adepta Sororitas defenders of Hyperia; working from the Aftermath Zone into the Triadine Plateaus, these redeployed forces vented their fury at being forced to concede Dirkden. One by one, the xenos in southern Hyperia were burned out of their lairs and put to flight, and the Ork-held territory cleansed with fire by vengeful Sisters of Battle.

With the sudden removal of Imperial foes from Dirkden, the Orks that had been attacking from Mekstop City swiftly turned on the Genestealer Cultists of that region instead. A new spate of battles rippled across the hivesprawl as the two rising xenos empires clashed in open war. Within a week of the Imperial withdrawal, over a quarter of the buildings above ground were on fire; seen from Hyperia, the horizon was blackened with smoke.

The true cost of this decision, of course, was to the civilians. With one curt order, Calgar abandoned tens of millions, damning them from Glaive Point to the Rescalid Underworks. Refugees fled in great crowds, seeking to be let along the Fortwall to Hyperia. They were held back by the Crimson Fists assigned to that region, for hiding amongst the unsullied citizens and even the Astra Militarum were Neophytes and brood brothers in thrall to the Pauper Princes. When rocks were thrown by protesters, the Space Marines opened fire. The resultant carnage was to form an indelible blemish on the honour of that Chapter, especially given that they were later forced to concede the Fortwall to the cultists. Still, Calgar was convinced their actions had been necessary.

corpses littered the steeples and rooftops.

Marneus Calgar and the Vigilus Senate took a stern and intense interest in the anomalies haunting the highest spires – for they occurred not in a single hivesprawl, but across every one of the planet's continent-sized cities.

To Calgar's mind, there was no way the blame for these high altitude occurrences could be laid at the door of their principal xenos foes. Preferring their wars loud, up-close and violent, the Orks had concentrated their air war on strafing runs, low altitude dogfights and dive-bombing. The cult uprising had shown no evidence of having air support to speak of. As a result, the Imperial Navy had, until now, confined their efforts to the skies below the cloud cover, only affecting the loosest patrols and transit engagements above the pollution line.

With the curfew forcing the populace inside at night and the prohibition against looking up at the Great Rift mercilessly enforced, few ever raised their eyes to the skies, and the entire planet was to pay the price. The Vigilus Senate discovered too late that whilst they had been focused on the ground war against the Orks, and the below-ground war against the Genestealer Cult, another war front had opened up high in the spires. That covert operation had been rendered all but invisible to those below by the thick pall of pollution that choked the Vigilus skies. The irony of the planet's populace being known as Vigilants became painfully clear to the Senate – for they had allowed an enemy force to claim a power base right over their heads.

The plague of nightmares that had assailed Vigilus ever since the breaking of the Noctis Aeterna grew more and more intense. The worst affected gabbled and muttered in their sleep, using the same phrase over and over again. They spoke not in Low Gothic, nor its High equivalent, but in a language that none amongst the planet's adepts could decipher.

It was the investigating Inquisitor Frenza of the Ordo Malleus that eventually codified the language – behind closed doors – as the Dark Tongue of Chaos. At first the babble was indecipherable even to her, but as time progressed the syllables hardened into distinct words. When several of the afflicted were gathered in the same place at the same time, it immediately became clear that they were all chanting the same thing, in unison: 'The Dark King is coming.'

The Vigilus Senate's investigation into the events taking place in the city spires soon bore ghastly fruit. Every hive spire's defenders had been slain, and the tips of each citadel claimed by an airborne host. The blasphemous text scrawled in blood on the spire-tips confirmed that this was nothing to do with the Orks, nor was it down to the actions of the Genestealer Cult or the Drukhari raiders. It was the work of the Heretic Astartes – airborne Raptors, Warp Talons and Heldrakes, apparently led by a murderous demagogue known as Haarken Worldclaimer, the Herald of the Apocalypse.

When Worldclaimer's voice echoed across the planet it proved terrifying in itself, but it was the woe promised by his speeches, the picture it painted of hells to come, that turned men's guts to water. His message rang out across the planet from countless hijacked vox-units tainted with scrapcode. It was bawled, crackling and distorted, from the gargoyle vox-sets of a thousand Raptors and Warp Talons. Its meaning was undeniably clear, and its message stark – the planet belonged to Abaddon the Despoiler, and he would soon be there to claim it in person.

14.010 POST – THE INFECTION SPREADS

As promethium fires blazed around Dontoria, the Iron Hands enforcing the quarantine allowed frustration and repugnance to overwhelm their nobler natures. Ruthless efficiency became sheer brutality, and desperation turned to terror amongst the trapped populace. Preferring to brave fire and pox than face the merciless Iron Hands, bands of resourceful Dontorians broke out of the restricted area and fled. Efficient as strategic cogitators, the Iron Hands deployed kill teams to contain these breakouts. However, their forces came under sudden heavy attack from the Death Guard still lurking in the city. Reports circulated of daemonic entities manifesting alongside Mortarion's sons.

14.641 POST – THE HERALD OF THE DESPOILER

Across every hivesprawl and slum on Vigilus, a darkly charismatic voice rang out. It was that of Haarken Worldclaimer, called by some the Herald of the Apocalypse. He broadcast his message to Human, Ork and Genestealer Cultist alike, and through arcane means ensured it reached every ear able to hear it. By spirit-linking his Daemon-tainted vox array to those of his widespread Raptor acolytes, his Heldrake fear squadrons and even the laud hailers of the hive spires he had already captured, he made sure that his ominous message was spread to every corner of the world:

'This planet is claimed in the name of Abaddon, Despoiler of Worlds. Know that you will kneel before him, or you will burn.'

THE RISE OF CHAOS

With the Imperium's armies fixed on the combined threats of Orks, Aeldari and Genestealer Cultists, the forces of Haarken Worldclaimer and the Black Legion had already inveigled themselves into the planet's upper spires. They were preparing the way for something much worse.

When the Vigilus Senate gathered in an emergency war conclave to discuss the new enemy that had revealed itself, there came a terrible rumbling crash from high above. The vaulted roof of the council room caved in as the giant golden colossus that once perched atop the Saint's Haven palace – a graven image of Lucienne Agamemnus IX – came smashing down through the stained glass.

The statue was so large and heavy that it crushed a dozen attendants and smashed the antique debating table to splinters, bowling over Calgar and his two Victrix Guard aides in the process. A great gout of daemonfire washed through the council hall in its wake, killing a handful of Primaris guards with its intensity as a Heldrake Daemon Engine roared a wordless challenge into the chambers below.

Marneus and the Victrix Guard fired upwards in response, shielding their eyes against the glowering Great Rift high above them, but the beast had already fled. Calgar thought fast, despatching a Thunderhawk and an escort of Stormtalons straight up into the clouds. An aerial clash ensued between the scrambled force and the Heldrakes that circled the broken tip of the hive. After a gruelling battle, the Adeptus Astartes prevailed – though none on the senate were foolish enough to think the matter at an end. Chaos was corrupting the planet in a dozen different ways.

In the far south, Kaelac's Bane had become ever more vital, for the planet's sources of water had dried up one by one. Seven Imperial armoured companies fought their way across the Ork-infested wastes

from Solor, the Sentinel Hive in Oteck Hivesprawl, towards the Tundric Perimeter of Kaelac's Bane. They passed through the Bastion force field network during a shut-down engineered by their accompanying Tech-Priest Enginseers, and united with the tattered remnants of the continent's garrison. Their respite was brief. The snows were haunted not only by Drukhari raiders, but also covens of automaton-like Thousand Sons. The Rubricae, clad in black as well as the cyan and gold of the Planet of Sorcerers, lit the snow with volley after volley of inferno bolts. The Lord Commissar providing the armoured company's spiritual backbone, one Barthold Dorst, ordered his tanks to effect a headlong charge, crushing several of the automatons in the process. Nonetheless, even the Leman Russ tanks were eventually melted under

the sorcerous warpfire sent their way, and only a handful made it to the glacier mines beyond.

The rulers of Mortwald, thrown into a state of high anxiety by the rumours of a Gellerpox outbreak on the northern borders of their coveted landmass, shut themselves in their strongholds – but not before issuing the order that all sterilised food and water available be seized and locked in there with them. Over the course of the next few months they bled the workers of Mortwald white, claiming far more sustenance than they could ever consume even if each of their number lived to be a thousand years old. Word of this reprehensible behaviour reached the demagogues and preachers of the worker populace, and within the week, an insurrection seethed on the continent's outskirts that had nothing to do with xenos cults or Chaos demagoguery.

The vox-waves and comms networks of the Imperial war effort, already rendered static-laced and inconstant by the baleful influence of the Great Rift, were haunted by whispers that detailed a thousand atrocities to come. At times, the susurrus of voices grew to be a hideous, deafening shriek that shredded the nerves of those who heard it. Over time, the auditory barrage took an ever greater toll on Vigilus' Astra Militarum defenders – eventually, many regiments stopped using their long-range vox altogether. With the breakdown of communication lines further hindering the cohesion of the war effort on the planet, the Vigilus Senate was forced to spread its assets thinner and thinner. The battered world had been brought to breaking point.

And the worst was yet to come.

14.782 POST – THE RAPTORIAL HOST DESCENDS

On wings of fire, the Raptor warbands that followed the Herald of the Apocalypse came down from vast Chaos ships on the dark side of the planet. They concealed themselves in the clouds, and from there attacked the upper echelons of the Vigilus hivesprawls. They came by the thousand, their jump-pack contrails scarring the skies until the night air appeared like a writhing nest of worms. Entire aristocratic dynasties were eradicated overnight as the Raptors fell upon the leaders and would-be rulers of each continent, aiming to destabilise the planet to the point of no recovery before their true master – Abaddon the Despoiler – arrived to claim it as his own.

14.912 POST – WAR AMONGST THE SPIRES

In the highest levels of those hive-spires still standing over Vigilus' troubled cities, the close assault specialists of the Necropolis Hawks, the Ravenwing, and the Ultramarines united to take war to the Chaos invaders plaguing the upper spires. Every hour, ceramite-clad corpses plummeted from the skies to crash into the dwellings and war fronts of the earthbound mortals beneath. With the Ork invaders forging through the cities' outskirts, the Genestealer Cultists boiling up from below, and the Chaos Raptors attacking from above, one thing became clear overall: nowhere was safe.

WAR ZONES

Vigilus was to feel the spiralling death toll of outright war, its defenders reeling in horror and confusion as the true nature of the Imperium Nihilus became clear.

The initial invasions of Vigilus, a planet that had long seen itself as a bastion of sanity and order in a tempestuous universe, were to reveal a terrifying truth. The world's facade of order was easily fractured, its structural integrity already critically damaged by the over-reaching ambitions of the Aquilarian Council and the delvings of the Adeptus Mechanicus.

The enemy that had grown unseen beneath the planet's surface had reached epidemic proportions, and the Orks had rampaged largely unchecked across the planet's wastelands. Meanwhile, that which came from the void to conquer the planet from the spire-tips down – the scourge of Chaos – was arguably more dangerous than the alien hordes. Even the Space Marines that came to safeguard Vigilus found themselves hard-pressed – not to secure victory, but to survive.

The interconnected nature of Vigilus' constituent continents meant that the system was inherently fragile. Rather than the sprawling regions being autonomous, each relied on at least one of the others for a commodity without which it could not function.

The majority of the planet's manpower, used to repopulate areas struck by seismic disaster, or to fill the ranks of such regiments as the Vigilant Guard, came from Dontoria Hivesprawl. Governance, strategic coordination and matters of the faith were set in motion from Saint's Haven in Hyperia. Megaborealis supplied and maintained the Bastion-class force fields that – in theory, at least – kept the other continents

safe. Storvhal was the planet's energy breadbasket, dotted as it was with vast geothermic generators. Mortwald grew and exported the bulk of the planet's food, whereas Kaelac's Bane and Oteck Hivesprawl supplied the vast majority of the water. Even the moon Neo-vellum played a vital role, coordinating the flow of information from the planet to the rest of the Imperium. Only Dirkden Hivesprawl failed to make an invaluable contribution, perhaps leading to its lack of development and status as the smallest and poorest of the planet's metropolises.

As long as the supply lines existed – be they networks of pipelines that tracked the wilderness, armoured convoys that moved freight the hard way, or aerial squadrons of bulk landers and rotorships that redeployed assets at speed – the needs of the continents could be met. But wherever hostile invaders disrupted, cut off or captured such routes, the planetary infrastructure – upon which many defensive assets relied in order to keep operating at full efficacy – was swiftly and severely impacted.

The situation on Vigilus was in many ways a microcosm of that which was occurring across the Imperium on a far grander scale. Out in the blackness, shorn of supplies, communication and the light of faith provided by the Astronomican, the worlds of the Imperium Nihilus were falling one by one. Roboute Guilliman had vowed that Vigilus would not be amongst them, and it was his trusted Chapter Master, Lord Calgar of the Ultramarines, that was sent to do everything in his power to ensure that oath was not broken.

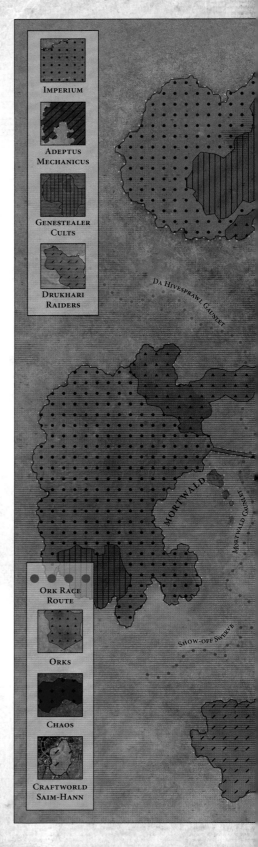

IMPERIUM

ADEPTUS MECHANICUS

GENESTEALER CULTS

DRUKHARI RAIDERS

DA HIVESPRAWL GAUNTLET

MORTWALD

MORTWALD GAUNTLET

SHOW-OFF SWERVE

ORK RACE ROUTE

ORKS

CHAOS

CRAFTWORLD SAIM-HANN

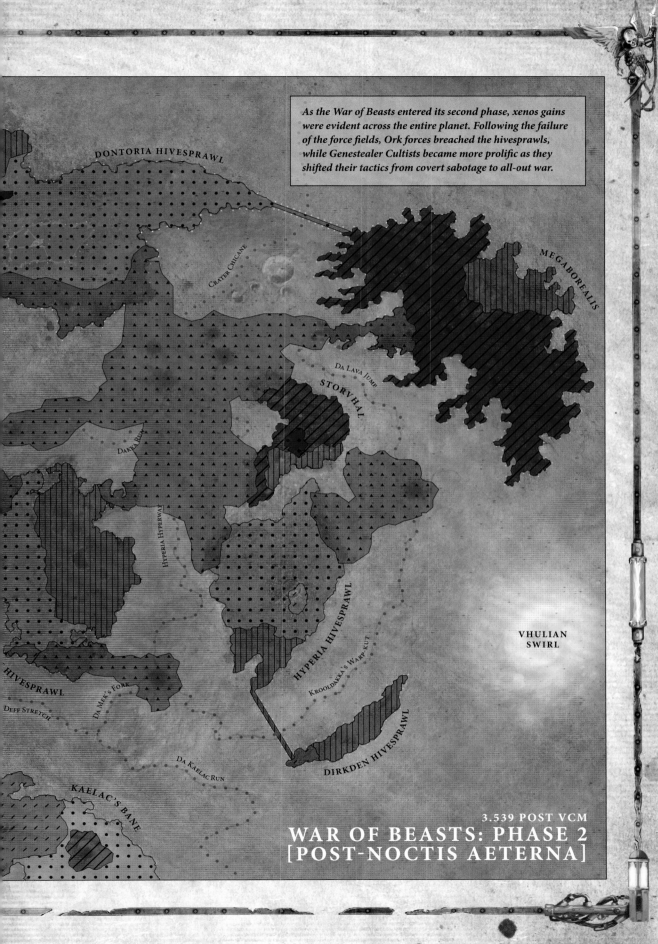

DONTORIA HIVESPRAWL

CRATER CHICANE

MEGABOREALIS

DA LAVA JUMP

STORVHAL

DAKKA BOX

HYPERIA HYPERWAY

HYPERIA HIVESPRAWL

KROOLDAKKA'S WARP-KUT

VHULIAN SWIRL

HIVESPRAWL

DEFF STRETCH

DA MEK'S FORK

DIRKDEN HIVESPRAWL

DA KAELAC RUN

KAELAC'S BANE

As the War of Beasts entered its second phase, xenos gains were evident across the entire planet. Following the failure of the force fields, Ork forces breached the hivesprawls, while Genestealer Cultists became more prolific as they shifted their tactics from covert sabotage to all-out war.

3.539 POST VCM

WAR OF BEASTS: PHASE 2 [POST-NOCTIS AETERNA]

THE TRINITY HIVES

At the start of the war, the Ministorum held de facto power over a trinity of massive hives, known as Sanctifi-Ultima, Hivespire Magentine and Martyr's Pyre. From these strongholds, the agents of the Ministorum and the Adepta Sororitas sallied out to punish any whose faith they feared might waver, and to spread inspiration and courage amongst those that remained true. A legion of Crusaders and Adepta Sororitas, acting under Canoness Superior Temperance Blaise and based at the Abbey Septimus of the Order of Our Martyred Lady, kept the citizenry under strict control, rooting out traitors and heretics, and stopping undesirable elements from disturbing their betters in Saint's Haven.

The Ecclesiarchy's head representative was the Pontifex Slyne Galluck, a man so obese he had to be conveyed about by a hover-bier. He maintained that it was the unceasing prayers of the Ministorum that had kept Vigilus safe for so long, and that as long as the Trinity Hives remained standing, the planet would endure.

The Ministorum controlled the water drunk by the people of Hyperia Hivesprawl, aqua sanctus, which was chemically treated as well as being blessed with holy writ. Their monopoly of this precious resource saw them gain even more power. Furthermore, any members of the Agamemnus Dynasty who stood against the Ministorum soon found their fortunes take a sharp downturn.

HYPERIA HIVESPRAWL

At the onset of the xenos invasion, Hyperia was the capital hivesprawl of the planet Vigilus, home of the Planetary Governor's palace and the Ministorum stronghold that surrounded it.

Together, the strongholds of the Agamemnus Dynasty and the Ministorum formed the city-state of Saint's Haven, high-walled, gun-studded and surrounded by a vast, moat-like chasm known as the Ring of Nothingness. It is said that this abyss was bottomless, though some who looked down from the bridges that crossed it at its eight cardinal points reported seeing lights in the deep darkness below.

Over time, the Ministorum presence in Hyperia went from being a loose confederation of advisors and chaplains to a vast military force with a controlling interest in the region. The

Ministorum were considered by most to be the power behind the throne, and none could deny them – they were doing the Emperor's will, and his was the ultimate authority.

To the west of this city-within-a-city were the Industrial Enclaves, an endless maze of manufactorums from which a large portion of the planet's war materiel came. The Negation District, also in the west, was once a well-maintained gothic quarter, used as neutral ground for the continent's factions to debate the planet's destiny. By the time the Great Rift split the sky, however, this region had become a slum district

populated only by itinerants and refugees of the faith. To the north were the Twin Chasms, mined exhaustively for amethyst since they yawned wide after the Greater Hyperian Quake of 882.292 previo. Nearby was Sanctifi-Ultima – a giant spiral-tipped hive with huge concentric rings of amaranthec manufactorums around its base. These liquor-sludge distilleries spewed out baleful magenta-hued emissions that were carried across the northern limits of the continent, known as the Magentine Veils. The citizens there were said to lead short and dirty lives.

The Macro-yard district to the north-east of Saint's Haven reclaimed spaceships consigned to disuse, and enjoyed a thriving black market as a result. Governor Agamemnus assigned troops to defend it in the early stages of the war, and it was put under the purview of the ramrod-

straight Proctor Venedar of the Astra Militarum Vigilant Guard. Venedar held the line against the Ork incursions from Hurrikane Rekk, despite constant Deathskull raids and headlong assaults led by war leader Stormboss Stampskul. Unfortunately, though the Macro-yards remained inviolate, they relied upon the adjoining Eastgate Bastion Nexus to ferry munitions, and this site was overrun by the Orks of Mob Kommander Grokker. Amidst allegations that the disaster had been the result of a diplomatic feud between Venedar and Lord Commissar Asdan, Tempestus Scions of the 23rd Betic Centaurs and 12th Kappic Eagles launched pitiless counter-incursion strikes to retake the nexus.

The south-east of the hivesprawl, including the hive of Martyr's Pyre, the Hubridon Sub-sprawl and the Triadine Plateaus, held fast against Ork incursion throughout

the war. By keeping the Van Gollick Macrohighway open and hence allowing Astra Militarum and Adepta Sororitas vehicles to redeploy at speed, the major Ork incursions were stymied and eventually forced to retreat. Meanwhile, the tireless efforts of Temperance Blaise's Adepta Sororitas kill teams saw each uprising of xenos insurgents swiftly exterminated before they could gain a foothold.

The southernmost point of Hyperia, known as the Cape of Lost Causes, became a stronghold for incursion elements that bled into the city via the Hyperia-Dirkden Fortwall. Though the Brazen Claws practiced a scorch-and-scramble program of incendiary war across the widest point of the Cape, its tip was still in enemy hands at the time of the Ultramarines' arrival and the skirmish with the Aeldari that came to define the strife in Saint's Haven.

MEGABOREALIS

The continent of Megaborealis was ceded to the Adeptus Mechanicus in an ancient treaty, and from that time to the dawn of the war, they strip-mined almost all of its resources. The rapacious industry of the Tech-Priests proved to be the perfect cover for the clandestine deeds that were occurring below ground.

Even before the war began, Megaborealis was one of Vigilus' most dangerous continents. This was thanks, in part, to its tectonic instability and the proliferation of volcanic mountain ranges that criss-crossed it. Yet it was the touch of the Machine God that truly cursed Megaborealis.

Over a thousand years before the War of Beasts broke out, the Magi of Stygies VIII forged a pact with Vigilus' then Planetary Governor, Donsor Agamemnus, giving them absolute ownership of Megaborealis. In return, it was agreed that the Tech-Priests would contribute the might of the Adeptus

Mechanicus and its aligned Knight Houses to the planet's defence. That agreement, known as the Pact of Fire and Steel, was swiftly ratified. The Adeptus Mechanicus began their excavations at once.

Though Megaborealis' bore-hives looked huge from above, their sprawl was greater still below. Where their immense excavator engines and macro-drills laboured ceaselessly, turmels, mine workings, underhabs and manufactorums radiated out like tree roots. The majority of these excavations brought up streams of ores and minerals, gems and crude fuels that were funnelled into the upkeep of

the bore-hives themselves, and the war efforts of Vigilus' many armies.

In the underdeeps, below even the sacred bore-points and sump-pits of Dredger's Abyss and Unguent Sprawl, lay the Black Levels. Worked by neuro-wiped servitors overseen by secretive Magi, these were the mines from which the blackstone veins within Vigilus' crust were painstakingly extracted. Gathered in sanctified haulage-reliquaries, the substance was stockpiled deep within each bore-hive, for the Tech-Priests would no more relinquish their grasp upon that precious substance than they would give up their own lives.

THE BORE-HIVES

The bore-hives began their existence as drill engines, each one several miles in length. They were so enormous that they had to be transported to Vigilus within dedicated space-faring barges. Painstakingly manoeuvred into precise low orbit trajectories, the drill engines were launched into the crust of Megaborealis like enormous harpoons, each churning its way down through the bedrock to anchor itself deep within Vigilus' planetary crust. The tectonic upheaval of this monumental act was so great that the planet's landscape was changed forever. Volcanic eruptions caused the lands to convulse for years to come. Earthquakes of phenomenal violence opened chasms that could have swallowed cities, while a pall of ash and smoke rose above the continent that blotted out the skies. The destruction was judged worthwhile, for deep beneath the planet's surface lay resources that the Xenarites of Stygies VIII believed to be incredibly valuable.

After that day – known as the Day of the Omnissiah's Claw – the drill engines were built up until they transformed into sprawling bore-hives. Thousands of levels and districts rose above ground, comprising laboratories, foundries, shrines, data-stacks, manufactorums, biologus dissection chapels, generatorums, weapon batteries, cogitator networks and countless other arcane facilities. So high did the bore-hives stretch that their uppermost levels pierced the atmosphere, meshing with space docks where lumbering ore barges and manufactorum ships were moored.

Underground, billions of labourers lived and died in service to the Machine God. Countless mining clans dwelt in subterranean cities, never knowing the warmth of any light save that of petrochemical lanterns, never seeing any future but one of endless toil amidst the mainways and bore-shafts. It was amongst these clans that an offshoot of the Genestealer Cult of the Pauper Princes spread, bringing corruption disguised as hope.

Deep beneath Hive Ankhar Tertius, the infestation first took root when a single, slinking Genestealer escaped from a harvested asteroid. Hidden away in the half-collapsed subterranean district of Piston's Hollow was the tainted brood cathedrum where the Genestealer Patriarch, Grandsire Wurm, often made his nest. The Patriarch was a terrifying figure even to the cultists that worshipped him, yet he was the spider at the centre of the infestation's web, and his will bonded millions.

Under this alien despot's influence, much of Ankhar Tertius' miner militia fell to the cult's sway. Over twenty miner clans based around the rebel hold of Tecton followed suit, concealing their corruption from their Tech-Priest masters by dint of diligent labour and ever-increasing yields.

This gene-sect was far from the only one lurking beneath Vigilus' crust. Only Grandsire Wurm himself knew the true extent to which his progeny had spread, undetected, through the infrastructure of the bore-hives and beyond. For long years they built their stockpiles of munitions and materiel, suborned positions of authority, stole codes, and laid plans for their day of ascension. This diligence lent them a critical advantage when the first stages of the war erupted on Vigilus.

The fabulous wealth of Mortwald's ruling aristocracy was largely due to its rejuvenat clinics and the system-famed adepts that worked within them. The bio-regressive procedures and neo-nascent surgeries conducted there were so advanced that so-called 'immortality pilgrimages' were once common practice.

The privileged inhabitants of the worlds under Astravigila's light would make the long journey to Vigilus, and though it cost them years to do so, they would leave looking decades or even centuries younger. There were rejuvenat clinics that dared to claim that they could lift the soul as well as the body, and in doing so honour an age-old tradition set down by the Master of Mankind himself. They maintained that the planet had the Emperor's blessing, and that evidence of his miraculous beneficence could be found in the tranquillity of the bio-domes. This same serenity could be conferred upon a visitor's soul – for the right fee, of course.

The coming of the Great Rift quickly put an end to safe space travel, all but eradicating this lucrative industry.

MORTWALD

Mortwald was the primary source of food growth and harvest on the planet Vigilus, as well as a centre for rejuvenat processing – but for all the life it gave, its guns promised death to those who approached unauthorised.

The majority of Mortwald's land was given over to the cultivation of hyperflora – massive swathes of cactus and other succulents that formed oxygen-generating forests. These were force-grown on an industrial scale to counteract the huge amounts of gaseous by-product that Vigilus' industry churned into the planet's air. The oxygenating effects of the Eastern Cactus Forests, the Ageless Weald, the Viridian Forests and the Emerald Strain did initially give the planet enough clean air for its ever-expanding population to survive. Unfortunately, the atmosphere-scrubbing effects of Mortwald's forests were soon surpassed by the rampant pollution produced by the hivesprawls; not only did the other metropolises grow larger, but the northern third of Mortwald itself was taken over by a sprawling cityscape much in the manner of its neighbours.

The rich and influential inhabitants of Mortwald lived in secluded enclaves far from the northern capital of Djodrolev Hivestar and its smaller but no less overcrowded sibling, Electros Hive. The domain of the rich and the indolent, these enclaves consisted of specially commissioned bio-domes, their interiors verdant oases of sanctity filled with trickling waterfalls, glittering lakes and sculptures of dynastic aristocrats past and present. They were called a paradise, and rightly so.

The domes appeared quite different from the outside, dotted with brutal-looking gun-nests and sentry crenellations constantly manned against aerial attack. No expense was spared to keep the bio-domes safe, for these complexes were ruled over by Grand Castellan Deinos Agamemnus, brother of Governor Lucienne, and he had grown accustomed to a life of unalloyed luxury. The Castellan was a famed Imperial history enthusiast who collected devastating archeotech weapons like they were trinkets, and spoke at length on the subject whenever possible. It is said that his personal collection boasted no fewer than six Deathstrike missiles.

Due in part to the suspicion that Deinos Agamemnus held for the Adeptus Mechanicus, Mortwald's perimeter was protected not only by force fields, but by a network of squat bastions, trenches and aegis lines. The Deinos Trench Network in the continent's north-eastern reaches was a superlative example, an overlapping labyrinth of raised revetments, gun emplacements and rockcrete roads lined with sentry towers some hundreds of feet tall. Over time, that trench network was expanded to cover the vast majority of the eastern border of Mortwald, joining with the 'Tzeller Line in the south to protect the region's most valued holdings: New Vitae Docks, through which the continent's wealthy visitors came and went; the Paradisiac Domesprawl, where the most high-end treatments took place; and Rejuvenus Strongport, where lesser nobility enjoyed having a few years stripped from them by more affordable treatments.

Those whose bodies were beyond recovery, should they receive permission from Deinos himself, were allowed to visit the Biosanctic Fleshplants. It was said that extreme methods of rejuvenation, such as the suturing of old heads to fresh young bodies, were not beyond the abilities of the complex's bio-magi and elite anatomagisters.

'COME TO MORTWALD, UPON THE PLANET VIGILUS, AND KNOW PARADISE! FLY IN YOUR PERSONAL CRAFT ACROSS ACRES OF LUSH CACTUS FOREST BEFORE MAKING PLANETFALL IN THE NEW VITAE DOCKS. THEN, ONCE YOU ARRIVE AT ONE OF OUR SYSTEM-FAMOUS BIO-DOMES, LET THE MUSIC OF THE SPHERES SOOTHE YOU INTO UNCONSCIOUSNESS. WHEN YOU AWAKE, YOU WILL FEEL AS IF THE YEARS HAVE BEEN FORCIBLY STRIPPED AWAY FROM YOU. A NEW LEASE OF LIFE AWAITS!'

- *Promotional pict-slate text found on the wreckage of the shuttle* Echo of Grandeur

OTECK HIVESPRAWL

The source of water for billions of Vigilus' citizens, Oteck Hivesprawl was best known for its five vast reservoirs, which were to become hotly contested during the war. An insidious Genestealer Cult uprising from beneath and five Ork Scrap Cities in proximity saw Oteck assailed from without as well as within.

Like the other hivesprawls on Vigilus, Oteck was made up of hab-blocks and manufactorums that rose only a few dozen storeys above ground level, but spread out over enormous distances. Limiting the height of buildings helped them to avoid suffering catastrophic collapse when the inevitable tectonic upheaval caused by the mining operations in Megaborealis hit the continent. Though there was a significant military presence in Oteck, the vast macro-districts were run by the Adeptus Arbites, who kept the labouring classes in check.

Water supply in Oteck was regulated through the Hollows –

five enormous reservoirs, more like inland seas than conventional containment sites. These gathered water from deep under the planet's crust via an elaborate system of pumps, capillary banks and pipe-ways, and were topped up with regular infusions from the island-like precipitation sites of Tzardonica, Luthvren Isle and the Lenkotz Chain.

Networks of macro-ducts pumped Oteck's water to the furthest extents of the continent, and even beyond. In return they brought back polluted water, industrial run-off and reclaimed biomass to be recycled into potable fluids. Much

of the purer water Oteck conveyed to its prime clients was transported via convoy under armed guard – it was not unheard of for Astra Militarum Hellhounds and Devil Dogs to carry two tanks of pure water alongside those filled with volatile fuel in their rear quarters. As well as ensuring safe delivery, this tacitly meant that the crew of the armoured convoy would not die of dehydration on the long journey from one continent to another.

The five reservoirs of Oteck were known as the Greigan, Mysandren, Trevig, Ostaveer and Agamemnus Hollows. This last was named for the Planetary Governor's dynasty,

and was maintained as a back-up water source in case Hyperia's own store should be compromised. The Hollows were linked by the Aquadine III Processor Districts, and overseen by Hive Dagda in the south. Dagda shared a fierce rivalry with Hive Pneumos, which generated the immense pressure needed to force the water supplies across the planet.

To the south-west of the Hollows was the Ellerophosus Hivebelt, a cluster of medium-sized hives that were classed as one vast conurbation. To the far south was Solor, the Sentinel Hive, which kept watch over the waste-grounds and shanties at the point closest to the freezing wilderness of Kaelac's Bane. Hive Zontanus and the Sumphall Districts were also overtaken by Oteck's sprawl, which reached all the way to the Siltid River in the north.

Perhaps the most coveted sites in all of Oteck – aside from the reservoirs – were the Turingsbane Datahives, whose foundations pre-dated Imperial settlement upon the planet. It was said that buried in their lower levels were rich troves of data so dense and meaningful they would make a Tech-Magos weep.

The Agamemnus Dynasty knew well how much the Adeptus Mechanicus coveted the ancient data contained in the catacombs of Turingsbane, and the Planetary Governor used access to these data vaults as a bargaining chip with which to manipulate her Adeptus Mechanicus rivals on the Council of Cogs. Part of the Pact of Fire and Steel stated that the priests of Megaborealis could never access the archives unaccompanied, though evidence suggests that the Magi eventually found a way to remotely access the data without permission.

My fellow Hivelords,

Our beloved planet is under attack from vectors so numerous I fear to count them. The insidious encroachment of off-worlders into our lands, be they refugees from unfortunate planets that could not defend themselves or unpleasant military types enlisted to die on our behalf, has been surpassed by threats even more thuggish and unpalatable. Most obvious amongst them is the ignoble Ork. We need not fear this beast, for though he has made sustained assaults on the fringes of our domain, there is no way he can reach us in our spires.

Similarly, these rumours of scuttling spider-beasts from the sewers and sub-levels need not concern us overly. It is my belief that, if needs be, we should forsake the common herd entirely and marshal the military assets upon which we can rely. With unlimited access to the planet's supply of water, we are in a strong position to continue living in the manner to which we have become accustomed.

I am sure we will have to endure the bleating of the other hivesprawls until the inevitably victorious conclusion of this war, yet I am equally sure we can endure it – and perhaps even profit from it if we apportion the water in such a fashion that our rivals find themselves lacking in extremis.

Yours in eternal service,

Danst T. Malaghust,
Lord Aquarian

- Missive parchment from the Spireheights of Hive Dagda, fished from the mouth of its author's corpse

Though only the highest-placed adepts and leaders on Vigilus had an inkling of its existence, there was an ancient Aeldari webway gate situated in the west of Kaelac's Bane. It had existed there for tens of thousands of years. Shrouded by permanent blizzards that were whipped up by the empyric energies howling from within, it divulged its secrets only to those who could survive the barrier of intense cold that surrounded it like a moat. Leading to the labyrinth dimension, it was an ingress point that the Drukhari used to attack Kaelac's Bane, Oteck and Dirkden on swift and deadly raids.

When the Deathwatch made a foray across the Dearthland Permafrost, they declared a region of some eighteen hundred square miles Quarantine Cryofernus – centred on the arcing structures of the xenos portal. No Imperial presence strayed within that cordon, with the exception of the black-armoured Space Marines themselves, and they reported their findings to none save the Chapter Masters of the Vigilus Senate. Even the Deathwatch, however, did not realise that an entirely different breed of enemy would emerge from that webway gate within the year.

KAELAC'S BANE

Kaelac's Bane was a frozen wasteland of permafrost, icebergs and glaciers. It was home only to ice-miners, arctic beasts, and secrets hidden deep in the snow.

Kaelac's Bane was one of the last areas of naturally occurring water on Vigilus, but by the time the Great Rift opened, it had shrunk considerably, the Tundric Perimeter that marked its outer edge moving inward with every passing year.

Kaelac's Bane was of little use as a dwelling place – the last testimony of the famed Vigilant pioneer Jonst Kaelac is proof enough of that. It was, however, invaluable as a source of the pure water known as aqua glacius, and the continent's glaciers were mined extensively by Adeptus Mechanicus clades optimised to endure subzero temperatures.

In the vast, continent-spanning mining operations that covered the sunward side of Kaelac's Bane, huge las-cutter engines sliced off perfect cuboids of ice from glacier fronts and the edges of the continent's craters. The Venstran and Heliostrike Impact Craters yielded the most bounty, harbouring the Glacia Betus and Glacia Omicroid macro-quarries respectively.

Each day, mining servitors, quarrymen and hook-handed ice-crawler drones crossed each glacial face of these enormous impact craters. As they did so, they hammered in pins and prepared

las-nets that, although low powered, were able to melt their way through even icy rock in time. Each cyborg worker was noospherically linked to his fellows, and they operated in complete synchronicity, as if in some choreographed dance perfected by endless repetition. From these sites, giant slabs and monoliths of ice were cargo freighted to Mortwald, Hyperia and other areas that could afford them.

It was not only water that was harvested from Kaelac's Bane, for in places the permafrost hid strata of valuable minerals and ores. Here too the Adeptus Mechanicus delved deep. The icy and featureless tracts of land protected by the force field web known as the Quixotine Loop were said to be rich in esoteric stone, and were mined extensively. Over time, the islands devolved to little more than landscapes of deadly ice crevasses.

These mining operations were risky indeed. As well as the logistical challenges of the punishing cold, the great white apex predators that prowled the region were as stealthy as they were violent. The truck-sized ice-stalker mantis was particularly fierce, frequently dragging ice-workers away to be devoured in their lairs, and the near-invisible whiteworm was a horrible threat that swarmed toward sources of heat and burrowed into the flesh of those too slow or preoccupied to evade it.

Even then there were worse predators snatching people from the snowstorms. Though no official Imperial sources existed to define their nature, rumours abounded, and the fact that so many glacier miners went missing was enough to cause grave productivity concerns in the upper echelons of the mining clades.

> *'The precise nature of the Quixotine Tracts to the north of Kaelac's Bane remains anomalous, as does the vast imbalance of resources sent to guard these seemingly featureless areas and the high proportion of Bastion-class force fields that defend them. All my attempts to categorise or analyse them have been rebuffed, glitched or scrambled. By this measure I can only conclude they are of great value to someone in a senior position in Kaelac's Bane, or perhaps even Megaborealis itself.'*
>
> *- Excerpt from the journal of Meta-Geologue Xanthran Tarendos*

FROM SHIPS TO FORTRESSES

The vector of the Ork invasion was straightforward enough – most of their spacecraft simply bullied their way through the stratosphere, pulling up over the last few miles and angling their landing so they did not dash themselves to pieces on the wasteland dunes. It was a haphazard invasion tactic, that much was sure, but it worked.

Some ships came apart in fiery arcs of destruction, spinning end-over-end as they flung burning scrap metal in all directions. The shock waves from these crashes rolled out across the deserts, battering far-flung monitoring stations and hammering refinery pipelines with each landing. Huge dust clouds were kicked up into the skies like atomic blasts, turning the air hazy for days.

The survivors were numerous enough to shrug off their early losses and repurpose virtually all of the scrap metal provided by their unfortunate comrades, using it to build immense, if ramshackle, fortresses.

Some ships, protected by powerful energy shields, made the landing all but intact. Their force-field generators were intact too – projecting a kind of matterphobic dome known as a bubble field. Adapted to protect the scrap fortresses, they remained functional throughout the War of Beasts, repelling many of the Imperial sorties sent against them. These shields, like the fortifications they guarded, were testament to the strange, innate genius of the Ork Mekaniaks that built them.

SCRAP CITIES

The Ork settlements and junkyards that sprang up in the planet's wilderness were known to all as Scrap Cities. From these came tides of barbaric xenos and an endless parade of war engines.

In the year 1.192 post, a vast agglomeration of Ork spaceships – each of which had uncharacteristically massive and powerful engines – ploughed through the hastily assembled Imperial cordon sent to blockade it and made straight for the surface of Vigilus. Most of the spaceships aimed not for the metropolises of the hivesprawls, but for the regions of wilderness between them that would act as ideal staging posts for the invasion.

Speedlord Krooldakka and his warlords were savvy enough to realise that to attack the cityscapes head-on would invite a vast amount of flak and defence laser fire – and that even if they somehow made a safe landing amongst the dizzying spires, arches and statues of the cityscapes, they would almost certainly be surrounded and picked apart before they could muster a cogent invasion force. Some of the Ork war leaders simply intuited that to invade via the wastelands would lend them a better chance of victory. Others wanted a chance to race their favourite wagons around their new home for a while before getting really stuck in – after years of being cooped up in the confines of a spacecraft, the scouring winds and open terrain of the desert were a welcome prospect.

The first wave of invaders, upon finding they could not get past the force field networks, built shanty-style encampments around their crash-landed spaceships. They set to work conquering the landscapes around them, attacking Imperial convoys wherever they tried to cross the wastes. As these running battles gathered pace, the resultant flotilla of Ork vehicles became known as the Speedwaaagh!.

The most part of the original armada came down in the same region of Vigilus' wastelands, to the north of Oteck Hivesprawl. This area came to be known as the Western Scrap City Cluster. With capital craft at the centre of each collection of Ork vehicles, they formed four Scrap Cities, the largest of which was Krooldakka's own stronghold, Fort Dakka. The other three were the domains of powerful Ork leaders whose mutual rivalry saw their power bases flourish

quickly. These became the hub of a primitive yet profitable economy of scrap metal, fuel and engine parts.

The westernmost was Tanka Spill. Characterised by vast slicks of black petrochemical fluids that spread out from ruptured fuel-haulers and cargo hulks, this city was the province of the Mekboss known as Big Tanka. To the north was Runthive, a township of squig-infested wrecks and grot scrap merchants under the purview of the noted Snakebite Warboss Ogrokk Bitespider. To the south was Drogzot's Crater, where the Deathskull hoardboss Drogzot and his Bad Moon customers piled salvage ever higher in an attempt to fill the vast impact crater to the lip with scrap metal. Fort Dakka was the easternmost city, a vast scrap metropolis that bristled with every gun and artillery piece Krooldakka and his Meks could get their oil-stained hands on.

Out in the Aquaphobian Wastes was the Goff base of Skumtown, a clattering mass of bone-dry structures that rattled against one another in the hot wasteland winds. To the north of Storvhal was Da Wheel Hub, which famously offered a drive-by upgrade service to those Speed Freeks patient enough to stop there. Nearby was Rakkuk's Mekmaze, into which many an aspiring racer drove his wagon, only to find himself walking back out with little more than a steering column, a small money-bag of teef and a confused expression. To the far south of Oteck Hivesprawl was Mekstop City, the premiere site for vehicle customisation. Its gargant construction fields were home to the legendary Drokk and his Rivet Krew. To the east of Hyperia lay Hurrikane Rekk, an early settlement that was all but abandoned when the storm of the Vhulian Swirl expanded to ravage its rusted buildings and shanties.

NEO-VELLUM

Vigilus' only moon, Neo-vellum, was an orb of white rock and swirling green gas storms. It was a stronghold of the Administratum – that branch of the Imperium dealing with the coordination, analysis, assessment and deployment of information.

Neo-vellum was a nerve centre of data for the Vigilus System, theoretically independent of the disparate factions on the planet, whose own agendas and bias might lead them to restrict or manipulate communications from the wider Imperium for their own purposes.

Amongst the moon's acid swamps and emerald gas storms were built massive, hermetically sealed scriptorums that churned out logistical analyses at a slow but steady rate. Each was a message-centre and an informational way-station, their legions of bent-backed autoquill scribes and lexicographers

literally chained to their desks, allowed to slumber for a few scant hours per cycle beneath their wooden workstations before getting back to their tasks. Together, these stain-fingered troglodytes processed hundreds of thousands of dataslates, parchscrolls and data cylinders with every new day. Only a tiny proportion of these reached their intended recipients, but this was of little consequence to the senior scribes – provided the ink flowed, they cared not how or why.

The normal protocol for despatching the message-scrolls produced by Neo-vellum's

scriptorums was to encase them in ablative packets fitted with grav-chutes before firing them at the planet via hyper-pneumatic tubes. Each metal-cased scroll was launched on a route devised by the complex, cog-driven machine known as the Datasaint, a wonder of ancient technology that calculated the trajectory of the missive against the rotation and orbits of the moon and planet in order to target the recipient's exact position at the optimal time.

Despite its fastidious computations, the Datasaint was so antiquated that its systems were corroded

by millennia of entropy. As such, many of the messages sent out from Neo-vellum were wildly off-course and never reached their targets. Grav-chutes also frequently failed to deploy. More than one accident was caused by a stray message tube falling from the sky at great speed. In one famous case, the message was so on target and travelling at such a velocity that it killed the intended recipient instantly. The message tube itself was also destroyed on impact, and all record of its existence was swiftly eradicated by the Administratum – but the tale lives on nonetheless.

Neo-vellum also had a well-maintained astropathic presence for those times when a message was of such high priority that psychic communion had to be attempted. The Lunar Choir, as it was known, was a body of powerful Astropaths with many centuries of experience between them; before the coming of the Great Rift it was said they were able to send visions of startling clarity across the stars.

After the Cicatrix Maledictum ripped open, the sending and receiving of psychic missives became more fraught with peril than ever before. The operatives of the Choralium, the torus-shaped building from which the moon's talented psykers sent their missives into the void, suffered dozens of seizures, fits and episodes of insanity in the months following the rift's appearance. Worse still, the complex was plagued by terrible manifestations of supernatural phenomena. This saw the Choralium all but shut down, and astropathic communiqués attempted only in extremis – the psykers knew well the dangers of opening their minds to the warp in such tumultuous times.

A BROTHERHOOD INFILTRATED

Neo-vellum was left alone entirely by the Ork invasion. Perhaps this was because the invaders sought richer pickings on the planet below, perhaps because the moon was simply on the other side of the planet at the time the Ork Waaagh! hit home. Yet the satellite was not untouched by the scourge of the xenos. Hidden amongst the data-stacks and grimoire nests of the Administratum's holdings, a secret cult thrived – and in the attics of the monastic hab-blocks, strange creatures skittered from pools of darkness to slash apart those who dared to venture into their lair.

The Cult of the Pauper Princes made it a priority to settle an infestation upon Neo-vellum shortly after establishing itself within Megaborealis. Ensrod Ghaul, the Primus of the brood sent to conquer the scriptorum moon, stowed away with a pair of dormant Purestrain Genestealers in the capacitor hold of the electro-freighter Zealous Blurt before the ship left for Neo-vellum on a routine resupply mission. Using a combination of forgery, charisma and murderous determination, he smuggled one container into the Scriptorum Primus district of Neo-vellum, and the other into the Stormwrack Citadel. As a result, two minor gene-sects propagated through the downtrodden ranks of Neo-vellum's workers. After the narrow escape of the quillslave Ghorrod from a xenos attack, and an anonymous message sent to the Inquisition, the Purestrain Genestealers themselves were hunted down and burned out by an Ordo Xenos purge, but their dark legacy remained.

THE WASTES

The wastes of Vigilus were vast, an endless desert punctuated by the hivesprawls that slowly encroached upon it. They were arid and dusty, broken up by gullies and chasms, and populated only by hardy survivors.

The wastes of Vigilus were anathema to life. They were not poisonous, nor acidic – they were simply empty of all but the remains of those who foolishly tried to conquer them. The landscape was almost entirely devoid of greenery, for the water table was so low that the ground was infertile and dusty, incapable of producing anything but the hardiest vegetation. There was little liquid to be found, other than the occasional river of lava vomited from some new seismic upheaval, and the odd stagnant mud hole. With nothing to bind the earth together, the landscape was a gigantic dustbowl, its substrate whipped up into the air with each passing landstorm to create great cyclones of grit that raged uncontrollably across the wilderness.

Despite the hostility of the region, there were areas where life found a way to eke out an existence. Some of the impact craters that scarred the planet's surface acted as bluffs, gathering a little moisture in their shadowed lees and allowing a rudimentary ecosystem to gain some purchase. In the same way a coral reef gives undersea fauna a chance to cling on to an otherwise featureless sea bed, these features allowed the hardiest of species to stubbornly hang on to life.

The mounds and chasms around Storvhal became home to a colony of ambulls; these claw-armed, subterranean giants preyed on isolated groups of travellers, hunting with their sonic and thermal senses. They learned to avoid the trundling tracks of weapon servitors and the lock-step thump of the metal-legged Skitarii, instead tunnelling up from below to scissor apart fleshier creatures that were usually meatier and less dangerous. Some amongst the Adeptus Mechanicus propagated the belief that the ambulls were a manifestation of the universe's displeasure at those that relied on flesh rather than metal.

The terrestine molerats that infested the northern reaches of the planet could grow to the size of locomotive carriages on a diet of giant sandroaches – the only other species that could thrive in the irradiated wastes to the west of Dredger's Abyss. Existing in great hives of several hundred individuals, these hideous, hairless moles honeycombed the giant ridged impact sites known as the Kenser Crater Network between Dontoria and Megaborealis. They occasionally ambushed those forced to go on foot across the wastes – for them, human flesh was a delicacy – though it is worth noting that they did not trouble any of the convoys that happened to carry individuals bearing the mutated DNA of the Pauper Princes.

THE VHULIAN SWIRL

The Vhulian Swirl was perhaps the most dangerous of all Vigilus' geographic features. A vast storm of dust and sharp, shredding particles, it birthed cyclones and hurricanes that continually ravaged the wastelands beyond.

To the east of Hyperia, there was a dust storm so immense that when seen from space it dominated a full quarter of the planet's surface. Near its centre it was so violent that the tiny stones, dust and sedimentary particulate could strip the skin from a man's body. Over time, the storm would abrade layers of subcutaneous fat, muscle, tendon and, eventually, bone. Ultimately, there would be nothing left of the unfortunate victim. The citizens of Vigilus, and their shadowy counterparts the Pauper Princes, knew well to fear the Swirl, and so avoided it at all costs, never straying past the Perimeter Extremis as defined millennia ago by the Astra Cartographica that founded the planet. Even the Ork invaders gave it a wide berth, for at times the Swirl raged so hard it could tip over their gunwagons and lift their light buggies clean into the air, only to dash them to pieces on the hard earth when its fury abated once more.

Smaller storms emanated from the Vhulian Swirl, cyclones and tornadoes bursting into the wastes along their own seemingly random trajectories. Carried by the hot winds that gusted from fault lines, they were flung eastwards by the pyroclastic blasts of Storvhal. These errant storms primarily scoured the unpopulated side of the planet, and were largely responsible for that part of Vigilus never being settled. Freak weather patterns would cause them to occasionally veer towards the hivesprawls, but the Bastion force fields, while active, dissipated them before they could do serious harm. Travellers who strayed outside the force fields risked having one of these gritty, choking hurricanes bear down on them out of nowhere. Even if it should not strip them bare, such a storm could foul an engine or cause an anti-grav vehicle to crash in a matter of minutes.

The barren side of Vigilus, known as the Dismal Waste, was commonly thought to include little of worth, and its dust storms were even more deadly than those thrown up over the deserts between the hivesprawls. However, the slow expansion of Megaborealis pushed fingers of industrial sprawl into the Dismal Waste as the Adeptus Mechanicus continued to quest for the bounty beneath the planet's surface. Dontoria likewise expanded, being vastly overpopulated, though those who lived on the barren side were often beset by toxic cyclones.

'There's something in there, you can mark my words on that. No storm without an eye, and that storm isn't dissipating, just as its Emperor-forsaken eye isn't moving anywhere but where it sits. I'll wager there's something in there, right in the middle, riling it up. But I'm not gonna be the one that goes in there to find out what.'

- Elder Ghara Jhaine, the day before her disappearance

DIRKDEN HIVESPRAWL

Dirkden Hivesprawl, characterised by its rudimentary cityscape, was a troubled metropolis indeed. It was abandoned by Vigilus' elite, and was home to as many subterranean, half-feral outcasts as it was productive civilians.

Dirkden long ago reached a threshold in its expansion, after which it was all but abandoned by the Agamemnus Dynasty. Unbeknownst to all but the Cult of the Pauper Princes, however, this discarded cityscape did indeed supply something to its fellows – the mutating genetic pattern known as the Genestealer's Kiss.

Dirkden's tallest and proudest conurbation was Ashenid Non-Hive, a half-finished skeleton of a hive city that, although teeming with life, was open to the stars. Its construction was never finished, for the architects that built it – now lost in the annals of history – changed tack halfway through, and began to build downwards into the naturally occurring cave networks beneath. From Glaive Point in the north to the Rescalid Underworks at the southernmost tip, the hivesprawl was shot through with subterranean levels. These had become so liberally infested with Genestealer Cultists by the end of the War of Beasts that if a census had somehow been taken, it would have revealed far more in thrall to Grandsire Wurm than to the Emperor of Mankind.

THE FORTWALLS OF VIGILUS

Dirkden was joined to the southernmost reaches of its parent hivesprawl by the massive Hyperia-Dirkden Fortwall, a vast double row of crenellated defences with a rockcrete macrohighway running between them. Mortwald was similarly linked to its neighbour by the Mortwald-Oteck Fortwall, and the Dontoria-Megaborealis Line connected the two northernmost continents to facilitate trade and transit. The original plans for these links between the hivesprawls were put into place by Deinos Agamemnus shortly before his fourth rejuvenation. Growing ever more irate at the toll the native hazards of Vigilus were taking upon his endeavours, and determining that his losses in export convoys were unsustainable, he leant on the Aquilarian Council to provide a more stable means of transit.

It was hoped that by allowing the faithful of Hyperia to flood along the highway to Dirkden they would raise the hivesprawl to new heights of productivity – and one day, should all go well, build outwards to merge the two into a single hivesprawl that would empower Hyperia all the more. Instead, the macrohighway seemed only to drain the capital of Vigilus of its manpower and resources – and in return, infect the Cape of Lost Causes in Hyperia with the gene-tainted xenos cult that plagued the subterranean levels of so many of Dirkden's districts.

Still, the Fortwall itself stood strong throughout the War of Beasts, even with the rampaging Orks that marauded around the wastelands occasionally mounting raids against it.

DONTORIA HIVESPRAWL

Dontoria was critically overpopulated, even amongst its fellow hivesprawls. So densely packed were its districts that it had access to incredible manpower – though when infection broke out in the populace, it could not be stopped.

Dontoria passed the standard metropolitan population density recommended by the Administratum in 943 previo. Over a thousand years later, it continued to pack more citizens into its earthquake-ravaged slums. The endless manufactorums and fabrication shanties that surrounded its numerous hives were so steeped in pollution their outer walls were blackened and flaking, and their insides were a sickly yellow reminiscent of a lifelong lho-stick addict's fingers. Hacking coughs and expectorant splutters were common there; the lands of Mesha's Delta, Smog Field and the Great Choke were swathed in a dense blanket of vile pollution that damaged the lungs of those without respirator augmetics.

This false continent's sole source of water, the inland sea known as Lake Dontor, was polluted to the point that no life could exist within it and it sickened any who dared drink from it. That did not stop floating shanty towns being built upon it. So desperate was the population to find living space that much of the lake was covered in walkways, rowing boats, decommissioned barges, flora batteries and sump haulers, all bound together in a latticework teeming with shouting merchants, hustling traders, merciless opportunists, tattooed thugs and smogwater urchins.

The scrap-built shanties of Tzimitria, Stump and Vostoyev Subsprawls were far from wealthy in the conventional sense, but as with many desperate populations, they were rich in faith. The Ministorum found it easy to sway the swathes of smoke-stained workers, so desperate for hope as the Great Rift glowered above, to the fervent worship of the Emperor at the exclusion of all else. Their daily task was to make the autosanctioned relics and holy weaponry with which the Ecclesiarchy waged its wars, and the strongest of their holy

gangers often went on to lead new lives in the Vigilant Guard. Grodholev, Pravdus, Hallordwight and Vostoyev were older; these subsprawls were considered to be the original foundation of Dontoria and hence were more heavily tithed. The extreme north of the continent, optimistically named New Horizon, was slowly encroaching on the wilderness in order to provide more living space. Similarly, Missionary Point to the south was extending towards Mortwald. Lord Tharenst, the Hive Marshal of Mesha's Delta, wished to link his province with the northernmost point of Mortwald, but his entreaties and proposals were met only with contempt, until the outbreak of war on Vigilus relegated them to the status of a distant dream.

> *'They're packed in like skinrats in an Ogryn's ration tin up there. It's a pressure cooker, no doubt. Just listen to the tales of violence and crime – they make even Dirkden seem civilised by comparison. Breeds tough fighters, though, does Dontoria. I swear half the Vigilant Guard comes from up that way. I pity anyone that takes on the Big Fug; they'll find its sons up in arms by the billion.'*
>
> *- Sergeant Goagan of the 342nd Immersite Skydrakes*

STORVHAL

Situated near the equator, Storvhal generated an incredible amount of energy from its volcano chains and geothermal chasms. It was home to countless worshippers of the Machine God, but still darker cults operated in the shadows.

The volcanic land of Storvhal was relatively small, but of exceptional value to the planet's infrastructure. Deliberately sited on a convergence of fault lines, it was originally founded as an annex by the Adeptus Mechanicus after the Pact of Fire and Steel was signed. It produced the planet's main source of power, its volcanic farms and generator arrays harnessing the energy created by the continent's frequently erupting volcanoes. Fabricator Vosch claimed to have adapted, overseen and optimised the technology used in the farms himself – basing his works upon the holy foundation of a Standard Template Construct, of course.

Rather than suffering from the seismic upheaval caused by the drilling in Megaborealis to the north, Storvhal reaped the benefits of each tectonic shift and volcanic eruption in great measure. Though hundreds of its workers, magma-servitors and Skitarii patrolmen died with each geo-spasm, its energy yield spiked massively as the volcanoes from the Phaestos Mound in the south to the Omnissiah's Tread in the north erupted. Fabricator Vosch considered the exchange more than worth it.

If the storage levels of Vulcanid Geohive, Hive Magmathermid and Phaestos Mound filled their enormous capacitors and generatorum caches to excess, the overflow of energy was sent along the Voschian Canals, and from there into a subterranean network of cables and macrofibres to Megaborealis. If that continent's needs were already met, the excess instead went to the hivesprawls that bid the highest to receive it.

Being a place of fire and fury, Storvhal inspired a lot of religious subcultures. Some of the cults burgeoning in the Pyroclast Districts believed the volcanic eruptions of their homeland to be the Emperor's work, and that their sacrifice was necessary to appease the volcanoes. Others saw the abuse of their Adeptus Mechanicus overlords for what it was, and sought recompense. The resultant unrest and civil ire was capitalised on by rogue elements working against the Imperium. Because of the inhuman toll on life, the agents that worked in secret in Storvhal found it easy to seed fire-cults, rebel sects and pyromaniacs throughout the slave populace. Some preached the notion that the fires of the volcanoes could be altered to transform the faithful into divine beings, a phoenix-like apotheosis from ashes to glory. Worse still, the underground demagogue known as Vannadan the Firebrand was able to garner power – not in the name of emancipation, but Chaos.

THE OMNISSIAN HOIST

The Greater Omnissian Hoist was a true marvel of the Adeptus Mechanicus' genius. Via this immense pulley, the Tech-Priests captured and processed ice-clad asteroids for their elemental bounty.

Reaching up from the Stygian Spires – the tallest hive in Megaborealis by some margin – was a vast construction known as the Greater Omnissian Hoist. This edifice was testament to the incredible willpower and vision of the Magi of the Adeptus Mechanicus, and was famed across the sector for putting into practice a hypothesis that had intrigued Tech-Priests for millennia.

The Hoist and its supporting structures rose so high that the tip was invisible to the naked eye. They linked the Stygian Spires with the wheel-shaped space station of Sacrus Tora Hawking in geosynchronous orbit high above. It did this via a complex system of microfibre carbon chains and duraplas capillaries. Partially telescopic and modular, these were created on an industrial scale by the workshops of Megaborealis' primary hive and hauled into the stratosphere by a succession of low orbit tugs.

Across the span of an entire century, the carbon chains were extended and reinforced until they not only reached Sacrus Tora Hawking, but passed through its specially constructed engine mills and back down to the planet's surface again. These chains were counterweighted with sections of the original space station in order to pull up replacement components from the hive below, the interstitial point of the Median Sacrus Way-station ensuring that each winchnode passed on in safety.

That was the first freight transaction made between the hivesprawl and the space station above it, but it opened the door for the tens of thousands of other exchanges that happened after. For its part, Megaborealis sent up manpower, food, repair parts and other necessities. In return, Sacrus Tora Hawking shipped down asteroids clad in thick layers of ice, a vital source of water for the planet.

The asteroids harvested by Sacrus Tora Hawking were native to a great band of space debris known as the Octiline Belt. Early auguries determined that the rocks drifting in that band were clad in ice water, and almost immediately a plan for the capture and exploitation of this resource was put into place – the thirsting citizens of Megaborealis cared little where their water came from. The plan to harness the Octiline Belt's seemingly endless bounty was so ambitious, and of such immense scale, that only one with the processing power of an Arch-Magos could dare to attempt it. But, with the help of his most trusted colleagues, Fabricator Vosch oversaw the Hoist program from beginning to end, adapting and installing banks of tractor beam cannons that could lock onto the asteroids within reach and slowly draw them into the space station's armature talons. From that day, the transit of ice from orbit to the processing factories of the Stygian Spires – where the meltwater was 'refined' with the addition of sacred oils and blessed lubricants – became a miracle so commonplace it was rarely considered worthy of mention.

FORCES OF WAR

'This entire planet is cursed. I am sure of it. It can be the only explanation for the sheer scale of destruction meted out upon it.'

- High Castellan Deinos Agamemnus

FORCES OF THE IMPERIUM

In the early phases of the war, the forces stationed upon the planet formed a cross-section of the Imperium's defenders. Most numerous amongst them were the soldiers of the Astra Militarum – though the presence of the Adepta Sororitas and arrival of the Adeptus Astartes made a vital impact.

Collectively, the unaugmented human soldiery defending Vigilus were known as the Imperium Vigilant. With so many military forces having made the star-spanning journey to the strategically vital planet, this brotherhood included everything from raw recruits and conscripts to the hard-bitten Adepta Sororitas.

In general, the military assets of each continent journeyed to other conurbations only to distribute vital supplies. The rulers of each hivesprawl jealously guarded the battalions and regiments seconded to their defence, though they did so out of a sense of pride rather than prudence. With the Bastion force fields protecting their assets, the amount of military force assigned to each area of Vigilus was seen purely as an indication of status rather than a pragmatic solution to theoretical invasions.

This over-confidence was present most of all in Lucienne Agamemnus and Pontifex Galluck, who were so embroiled in their own power struggles they had little time to devote to protecting the planet against some hypothetical danger from off world – nor even from the downtrodden masses, who they had come to see more as sheep and cattle than as living citizens whose allegiance could not always be counted upon.

The aristocracy's failure to treat the ever-present threats of the alien, the heretic and the mutant as very real dangers antagonised many of the Astra Militarum commanders assigned to the defence of each hivesprawl, but short of actually leaving the planet, there was little they could do about it. Instead, they looked to the defences of each hivesprawl as best they could, ensuring their men were familiar

with the planet's geography and learning to deal with the frequent earthquakes that could throw all their preparations into disarray in a matter of minutes. A loose confederation of sharp military minds began to take shape across Vigilus, the lord commander of each military body in correspondence with several of his peers so that the Astra Militarum would have a safety net should the political rulers of the planet act in a fashion that threatened the war effort.

The coming of the Noctis Aeterna shattered that long-range web of cooperation and coordination beyond recovery. With communications disrupted everywhere and the populace under attack from within and without, the truth of the situation soon became clear – it was every continent for itself.

Marneus Augustus Calgar of the Ultramarines restored a semblance of order to Vigilus' war effort in the war's latter phases, but for many areas it was already too late.

Fabricator Vosch of the Adeptus Mechanicus addressed war as an exercise in logistics. His callous approach added fuel to the fires of many a slow-burning rebellion.

IMPERIUM VIGILANT

Because Vigilus was so strategically situated, the Astra Militarum stationed there were very disparate, hailing from a dozen war zones. Though in the years previous to the opening of the Great Rift the many regiments' different agendas had sometimes caused conflict to arise between them, they united in a common cause upon the initial invasion of the Orks, and remained in the Imperium's service from that point on.

HYPERIA GUARD AGAMEMNUS

Sonasthi Royal Guard	8 regiments
Vigilant Guard	32 regiments
Vigilant Creedsmen	19 regiments
Dragoons Demonstratus	6 echelons
Vyacine Adepts	2 regiments
Adamant Rifles	4 regiments
Dagmar Guard	8 regiments
Nord Lothan Vanguard	1 regiment
Expadar Vengers	2 regiments
Golohastus XIIth 'Decapitators'	1 regiment
Black Torus Scout Companies	3 companies

ADEPTA SORORITAS

Order of Our Martyred Lady	11 preceptories
Order of the Bloody Rose	7 preceptories
Order of the Ebon Chalice	3 preceptories
Order of the Argent Shroud	5 preceptories

VIGILUS ARMOURED ELEMENTS

Sondoran Gearheads	4 armoured regiments
Cadian Heavy Armoured	6 armoured regiments
Ustenoran Gundogs	9 armoured regiments
Kharbys Iron Cavalry	4 armoured regiments
Vostokh 44th 'Crushers'	1 armoured regiment

OTECK DEFENCE GROUP

Vigilant Guard	12 regiments
Vigilant Creedsmen	7 regiments
Utica Pikemen River Guard	2 regiments
Palladion Rifles	6 regiments
Tallarn Raiders	4 cavalier regiments
Miasman Redcowls	7 regiments
Hydroplant Water Hounds	5 castellanries
Vastadt I Expedrines	3 sabot groups
Gharti Volunteers	7 regiments
Tekarn Iron Men	2 iron phalanxes
Vresh Grenadiers	11 regiments
Anark Zeta Bullgryn Auxilla	2 brute regiments

ADEPTA SORORITAS

Order of the Last Prioress	7 preceptories
Order of the Martyr's Shroud	3 preceptories

DIRKDEN RECLAMATION GROUP

Vigilant Underhivers	13 regiments
Dharan Bloodfists	5 regiments
Anark Zeta Abhuman Auxilia	2 detachments
Kanak Skull-takers	1 regiment
Cthonol Nineguards	7 regiments
Miasman Redcowls	3 regiments

++**CONTINUED IN FILE IMP.VIG/PGS2/1-12**

Participants in second and third stages of Vigilus conflict codified 'War of Beasts' codified in auxiliary dataslate Imp.Vig/PGS3/13-119.

DONTORIA SPRAWLGUARD

Vigilant Guard	8 regiments
Vigilant Creedsmen	3 regiments
Mordian Iron Guard	2 regiments
Gantor Rough Riders	3 cavalier regiments
Indigan Praefects	5 regiments
Ezelti Lancers (8th)	7 echelons
Ocanan Rad Waste Troopers	9 regiments

MORTWALD RESERVE

Cadian Shock Troops	12 regiments
Catachan Jungle Fighters	4 regiments
Vigilant Guard	34 regiments
Vigilant Creedsmen	32 regiments
Ventrillian Nobles	14 regiments
Sonasthi Royal Guard	15 regiments

KAELAC'S BANE TASK FORCE

Truskan Snowhounds	19 regiments
Catachan Jungle Fighters	2 regiments
Valhallan Ice Warriors	4 regiments

OFFICIO ASSASSINORUM

Imperial Assassins	CLASSIFIED

Temperance Blaise of the Order of Our Martyred Lady was considered humourless and dark-tempered – though those who saw her fight treated her with great respect.

The unyielding Proctor Commander Venedar of the Vigilant Guard was the leader of the Astra Militarum battle group Hyperia Guard Agamemnus.

Legend

- **BRAZEN CLAWS** DROP ZONE
- **BRAZEN CLAWS MULTI-PRONGED ARMOURED ASSAULT**
- **BLOOD AXE HORDE** TANKBOSS DEEZULFIST
- **SISTERS OF BATTLE** ORDER OF OUR MARTYRED LADY
- **CADIAN 8TH** 'CREED'S LEGACY'
- **CADIAN 122ND** 'BAYONET BARONS'
- **CULT-HELD ANNEX** [CF. HYPERIA-DIRKDEN FORTWALL]
- **BAD MOONS** WARHORDE

TRIADINE PLATEAUS

CAPE OF LOST CAUSES

HAMMER AND ANVIL

Gauntlet Master Sharrack's Brazen Claws hit the xenos of southern Hyperia in two trident-shaped attacks, breaking their inhuman foes against the bulwark of the Imperial Guard.

HEROES ON HIGH

Though the decisive battles of the War of Beasts were won on the ground, crucial victories would have proven impossible were it not for the stalwart efforts of the Aeronautica Imperialis. As the Orks established their Scrap Cities and rapidly increased their production of war materiel, scores of Dakkajets, Blitza-bommers and other greenskin aircraft rolled off their ramshackle assembly lines. Droning waves of deadly xenos attack craft filled the skies over Vigilus' hivesprawls and screamed down to strafe transport columns and hammer manufactorums with barrel-like incendiary bombs.

In response, Imperial commanders threw every air asset at their disposal into interdiction missions and combat air patrols. Flights of Thunderbolt and Lightning fighters spiralled madly through the Ork air-armadas, their cannon-fire lashing out to punch one greenskin pilot after another from the skies. Heavy wings of Marauder Bombers lumbered out over the wastes to rain explosive death upon the Ork airfields; despite heavy casualties amongst the air crews, their efforts stripped away the xenos' aerial capabilities bit by bit, and prevented a desperate battle from becoming an untenable slaughter.

The heart of the greenskin aerial efforts on Vigilus was Rakkuk's Mekmaze, a warren of scrap-metal shanty towns behind whose defences a quartet of airfields sheltered. Rakkuk led a loose assemblage of airborne tribes that outnumbered any other Ork airforce on Vigilus several times over, and staged repeated raids upon Megaborealis.

The silhouettes of Blitza-bommers became a thing of dread to the Imperial forces guarding the Megaborealis supply convoys. Yet for all the terror the Ork Flyboyz caused, it could not outweigh the furious elation of the Imperial ground forces as they witnessed the intervention of the Aeronautica Imperialis pilots. As macro-tankers and speeding Tauroxes raced across the Vigilus wastes, outnumbered bands of heroic pilots fought ferocious duels against swarming greenskin craft to ensure the convoys made it to their destinations in safety.

The Imperial propaganda machine was quick to seize upon the seemingly glamorous and adventurous exploits of these knights of the air. Pilots such as Flight Lieutenant Brandyn MacElroy, Lucretia 'the Red Marquess' Jenst and Bomber Captain Brokmann Gallister became overnight sensations amongst the common soldiery of Vigilus, and their names were plastered on Commissariat bill posts from Oteck to Hyperia. The fact that barely any of these famed heroes survived the horrors of the Vigilus air war was not so well-publicised.

HAMMER AND ANVIL

The Astra Militarum is often likened to a sledgehammer, but on Vigilus they played the part of the anvil. Forced by circumstance to keep the bulk of their armies within the boundaries of the hivesprawls, they fought with a largely defensive stance in the early stages of the war. Though the call for aid had gone out into the stars – with many astropaths paying the ultimate price in the process – there was little hope it would yield swift results. Though none gave voice to their suspicions too openly, almost all of the commanders of the Imperial war effort harboured a fear that the Bastion force fields would give up before the Orks did. Even should they last, the greenskins that roamed the wastes had effectively mounted a siege that would eventually starve out the defenders of Vigilus and force them to commit to open war. That they had done so seemingly by accident was cold comfort indeed.

Then came the Space Marines. Striking without warning from high above the smog line, Adeptus Astartes cruisers hurled their Drop Pods from launch bays down to the planet with stunning force.

The Brazen Claws struck hard to the south of Hyperia, for even with the Hyperia-Dirkden Fortwall heavily garrisoned it was only a matter of time before Cult infiltrators rose up and Orks from Mekstop City took their war further inland. A Drop Pod invasion into the Ork-held city outskirts would have quickly

been surrounded, so the Brazen Claws launched a multi-pronged, mechanised attack that fell upon the Orks' rearguard and drove them into the guns of the entrenched Imperial Guard. Caught between an irresistible force and an immovable object, the Orks were scattered, hunted down, and destroyed.

Outside Megaborealis, the White Scars and Ravenwing used their mobility as a weapon, blunting each Ork spearhead with well-timed pincer movements that left the Orks nowhere to run. To the north of Kaelac's Bane, the Primaris Marines of the Void Tridents and Castellans of the Rift made similar attacks, their individual companies splitting up to take on the Orks – and in one region, raiding Drukhari – in a series of well-chosen engagements that kept their foes on the back foot and forced them to retreat or be utterly eradicated in a storm of bolt rifle fire. For a time, Vigilus knew hope once more.

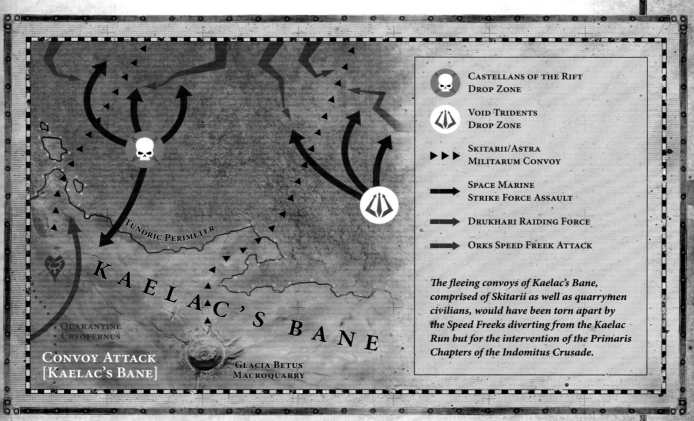

CONVOY ATTACK
[KAELAC'S BANE]

TUNDRIC PERIMETER

K A E L A C ' S   B A N E

QUARANTINE
CRYOFERNUS

GLACIA BETUS
MACROQUARRY

	CASTELLANS OF THE RIFT DROP ZONE
	VOID TRIDENTS DROP ZONE
▶▶▶	SKITARII/ASTRA MILITARUM CONVOY
➤	SPACE MARINE STRIKE FORCE ASSAULT
➤	DRUKHARI RAIDING FORCE
➤	ORKS SPEED FREEK ATTACK

The fleeing convoys of Kaelac's Bane, comprised of Skitarii as well as quarrymen civilians, would have been torn apart by the Speed Freeks diverting from the Kaelac Run but for the intervention of the Primaris Chapters of the Indomitus Crusade.

FORCES OF THE ULTRAMARINES

The warriors of Ultramar came to Vigilus in force – though they were amongst the last to arrive, they made such a vital contribution to the war effort that they arguably turned the stricken planet's war footing from a total collapse to a grinding stalemate – and, for a time, brought a chance of victory.

The Ultramarines hail from the Macraggian tradition of leadership, producing great statesmen as well as warriors. On Vigilus it was their skills in the art of diplomacy that saw them restructure the planet's war machine from the inside out.

Few in the Imperium could have matched the strategic mastery displayed by Lord Calgar as he cut out the corruption of the Aquilarian Council and reshaped it in the image of a Macraggian senate. He despatched the failed and the corrupt in a single night, all the while keeping the delicate balance between the Agamemnus Dynasty, the Priesthood of Mars, and the Ecclesiarchy. So reformed, the senate was able to focus on the true enemy rather than their old rivalries and feuds. From the debating tables of the Aquilarian Palace, he organised a new war, abandoning the status quo that saw each continent looking to its own defences and bringing in a complex, overlapping methodology that combined all of Vigilus' disparate forces. His strategic command saw the armies of Vigilus working together, crushing hordes of Orks and seething infestations of Genestealer Cultists beneath the Imperial sledgehammer.

By the end of the war's third phase, Calgar had not committed his own forces far beyond Hyperia – beyond Saint's Haven, come to that. Instead he focused three companies and two demi-companies of Ultramarines on the inner metropolis defence. He had his warriors mount hit-and-run strikes from Saint's Haven as and when a Genestealer Cult uprising, Ork air assault or rebel horde threatened the stability of inner Hyperia,

for maintaining a solid base of operations was of paramount importance. Any strike forces sent out of the capital quickly returned once their task was complete, ensuring that Calgar always had a bulwark of Ultramarines as part of the senate's defence.

The only standing deployment consisted of five squads of the 9th Company, each assigned to one of the bridges that crossed the Ring of Nothingness around the inner territories of Saint's Haven. With any who sought passage across these bridges subject to stringent checks, and any foe attempting to force their way across coming under heavy fire from Devastators and Centurions, this fortified position meant that there was no easy invasion route into the Aquilarian Palace on foot or by wheeled conveyance.

The vengeful Aeldari of Saim-Hann mounted a cogent assault on the senate despite these measures, for their jetbikes and skimming anti-grav transports evaded the 9th Company and darted straight over the Ring of Nothingness with alarming ease. Though they took a heavy toll on the Militarum Tempestus and slew no few Ultramarines, ultimately they were dealt with by the quick thinking of Lieutenant Eothrus.

There were those in the Imperial war effort that accused Calgar of holding back. The Victrix Guard that formed the inner circle of defence for Calgar and the rest of the Vigilus Senate saw action but rarely, and the majority of his Ultramarines had mounted search-and-destroy missions, but little else. Eothrus went on record stating

that he believed Calgar was waiting for something.

Only when the spires of the Vigilus hives were found dotted with mutilated corpses did that menace make itself known, and a new phase of the war for Vigilus begin. The Ultramarines were the first to respond in force, sending their strike teams high into the spires to duel with the Raptors, Warp Talons and Heldrakes that blighted the cityscape above the clouds. Had they been despatched in force to other war fronts, they would never have been able to respond to the Chaos threat with such speed and efficacy.

Only a leader of visionary insight could have looked upon a world assailed on all sides by not one but three xenos races, and realised that an even viler threat might yet cast its shadow over the planet. Each decision Calgar made that was questioned by others proved to be a calculated move, be it consigning entire war zones to damnation in the name of the wider war, or sacrificing valuable holdings to burn out an insidious foe. Calgar's seemingly callous rulings and commands besmirched the reputation of the Ultramarines in the eyes of the planet's aristocracy, but in truth they were necessary. Because of Calgar's wisdom the scourge of Chaos was prevented from turning its early gains into a lethal momentum.

Only those closest to the Lord Macragge suspected there was another, more personal reason for Calgar's reticence to commit in person – he was still recovering from the ordeal of the Rubicon Primaris.

THE RUBICON PRIMARIS

The induction of the Primaris Marines into the Adeptus Astartes was not an easy process by any means. The Chapters of the Space Marines are arch traditionalists, and some are conservative in the extreme, having upheld the same warrior traditions for thousands of years. Of course, the express command of Roboute Guilliman, Lord Commander of the Imperium, eased the transition into the new era. For the Ultramarines and the vast majority of their successors, the word of the risen Primarch was good enough, and many Chapters welcomed the Primaris battle-brothers gladly. But there were those especially secretive or wilful Chapters who saw the incorporation of the Primaris Marines into their ranks as a dilution of their gene-stock and a betrayal of their long-held culture.

Some amongst the Adeptus Astartes suspected that the Primaris Marines, being stronger, more durable, and closer in blood to the Primarchs themselves, represented the obsolescence of traditional battle-brothers. No amount of reason – of pointing out that what the Primaris offered in raw ability, they lacked in experience and versatility – could salve the spiritual wound dealt by the sight of the newcomers wearing their heraldry. The Primaris Marines of the Ultima Founding had been swiftly inducted into brotherhoods that the incepted aspirants of yesteryear had given everything they had to join. Questions, heavy with the weight of destiny, hung in the air. Would the Primaris Marines ultimately make the traditional Space Marines extinct? Would the identity of each Chapter's home world be diluted, with so many thousands of new recruits sourced from the stasis vaults of Mars? And was it possible for a Space Marine to be transformed into a Primaris, inheriting the benefits of Adeptus Mechanicus arcanoscience whilst retaining his personality and experience?

This last question had been raised in Adeptus Astartes Chapters across the galaxy. It was a query Lord Calgar had asked of Belisarius Cawl himself, and had discussed with those of his fellow Chapter Masters he was able to meet in person.

Debate raged as to whether such an act was even possible without having deadly consequences for the recipient – for data that Archmagos Cawl had already amassed on the subject suggested there would be a 61.6% failure rate until the process could be perfected, which would take time. Then there was the moral concern of whether the process should be attempted at all.

The dilemma was proving divisive indeed. There were those who claimed this was the ultimate destiny of all Adeptus Astartes, while from other quarters came whispers of rejection, even mutiny, at the prospect.

The lords of the Ultramarines came to the conclusion that to ease the transition from centuries of Imperial tradition to a new order, the theoreticals of that raging debate would have to be put into practice. It was Marneus Calgar that stepped forward as the first test subject from the ranks of his storied Chapter. It was a process he did not survive – though like his Primarch before him, he was to rise from the threshold of death once more.

The operation to transform Calgar from a traditional Space Marine into a Primaris Marine was conducted in an auto-sterilised med vault. Thick with the tang of counterseptic and crowded with elaborate medical servitors, the room was dominated by the vast marble slab at its centre, artfully carved with runnels to collect the copious streams of blood that would result from the procedure. The surgery was to be extensive and agonising, a fact Marneus knew well from Cawl's tediously thorough descriptions of his masterwork process. A Primaris Marine is gifted three new organs in addition to the nineteen grafted, sutured and chemically implanted into an aspirant Space Marine. These are the Magnificat, which is buried deep within the brain to stimulate growth and to intensify other organ functions; the Belisarian Furnace, which releases a burst of hypersteroids and corticostimulants when a mortal blow is dealt so the Primaris may fight on; and the Sinew Coils, cable-like lengths of durasteel that encase every tendon and sinew in a metallic sheath that gives tremendous resilience and strength.

During the implantation of these advanced organs, Marneus Calgar was cut open from crown to heel. His ribcage was cracked apart and – at the climax of the operation – his physiology suppressed to the point that his life slipped away. Choirs of cyber-cherubs sang blissful, overlapping requiems, swaying their aspergillums that sacred incense might guide Calgar's spirit back to his body. The corpse lay in state, its flesh rent and open to the air, for what seemed to those watching like an age. Ten long minutes ticked past, then twenty. Skull-faced surgeons clicked and muttered and stabbed at the tortured flesh. Those around the periphery of the apothecarium theatre held their breath in dread.

Then, with his wounds stitched closed by a thousand jabbing needles and his mighty heart electrified to beat once more, the newly forged Lord Calgar was brought back to life. He broke his bonds with a strangulated, blood-flecked roar, stumbling to life as his Belisarian Furnace brought him to battle readiness. Calgar had clawed his way back from beyond the brink of death, and in doing so, he had shown to his Chapter that the transformation was possible. The Rubicon Primaris had been crossed, and a new path opened for the Adeptus Astartes.

FORCES OF THE DARK ANGELS

Where the White Scars and Crimson Fists worked closely with the Vigilus Senate, the Dark Angels that responded to Vigilus' plight largely followed their own path. Nonetheless, they fought with sudden and effective fury in many of the planet's war fronts.

The Dark Angels delegate that approached the senate was the young Primaris Lieutenant Kodden – a measure that even Marneus Calgar had not foreseen, as he had expected at the least a senior veteran of the Deathwing. Kodden honoured the war council to the smallest possible degree before leaving; though his protocol and manners were impeccable, his reluctance to divulge the strategies of his brothers said something in its own right. Only Chapter Masters Calgar and Kantor suspected the truth – that Kodden simply did not know the Dark Angels' plans.

Word had spread amongst the delegates of the Vigilus Senate that the Dark Angels typically kept their Primaris contingents separate from the traditional echelons of their legendary brotherhood. Though some Primaris Space Marines occupied veteran positions, the least experienced were rarely deployed alongside the rapid strike forces of the Deathwing or the Ravenwing. Instead they formed the spearhead of frontal assaults, plunging right into the enemy force whilst their brothers went about their own initiatives elsewhere. Through his acquaintance with Kodden, Calgar came to realise that the Dark Angels were using the Primaris officer and his honour guard of Intercessors in much the same way – and shielding the Dark Angels' true purpose.

As to what this was, none could say for certain. In the early months of the third phase of the war, word reached the senate that a Ravenwing strike force was acting strangely. Fighting in support of Olujin Khan's forking White Scars attack on Fort Dakka, the Ravenwing force had struck hard at the Ork fortress city before veering off east as the battle reached its crescendo. Abandoned by their allies, the White Scars were forced to withdraw before they could destroy the command centre of the Ork war effort. Kodden had little to add after giving this report, maintaining that the Ravenwing were not beholden to one such as he. Only Calgar picked up on the slight hint of bitterness in his words.

Over the course of the third phase, Calgar began to piece together the puzzle presented by the actions of the First. Wherever the Dark Angels fought, they never strayed far from the Vhulian Swirl, that vast dust storm to the east of the planet. He knew, with the fate of Vigilus hanging by a thread, that to delve into the reason why would likely destabilise his war council when cohesion was needed above all else, and so he withheld judgement.

When the revelation came that a Chaos insurgency had struck the planet from the tips of its spires down, the Dark Angels committed to the fight in full force alongside the Ultramarines. Deathwing and Ravenwing alike, so conspicuously absent from the annals of the war effort thus far, blazed into the fray with such spectacular force that the Chaos invaders were blitzed from several spires in the space of a single hour. There were after-action reports of some of the enemy being spirited away in the strange winged sepulchre-craft that Kodden referred to as Dark Talons, but again Calgar did not press the matter. If the current situation was to escalate any further, the Lord Macragge would have need of the Sons of the Lion and their devotion to the cause, no matter what other agendas might be at work.

ADEPTUS ASTARTES

Though all of the Space Marine Chapters present on Vigilus fought in several theatres of war, redeploying at need and at the behest of the Vigilus Senate, the majority operated within specific areas of Vigilus. With the xenos cult uprising occurring shortly after the Ork invasion, the urgent spectacle of war was never far away, and the Adeptus Astartes united their forces and divided once more at need.

HYPERIA
OPERATING OUT OF SAINT'S HAVEN
Ultramarines	3 companies, 2 demi-companies
White Consuls	5 companies
Black Templars	1 company
Praetors of Orpheus	2 companies
Silver Skulls	1 company
Genesis Chapter	2 companies
Hawk Lords	2 companies
Howling Griffons	3 companies
Novamarines	1 company

++CONTINUED IN FILE IMP.VIG/AAS9/1-5
Participants in second and third stages of Vigilus conflict codified 'War of Beasts' listed in confidential dataslate Imp.Vig/PGs1/1-19.

OTECK
Space Wolves (Haldor Icepelt)	1 strike force
Space Wolves (Brand Sabrewulf)	1 strike force
Mortifactors	2 companies

MORTWALD
Imperial Fists	3 companies, 1 demi-company
Mortifactors	2 companies
Fire Lords	2 companies

MEGABOREALIS
Iron Hands	6 clan companies
Brazen Claws	2 companies

DONTORIA
Iron Hands	2 clan companies
Necropolis Hawks	7 companies
Silvered Blades	4 companies

DIRKDEN
Crimson Fists	5 companies
Sons of Medusa	5 companies

PERIPATETIC FORCES
SONS OF THE LION
Dark Angels	4 companies
• Deathwing elements (unlisted)	
• Ravenwing elements (unlisted)	
Consecrators*	1 company
Blades of Vengeance*	2 companies
Angels of Redemption*	1 company

*Note these are estimates, no formal number given

SONS OF THE KHAN
White Scars	4 companies
Solar Hawks	3 demi-companies
Storm Reapers	2 demi-companies
Destroyers	1 demi-company

INDOMITUS CRUSADE FORCES
Sons of the Phoenix	6 companies
Void Tridents	3 companies, 1 demi-company
Castellans of the Rift	2 companies

Rather than sporting their company colours on their pauldrons, the Dark Angels wear them on their left kneepad. This practice harks back to the knightly traditions of ancient Caliban, which was all but destroyed in the tragic aftermath of the Horus Heresy.

FORCES OF THE WHITE SCARS

Even amongst the Adeptus Astartes, the White Scars are considered the masters of high-speed mounted warfare. Given that the majority of Vigilus' surface was wasteland, they were well-suited to battle against the menace of the Speedwaaagh!. Their style of attack came into its own in a dozen theatres of war.

The White Scars take great joy in the thrill of battle. They relish the singing of war songs, the spray of hot blood in the air, and the sensation of wind rushing past them as they push the engines of their bikes and transports to the limit. Following the events of the Great Rift, they had become a troubled Chapter, scattered across the galaxy just when they needed cohesion and concentration of force more than ever. Despite this setback, or perhaps because of a need to overcome it, they rose to meet the challenges presented by Vigilus with admirable determination.

The White Scars on Vigilus fought under Olujin Khan, a captain known for his bombastic and passionate character. A pupil of the famed Huntmaster himself, Kor'sarro Khan, Olujin was entrusted with the leadership of the Vigilus expedition that comprised the Sons of the Khan and their successor Chapters. The Chapter sent two full companies of White Scars alongside demi-companies from three successors: the Solar Hawks, the Storm Reapers and the Destroyers. That the White Scars did so speaks to the nobility of their character, for they were engaged on several fronts elsewhere in the galaxy.

The addition of Primaris Marines from the Indomitus Crusade had bolstered the Chapter's ranks and allowed them to break the stranglehold that Chaos had upon their home world of Chogoris, but the wider system was still reeling from the damage inflicted upon it by the forces of Huron Blackheart. Their Great Khan, Jubal, was still missing in action after the raid upon the *Seethnar*, they had suffered heavy losses against the T'au in the Damocles Gulf, and their fortress of Quan Zhou was still in the process of being reconsecrated following Chaos attack. Olujin felt a strong desire to work alongside his brothers to secure the Chogoris System once more, but their duty to the wider Imperium could not be put aside.

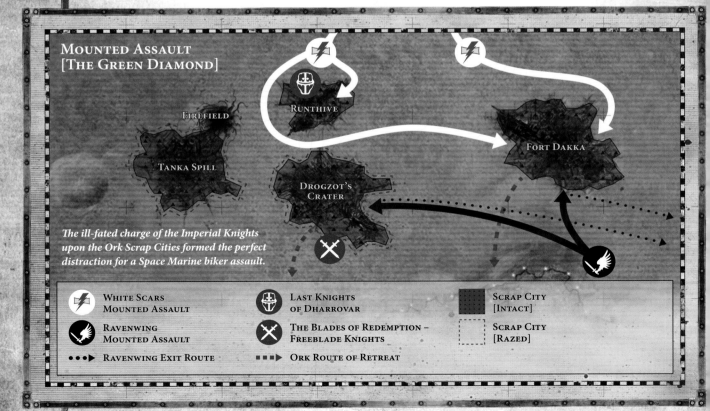

MOUNTED ASSAULT [THE GREEN DIAMOND]

FIREFIELD

RUNTHIVE

FORT DAKKA

TANKA SPILL

DROGZOT'S CRATER

The ill-fated charge of the Imperial Knights upon the Ork Scrap Cities formed the perfect distraction for a Space Marine biker assault.

WHITE SCARS MOUNTED ASSAULT

RAVENWING MOUNTED ASSAULT

RAVENWING EXIT ROUTE

LAST KNIGHTS OF DHARROVAR

THE BLADES OF REDEMPTION – FREEBLADE KNIGHTS

ORK ROUTE OF RETREAT

SCRAP CITY [INTACT]

SCRAP CITY [RAZED]

The Chapter's Stormseers, fulfilling the role of Librarians in their warrior fraternity, had seen in visions that the sentinel world of Vigilus was soon to be overrun by a tide of anarchy, and at the forefront of that tide was the greenskinned beast. Part of Olujin rejoiced that they were to fight the Orks, and Speed Freeks at that, for mounted warfare was his forte. More than that, the Orks were solid, brutish and predictable in comparison to the mind-bending hosts that he had fought in his last crusade on the Slaaneshi cult world of Vondrel Magnificat. There was honest glory to be had on Vigilus, won with bolt and blade. Some amongst Olujin's veterans – the Ivory Blades – had suggested that maybe, if their captain was instrumental in securing Vigilus for the Imperium once more, he might be considered as the next Great Khan if Jubal was truly lost.

The White Scars first made an impact not in defence of the Imperial cities, but in swift and vengeful assaults. Landing just north of Fort Dakka with the 2nd Company, Olujin Khan led a strafing, running battle along the outskirts of Krooldakka's own territory, a hurricane of bolts and las beams smashing industrial sites and blasting apart half-built effigies of war. The Orks responded quickly, roaring out from their workshops and hangars to engage the White Scars in a high-velocity chase, and several of the Sons of the Khan were shot out of the saddle or even blasted high into the air by the guns of Fort Dakka.

Nonetheless, the blinding speed of the White Scars armoured spearhead, combined with the thick clouds of dust thrown up by the skids and slaloms of their assault, protected them well enough. With the vast majority of Orks already on campaign, they were able to swathe the north of Fort Dakka in fire and smoke, intensifying their attack by blasting their way into the city

with enough Land Raider, Repulsor and Predator fire to destroy the gatehouse ship *Punchin' Fist*.

Almost simultaneously, the White Scars 3rd Company joined the assault from the west after setting their own ring of fire around Runthive. Their thunderous assault was well-timed to coincide with a mounted attack from the Ravenwing in the south of the city, for the Dark Angels had struck at both Fort Dakka and Drogzot's Crater to maximise confusion. The black-armoured bikers, obscured by the great rolling banks of dust and smoke thrown up by the northern attack, gunned down hundreds of Orks with each passing minute. Attacked on all sides, many of the lesser greenskins of Fort Dakka fled the city through the south-west speedway. All was in place for the noose to close, and the Orks, milling in confusion, to be burned alive in their own fortress. Then, without warning, the Ravenwing changed direction and sped off to the east, leaving the Orks to concentrate their forces upon the White Scars alone. Olujin Khan called off the attack soon after, having done considerable damage to Krooldakka's power base. He did not forgive the Ravenwing for abandoning the chance to strike a truly telling blow.

Over the course of the next few months, the White Scars collaborated closely with the Astra Militarum to harness as much

information as possible about the force dispositions across the planet. Olujin Khan attended Marneus Calgar's new senate in Saint's Haven, and there struck a deal with the Imperial Guard supremo Proctor Commander Venedar. The Sentinel Recon Companies of the Vigilant Guard, pacing the wastelands between hivesprawls, and even travelling to the featureless ocean of dust on the opposite side of the planet, would share their information about Ork racing routes and dust trails whenever comms contact would allow it. In return, Olujin Khan shared his own findings with Venedar and two other officers – Tank Commander Jaesman of the Vigilant Armoured Spearheads, and the leader of the Tempestus Scions that fought planetside, Tempestor Prime Ghallaghan. This latter would not deign to deal with mere Astra Militarum officers, but always made time for vox contact with the Adeptus Astartes. Through Olujin Khan, the greater war effort found a cohesion it had been sorely lacking, for where the Ultramarines masterminded matters strategic from Hyperia, the White Scars roamed far and wide – and hence came into range for conventional vox contact even when the communications networks were riven by warp storms.

Thanks to Olujin Khan, dozens of the Astra Militarum mechanised regiments that were escorting vital convoys of water tankers and war materiel from one hivesprawl to another fulfilled their missions without incident, despite Ork raids being levelled against them. This accord paid dividends over the latter half of the war, enabling the White Scars to strike quickly and efficiently at the Orks and then withdraw before untenable force was brought against them. In this way Olujin won the glory and respect he sought – not through combat, but through wisdom, diplomacy, and a desire for unity in the name of the Emperor.

FORCES OF THE IMPERIAL FISTS

The Sons of Dorn are archetypal defenders of the Imperium, and they showed their mettle upon Vigilus time and time again. Ever since their Primarch, Rogal Dorn, was entrusted with defending the Emperor's Palace on Terra they have been expert siegebreakers and tenacious castellans of the Imperium's holdings.

It was Captain Dravastis Fane of the Imperial Fists 5th Company that led his Chapter's war effort upon Vigilus. He was amongst the first to work with Marneus Calgar to restore order to Vigilus, just as his Primarch Dorn had worked with Roboute Guilliman in the dark days after the Heresy to restore sanity to the shattered empire of Mankind.

The majority of Fane's forces were stationed on the eastern trench lines of Mortwald shortly after planetfall. They fought in that false continent's defence for the duration of the war's second and third phases, thereby fulfilling a vital function – shoring up a wall against an Ork invasion that otherwise may have run roughshod over the planet's single

largest source of food – the cactus forests of Mortwald. With the Imperial Fists working alongside not only the fine regiments of Cadia and Catachan, but also the Knights of House Terryn and the Freeblades hailing from cursed Dharrovar, they made the invading Orks pay dearly for every foot of land, throwing them back time and time again.

IMPERIAL FISTS TRENCH FIGHTERS

FANE HIGH COMMAND

CADIAN SHOCK TROOPS

FREEBLADE ADAMANTIUM LANCE

HOUSE TERRYN KNIGHTS

DROKBURNA'S SPEEDMOB

DREAD MOB TANKA

KILLBOSS WREKKFIST'S STOMPA MOB

The defence of the Deinos trenches saw a deliberate withdrawal of the Cadian regiments, drawing the Orks into a kill zone between the Imperial Fists and the Knights of Terryn. Only the Freeblades of Dharrovar broke formation, forging into the wastes.

TRENCH NETWORK

— BUNKER NETWORK
— COMMS TRENCH
— SUPPORT TRENCH

— GUN EMPLACEMENT

TO DJODROLEV HIVESTAR

MORTWALD

MORTWALD-OTECK FORTWALL

DEINOS TRENCH NETWORK

Many of the Astra Militarum troopers joked of the Thin Yellow Line, for the Imperial Fists were conspicuous indeed amongst the drab earthen camouflage of the Deinos Trench Network, but their ribaldry came from a place of utmost respect.

The Imperial Fists see siege warfare as the ultimate test of martial ability, courage and resolution, and their stubborn, intractable nature makes them ideally suited to trench combat. Where the Dread mobs of the Ork vanguard drove their assault home, they found the Devastators and Centurions of the 5th Company ready to blast them to scrap. Where the Astra Militarum fell back from a rampaging tide of greenskins no human force could hope to stop, the Imperial Fists held the line. Where the Orks broke through the Imperial defences and appeared to gain some ground, they found themselves caught in a pincer movement between the Imperial Fists and their allies on the other side; with their quarry trapped, the Sons of Dorn wasted no time in gunning down the now-stranded invaders with relentless hails of bolter fire. When ammunition ran low, or even ran out entirely, it was the blades of the Imperial Fists that drove the xenos back, repelling wave after wave. For if there is a way to defend a muddy trench against a xenos horde or a looming war machine, the Imperial Fists will be the ones to find it.

The Company Banner of the Imperial Fists 7th Company, held aloft over the Tzeller Line's Fortress of Redemption in the south of Mortwald.

Captain Dravastis Fane changed radically after his first encounter with Chaos. Even during the xenos-hunting phases of the Vigilus counter-invasion, his preoccupation with heretics bordered on paranoia.

FORCES OF THE CRIMSON FISTS

The Imperial Fists were not the only Sons of Dorn to defend Vigilus against the alien. With them came their foremost successor Chapter, the Crimson Fists, who had lost so much to the greenskin race upon their home planet of Rynn's World. On Vigilus, that debt would be paid in blood.

The Crimson Fists were amongst the most numerous of the Chapters upon Vigilus. That in itself was a significant achievement, given their tragic past. After the disastrous missile detonation that had destroyed their fortress-monastery and killed the majority of their Chapter in a single blinding instant, the Crimson Fists had numbered less than four-tenths their original strength. But it was not in them to give up. Shorn of their fortress, their vehicle pool, and even their gene-seed, they fought on against the Ork invasion of Rynn's World. United under the unyielding will of their Chapter Master, Pedro Kantor, they consolidated squads and used every acre of their homeland as a weapon until they formed a cogent fighting force once more. Though they took many further casualties, they brought something akin to order back to their home world.

When the Indomitus Crusade reached Rynn's World, it brought a new breed of warrior with it. Guilliman had learned of the stricken Chapter's misfortune, and assigned over five hundred Primaris Space Marines to its reinforcement. This was an event of such destiny-altering magnitude it has been celebrated as the Day of Renewal ever since.

The Crimson Fists were beyond joyous at this turn of fate, for they had all but given up hope of attaining Chapter strength once more. To have their numbers doubled overnight, to have a real chance of redemption afforded to them, was a boon of historic magnitude. They worked hard to bring their new Primaris brethren into the fold, teaching them the rites of battle and training alongside

them night and day until the new warriors fought seamlessly with the old. Each new recruit to the Chapter underwent the trials of the Bloodied Fist, returning with his bare hands stained with the gore of a barb-dragon and the right to wear crimson upon his right hand. There were a few traditionalists of the Chapter who saw the induction of so many off-worlders into their ranks as permanently changing the soul of their brotherhood, but with Guilliman and Kantor united in their new vision for the Imperium, they kept their counsel.

The Crimson Fists too had heard tell of Vigilus' plight. Resolving to harden the bonds of kinship between newcomer and veteran, Kantor led five entire companies – a full half of his Chapter – to battle in the Nachmund Gauntlet. It was a statement, after a fashion, its intent as clear as the clarions that announced their arrival and the stark blue-and-red heraldry of their battle plate. The Crimson Fists were back in force, ready to fight and die not just for their home territory, but for far-flung worlds that the Imperium at large could not do without.

Upon making planetfall at Saint's Haven, the Crimson Fists did not plunge straight into battle, raining from the skies in thunderous drop assaults as did so many of their fellows. Instead they deployed via Thunderhawk Gunship – many of which had yet to earn a single battle scar, for the armorium of the Chapter had been replenished alongside its warriors by the grace of Guilliman's crusade. Pedro Kantor presented himself to the Vigilus Senate, consulting the war leaders of that august assemblage and seeking the wisdom of Marneus Calgar himself. He was there to serve, not to win glory – he would pay back the faith that Primarch Guilliman held in him through solemn duty.

Much to the disappointment and simmering anger of many Crimson Fists, the companies from Rynn's World were not despatched to shatter the Ork forces upon Vigilus. Instead, they were given orders to aid the war effort in Dirkden. Their task was to slow down the Genestealer Cultists that had boiled out of the subterranean levels of Dirkden, rising up in such impossible numbers that many thought that misbegotten continent already lost.

Without a word of protest, Kantor made haste for the Hyperia-Dirkden Fortwall – in doing so coming under attack from elements of the Pauper Princes – and crossed to the war-torn hellscape of the Rescalid Underworks. His forces fought nobly and without pause against the Purestrain Genestealers that scuttled like hideous alien insects through the streets, purging nests of the vile creatures with flame and sustained volleys of bolter

fire. Their aim was not simply to exterminate, for even with their newly bolstered companies, there was no way they could have taken on an entire nation of Genestealer Cultists and survived. Instead they fought a complex, overlapping web of battles designed to buy time for the Imperial citizenry to escape.

The populace of Dirkden, having been plunged into a nightmarish existence where every building, hab-site or bunker could harbour twisted alien mutants, had all but given up hope. With the Crimson Fists working alongside the Cadians to clear as many citizens as possible, tens of thousands of lives were spared, flowing in refugee convoys into the dusty southern reaches of Hyperia, where the Brazen Claws had so recently hurled back the Ork invaders. When the Ministorum decreed that they had overloaded the capacity of Hyperia to harbour more unfortunates, and that agents of the Pauper Princes were also escaping Dirkden disguised as refugees, Pedro Kantor argued for a stringent checking procedure at the southern gate of the Fortwall. He did so with such passion and eloquence that the Ministorum agreed to a compromise, and put into place the checkpoints requested under the purview of veteran Cadian regiments. In the end, even that was not enough – the Fortwall and Dirkden both ultimately fell to the xenos cultists that had so long prepared the way for their ascension. Yet without the efficiency, conviction and compassion of the Crimson Fists, the false continent would have fallen long before the culmination of the War of Beasts, and doomed millions of innocent souls.

The Chapter Banner of the Crimson Fists flew high and proud on Vigilus, held aloft by the Chapter Ancient Endigio Gomarex. Those lost in the Rynn's World disaster were remembered on its insets.

THE CHAPTERS PRIMARIS

Amongst the Chapters on Vigilus were those of the First Founding and their immediate descendants from the Second – but also several from the Ultima Founding. Though their legends were barely a century in the making, they were soon to earn the respect of their fellow Space Marines through skill at arms.

CASTELLANS OF THE RIFT

The Castellans of the Rift have a dire duty entrusted to them by Roboute Guilliman himself. Since the Primarch despatched them to the Nachmund Gauntlet, they have been locked in a struggle to drive back the hordes of daemonic war machines and Renegade Knights blighting that channel of space. When war broke out on Vigilus, the greater part of the Chapter was engaged in warfare against the heretic forces that had revealed themselves on Dharrovar. Still, two companies joined the war on Sangua Terra and a further two travelled to Vigilus. With experience fighting against the machinations of Chaos, in the third stage of the War of Beasts they hunted the dark cults of Storvhal with commendable efficiency and resolve.

The Chapter symbol of the Castellans includes crossed chains – a symbolic barrier against the evil that these Space Marines fight.

Battle-brother

Sergeant

Veteran Sergeant

Lieutenant

The Castellans of the Rift use High Gothic alpha-numerals to reflect their Ultramarines heritage. Their squad number is shown on the right pauldron and their company number on the right knee on a field of black.

NECROPOLIS HAWKS

Trained extensively in close-quarters warfare and veterans of a dozen city fights, the Necropolis Hawks are stoic and efficient in their warfare. They bear their battlefield role insignia upon their backpacks as well as their pauldrons so their comrades can identify them even in the smoke and dust of urban war.

On Vigilus, the Necropolis Hawks turned the tide against the xenos insurrection and Gellerpox infection that rocked Dontoria to its foundations. Taking control of the city building by building, they established several safe zones that were expertly defended – and pitilessly demolished those that they considered lost causes.

Higher ranks amongst the Necropolis Hawks are often denoted by the wearing of an embellished white Chapter badge.

The sword and halo was a device worn by those in Dontoria Hivesprawl who slew a heretic from the infamous Death Guard legion.

The Chapter icon of the Necropolis Hawks symbolises the sharp wits and visual acuity that make them such formidable urban fighters.

Battle-brother

Sergeant

Veteran Sergeant

Lieutenant

The blue-grey and white of the Necropolis Hawks is well chosen, for it enables them to blend into the ruined urban landscapes, cordite-scented smoke and dirt-smog typical of war in a dense cityscape.

SONS OF THE PHOENIX

Faithful to the Emperor and ritualistic in their battle cant, the Sons of the Phoenix pride themselves on plunging into the flames of battle. Their crusades are so impressive in spectacle they pave the way for the Imperial Creed to spread, and hence are followed by a great many holy men and women. Their presence in Hyperia Hivesprawl had a galvanising effect on the Vigilant Guard and Adepta Sororitas who had long anticipated their coming. Though the Sons of the Phoenix are a relatively new addition to the armies of the Emperor, during the Wars of Antipathy they won a reputation for levelling spectacular firestorms against the foe – and for the fact that they would fight on through those flames without hesitation.

The pauldrons of the Sons of the Phoenix are often richly embellished, sometimes with sanctus bones and other sainted relics.

Sergeants usually wear their squad number on their left pauldron, often framed by the laurels of victory.

On the left pauldron is worn the insignia of the battlefield role, and on the right, the Chapter symbol, a haloed helm with aquilan wing.

Battle-brother   Sergeant

Lieutenant

The off-white armour of the Sons of the Phoenix symbolises their purity. Rather than using the shoulder trim for company identification, they display their company number and often battlefield role in gold upon the left knee.

VOID TRIDENTS

Recruited from the ocean world of Talassar, the Void Tridents follow the naval traditions of the Ultramar empire. They are fast becoming known for their aptitude in space-faring and void warfare. Under their Chapter Master, Lord Commodore Theodro Vethrus, they were the first Chapter to cross the Nachmund Gauntlet from Sangua Terra to Vigilus. They outran the Daemon fleet of Warpsmith Tzungdan as they cut a path past Omis-Prion. Had it not been for the distress signals their Librarian picked up regarding Vigilus, they would have likely been able to outmanoeuvre Tzungdan and destroy his base. In the end, they diverted to Vigilus and fought a series of board-and-slay missions against the Ork cordon there instead.

The shoulder pads of Void Trident veterans often show one Aquila per decade of active service.

The astral halo, displayed alongside the laurel, is worn by warriors who have fought a boarding action that resulted in a total ship kill.

The Void Tridents show their role and squad markings on the right pauldron, and their tripartite Chapter symbol on the left. The company number is displayed on the left knee.

Sergeant   **Lieutenant**

The deep blue of the southern Talassarian oceans is echoed in the Void Tridents' battle plate. They keep an Ultramarian tradition, and on Vigilus relished the opportunity to fight alongside Marneus Calgar himself.

FORCES OF THE ADEPTUS MECHANICUS

Several dozen macroclades of the Adeptus Mechanicus were in action upon Vigilus when the War of Beasts began. These were not confined solely to the agents of Stygies VIII – though the Cult Mechanicus troops who wore the colours of that forge world fought the hardest of all to defend their domains.

After the Pact of Fire and Steel ratified what they saw as their divine right to Megaborealis, the Adeptus Mechanicus forces on Vigilus busied themselves with an agenda that none outside their mysterious priesthood truly understood. Their reputation for being inhumanly insular and at times infuriating was not helped by the behaviour of their representatives on the Aquilarian Council. These figures were politicians as much as they were priests, and they deflected, confounded and ignored any who questioned their true motives.

The Adeptus Mechanicus of Stygies VIII are seen as untrustworthy and peculiar even by their fellow Tech-Priests. The history of their forge world is defined by the events of the Horus Heresy, when their planet was saved by the quixotic Aeldari. Following this, the adepts of Stygies pursued a controversial interest in aliens and alien relics. This willingness to delve into xenos technology has coloured outsiders' perceptions of Stygies VIII's agendas ever after.

Though they never spoke of it to others, the priests of Megaborealis and Storvhal mined the planet's crust extensively for deposits of the precious substance known as noctilith, or blackstone in the common parlance. This material was of some interest to the wider Cult Mechanicus – especially after the discoveries at Amontep II came to light, and the expeditions of Belisarius Cawl of Mars became the subject of debate as he pursued deposits of this strange material in a dozen locales across the galaxy. But a peculiar quirk of the blackstone deposits upon Vigilus confounded even those who claimed to know its core properties.

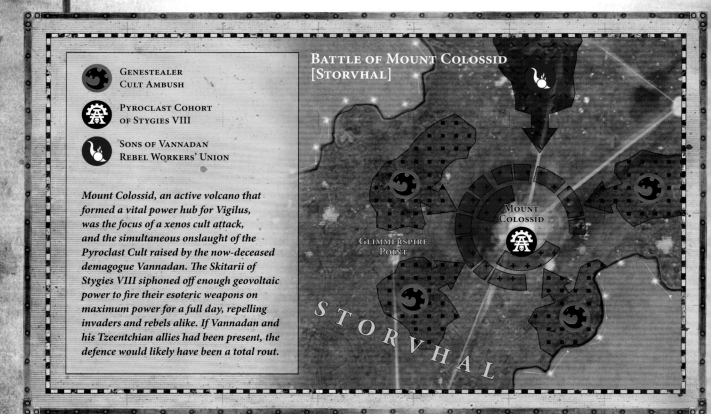

GENESTEALER CULT AMBUSH

PYROCLAST COHORT OF STYGIES VIII

SONS OF VANNADAN REBEL WORKERS' UNION

Mount Colossid, an active volcano that formed a vital power hub for Vigilus, was the focus of a xenos cult attack, and the simultaneous onslaught of the Pyroclast Cult raised by the now-deceased demagogue Vannadan. The Skitarii of Stygies VIII siphoned off enough geovoltaic power to fire their esoteric weapons on maximum power for a full day, repelling invaders and rebels alike. If Vannadan and his Tzeentchian allies had been present, the defence would likely have been a total rout.

BATTLE OF MOUNT COLOSSID [STORVHAL]

MOUNT COLOSSID

GLIMMERSPIRE POINT

STORVHAL

It was rumoured amongst the Priesthood of Mars that raw deposits of blackstone could not only be shaped and polarised to attract empyric energies, but also to repel them. There were wild theories that extrapolated from this, hypothesising that perhaps the blackstone structures dotted across the galaxy were partially responsible for reinforcing the barrier between material space and the warp. None amongst the Xenarites of Stygies VIII claimed to be able to replicate this, but they studied it with voracious and endless curiosity.

It was this boundless hunger for knowledge that saw the pioneering Tech-Priests of Vigilus delve deep under the planet's crust after their equipment showed strange readings at certain geomantic points. When they discovered the blackstone deposits there, what they found boggled the mind – the linear, spear-like shards of blackstone were held in hollow spheres that had somehow formed in the substrata, themselves filled with a viscous black suspension. As the planet turned upon its axis, the blackstone spears always remained pointing in the same direction – straight towards Sangua Terra in the Imperium Sanctus.

That discovery saw the Xenarites of Stygies reinforce their holdings a dozen times over. Whatever phenomenon of cosmic engineering they had beneath their feet had to be protected at all costs. A full sixteen macroclades – each of four cohorts consisting of three maniples – joined the eight that were already sworn to Vigilus' defence. Several other forge worlds sent macroclades to 'bolster' the forces of Vigilus, though in truth they were mobilised purely to ascertain why Stygies VIII considered the world so vital. The priests of Stygies at first rebuffed these 'reinforcements', but when the War of Beasts drove the planet towards disaster, the various forge worlds combined their efforts without further protest.

The symbol of Stygies VIII is a mark of utter dedication to the Omnissiah, and it is known on a thousand worlds. Sometimes worn with a 'VIII' numeral emblazoned beneath it, it symbolises knowledge attained at any cost.

The Skitarii Rangers of the Culax Black Guard were shipped to Vigilus as penance after their sacred charge, Arc Reactor LCVII, was destroyed by a stray orbital bombardment. They fight hard to clear their name.

FORCES OF THE ASTRA MILITARUM

The defenders of Vigilus hailed from a hundred different brigades and regiments, some amongst them the most famed in all the Imperium. The finest of these were seconded to Mortwald, where their excellence in the arts of conventional warfare enabled them to hold the line against dozens of Ork attack waves.

The strategic value of Vigilus saw it reinforced by regiments of Cadian Shock Troopers many times. They proved perfectly suited to the conditions in the hivesprawls, and were soon put to work training Vigilus' indigenous warriors in the arts of close-quarters fighting, urban escalation and quadrant pacification. Cadia had been a world where the cities were militarised to such a degree they resembled labyrinthine trench networks as much as they did conurbations – a fact that Deinos Agamemnus had long known, for he had visited Cadia as a youth.

With the Cadians manning the trench networks that protected the northern fringes of Mortwald, Lord Deinos turned his attention to the interior of his prized false continent. When a regiment of Catachans made planetfall he was quick to garrison them in the barracks of Mortwald's succulent cactus forests – though each plant was tangled and thick with foot-long, steel-hard spines, these were little impediment to the Catachan troopers stationed there. When the Ork bommer squadron known as the Dakkanaut Flyboyz made it through the flak-spitting Icarus

networks of the Deinos Trench Network and disgorged hundreds of Stormboyz from their bomb bays, the Catachans were waiting for them. The battle in the cactus forests was short and bloody. Soon Ork heads adorned many of the tallest cacti.

The Vostroyan Firstborn were stationed largely at Dontoria. Noble and selfless, they volunteered to guard the quarantine there. They paid a heavy price. When the lines failed, four out of every ten Firstborn troopers fell to plague, and the rest were incarcerated.

THE VIGILANT GUARD

The Astra Militarum are recruited from hundreds of thousands of Imperial worlds across the galaxy, and each regiment has its own customs and traditions as a result. The guardsmen recruited from Vigilus were known for one thing above all – their unwavering faith in the Emperor. They were already aligned with the Imperial Creed upon inception, for most of their number hailed from Hyperia, where religion was a way of life. The appointment of a standing body of Ministorum Priests to their ranks saw their ever-burning belief in the God-Emperor fanned to a blazing inferno. Sent to fight alongside the Vigilus-based orders of the Adepta Sororitas on hundreds of occasions, they witnessed so many miracles over the years that they had iron-clad faith in the old Astra Militarum maxim, 'The Emperor Protects' – and, if the logisticians of Hyperia were to be believed, they were quite correct. Many are the stories of true and faithful Vigilants having enemy

kill-shots turned away by their devotional medallions, lights in the sky guiding them to lost comrades, or ruined buildings suddenly collapsing upon ravening xenos raiders just before they could plunge into the Vigilant lines.

This intense belief manifested in several ways. Firstly, the Vigilant Guard were far more superstitious and reverent than their more pragmatic peers in other regiments. In early M41, when several battalions from the Cadian Gate were shipped to Vigilus and given the ongoing task of training the defenders to a high standard, this dissonance was a cause of conflict between the more military-minded Cadians and the faithful of the Vigilant Guard. The endless rites, services and obeisances that the high command of the Vigilants demanded of their men rankled many of the Cadian officers. Proctor Commander Hallatar of the 23rd Vigilant Guard was

so unbending in his insistence that every tradition and rite be adhered to that some Cadian footsoldiers started to call him the Little Pontifex. For them, this behaviour was a drain on their resources, a drag factor on their teachings – an unnecessary indulgence that would ultimately do more harm than good.

All that changed with the opening of the Great Rift. The Vigilant Guard were not troubled by the nightmares that afflicted the rest of the populace; they awoke fresh and rested after each sleep. Where the Vigilants fought they fought hard, fixing bayonets and charging gene-cursed Aberrants and even Purestrain Genestealers when needed. The Cadians grew to respect their allies, and even attended their services. Though they were strange company and believed every war hymn to be literal truth, something about the Vigilant Guard inspired hope in the time of war.

FORCES OF THE MILITARUM TEMPESTUS

The war for Vigilus saw several famous Militarum Tempestus regiments fight as elite troops in the prosecution of high-priority targets – and, when members of the aristocracy went missing, were abducted or required safe passage, as search and rescue teams, extraction specialists, and escort details.

The Militarum Tempestus are primarily known for three things – their absolutism, their exceptional degree of training, and the high quality of their wargear. They are not well liked amongst the footsoldiers of the Imperial Guard, and are held in loathing by those who resent their privileged position and wargear. This is a fact the Tempestus Scions care little about, for they are sent into battle when the Astra Militarum are found wanting, and must face some of the worst war zones the galaxy has to offer. On Vigilus they let their deeds speak for themselves.

The Schola Progenium, working hand-in-glove with Vigilant Lord Vaargan of the Aquilarian Council, recognised that the morale of the Imperial forces was of paramount importance. With the Genestealer Cult growing within and the uprisings spreading across the hivesprawls, rumours of catastrophe were causing panic in the streets.

Tempestor Prime Liocardus of the Betic Centaurs determined that the greatest impact his Scions could have was in saving the figureheads of the Vigilus world order. By thwarting the assassination attempts of the Genestealer Cultists and acting as an extraction detail for fleeing dignitaries, the Antrell Lions and Zetic Tygers under Lord Commissar Asdan saved the lives of three members of the Aquilarian Council attacked by the lumbering Aberrant horde of cult leader Hollun Desh. Meanwhile, when Hivespire Magentine was assaulted by Speed Freeks seeking to topple the hive from below, it was the Kappic Eagles that fought them to a standstill and escorted Pontifex Slyne Galluck to safety. Without their figurehead, the Ministorum would have suffered a serious blow.

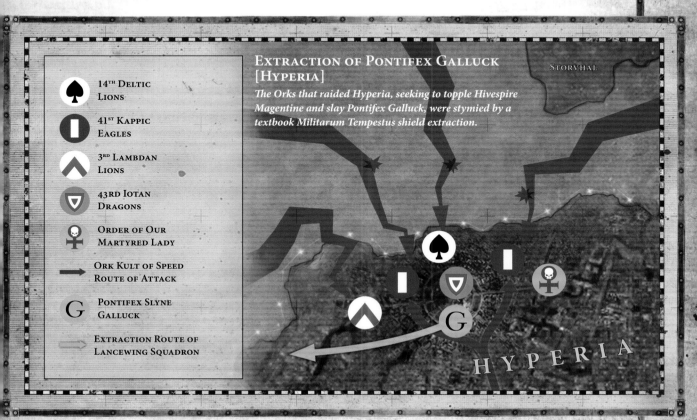

Legend

- ♠ **14ᵗʰ Deltic Lions**
- **41ˢᵗ Kappic Eagles**
- ▲ **3ʳᵈ Lambdan Lions**
- ▽ **43ʳᵈ Iotan Dragons**
- **Order of Our Martyred Lady**
- → **Ork Kult of Speed Route of Attack**
- G **Pontifex Slyne Galluck**
- → **Extraction Route of Lancewing Squadron**

Extraction of Pontifex Galluck [Hyperia]

The Orks that raided Hyperia, seeking to topple Hivespire Magentine and slay Pontifex Galluck, were stymied by a textbook Militarum Tempestus shield extraction.

STORVHAL

HYPERIA

FORCES OF THE ADEPTA SORORITAS

The Sisters of Battle that fought upon Vigilus were a vital part of its defence. Without their faith, surety and swiftness of purpose, the hivesprawl of Oteck would almost certainly have fallen – and likely Hyperia too. Some amongst the citizens have described the feats of martial prowess they exhibited as miraculous.

The Adepta Sororitas have a proud tradition that saw their founders talk in person with the God-Emperor himself. They are more than a mere military presence, for they embody the Imperial Creed, and back it up with fire and fury. On Vigilus, they kept the hivesprawls safe from countless threats, ranging from mundane rebellion to supernatural manifestation.

The Order of Our Martyred Lady had fought to keep Vigilus unsullied by the scourge of Chaos for nearly four thousand years. They had

garrisoned Saint's Haven ever since it was a simple basilicanum, and patrolled hundreds of miles of alabaster ramparts and tower-dotted boulevards in force. Being urbanised to such a degree, they fought almost exclusively in the built-up areas of the hivesprawls, and the Adepta Sororitas of Hyperia became a largely mechanised force. They had a great many transports at their behest, and were well-versed in citizen control during times of strife – so much so that the sight of their midnight-black vehicles sent the populace of Hyperia scrambling to move out of the way. Each

Canoness and Sister Superior knew the city streets well, having made a study of them for her entire tenure. With the data-harvests of the Order Dialogus predicting likely threat zones and guiding their optimal passage from one hivesprawl district to another, the Sisters of Hyperia were masters of their territory. Should the unbeliever, the heretic or the abomination threaten a city district, the Sisters of Battle were swift to respond. It was this home advantage that saw them hurl back the Ork invaders time and time again in the War of Beasts' opening stages.

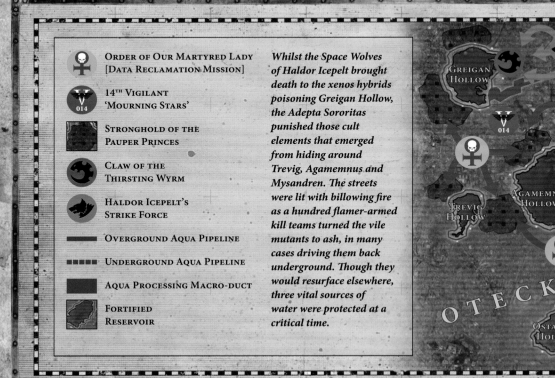

ORDER OF OUR MARTYRED LADY
[DATA RECLAMATION MISSION]

14ᵀᴴ VIGILANT
'MOURNING STARS'

STRONGHOLD OF THE
PAUPER PRINCES

CLAW OF THE
THIRSTING WYRM

HALDOR ICEPELT'S
STRIKE FORCE

OVERGROUND AQUA PIPELINE

UNDERGROUND AQUA PIPELINE

AQUA PROCESSING MACRO-DUCT

FORTIFIED
RESERVOIR

Whilst the Space Wolves of Haldor Icepelt brought death to the xenos hybrids poisoning Greigan Hollow, the Adepta Sororitas punished those cult elements that emerged from hiding around Trevig, Agamemnus and Mysandren. The streets were lit with billowing fire as a hundred flamer-armed kill teams turned the vile mutants to ash, in many cases driving them back underground. Though they would resurface elsewhere, three vital sources of water were protected at a critical time.

GREIGAN HOLLOW

TREVIG HOLLOW

AGAMEMNUS HOLLOW

MYSANDREN HOLLOW

OSTAVEER HOLLOW

OTECK

Such was the influence of the Ministorum over Vigilus that the Sisters of Battle under their command had priories and abbeys in every hivesprawl. They were initially placed there to further the reach of Saint's Haven – or rather, the Ecclesiarchy's presence there – and for a time, Lucienne Agamemnus resented them. But as the Orks slowly closed on the planet's metropolises and the Genestealer Cult rose up in dizzying numbers from beneath the streets, the true value of the Adepta Sororitas became clear. Where the Sisters of Battle walked, the grace of the Emperor held back unnatural magic and banished nightmares like the morning sun. Where they fought, the populace fought with them.

The Canoness Superior in charge of the Adepta Sororitas upon Vigilus, a fiery and short-tempered individual known as Temperance Blaise, was so roundly feared that she was given free rein by the entire Aquilarian Council to prosecute the Vigilus campaign as she saw fit. Beneath her was a network of trusted Canonesses and Celestian Superiors she had named the Sacred Thorns, each of whom was entrusted with the defence of the Ministorum's interests in a different hivesprawl.

When the Space Marines made planetfall upon Vigilus it was Temperance Blaise that dealt in person with the Chapter Masters. In the first few weeks of the war, Blaise had taken the invasion of her planet hard, and had led many a counter-strike in person, taking out her righteous indignation upon every malcontent and coward she could find, as well as the xenos invaders that threatened her cordons. Only when the war ground into more of a stalemate did she resume her role as war leader, coordinating the defence of Hyperia with lethal efficiency, and leaving the killing to her sisters.

Used to all but ignoring the officers of the Astra Militarum, the Adeptus Astartes conversely worked closely with Blaise, for they saw in her a powerful ally with vital knowledge of each theatre of war in which they fought. Working together, they proved far greater than the sum of their parts. Though the Sisters of Battle kept largely to the hivesprawls, they held the line when even a whole regiment of Imperial Guardsmen would have been found wanting, defending the interior districts with bolter, flamer and melta blast.

The icon of the Order of Our Martyred Lady was a common sight across Hyperia.

THE KNIGHTS OF VIGILUS

Dozens of Imperial Knights fought on Vigilus – some Questor Imperialis, some scions of the Mechanicus, and some Freeblades from the forsaken world of Dharrovar. Some hailed from as far away as Voltoris, the home world of House Terryn; these noble veterans played a large part in taking on the Ork Scrap Cities.

As war erupted in the outskirts of the urban sprawls, the defenders of Vigilus were outclassed by the massive, heavily armoured war engines constructed by the Ork Mekaniaks that oversaw the industry of the Scrap Cities. Only the march of the Imperial Knights turned the tide against these war machines. Yet such was the unremitting violence of the War of Beasts that at its end, only four Imperial Knights were left standing.

The first of the clunky, fat-bodied walkers that assailed the hivesprawls were crewed by gretchin and lesser Orks, their war machines dwarfed even by the Armigers that fought in support of

the nobles of the Imperial houses. The Ork vehicles were cut down by the dozen, smashed to pieces by the devastating charges of lance formations, and put to waddling flight on more than one occasion. But the longer the war ground on, the larger the war engines became, until the Ork walkers made even Dominus-class knights seem small.

When the Gargants of the Ork war tribes loomed into view on the horizon, several of the Questor Mechanicus detachments from Megaborealis calculated that they would suffer untenable casualties if they engaged them, and simply fought elsewhere, taking a deadly tally on the Ork Speed Freeks that

ventured into the interior of their home continents. The Freeblades hailing from Dharrovar were eager to fight the largest of the Ork war machines, forsaking the Imperial lines in what many saw as a reckless quest for glory. Their dauntless aggression carried them far, but in the end, they were outmatched and slain to a man.

'Honour comes from within, not from circumstance. Though it asks not for reward, it forms a shield against corruption more potent than any other.'

- Taurus of House Terryn

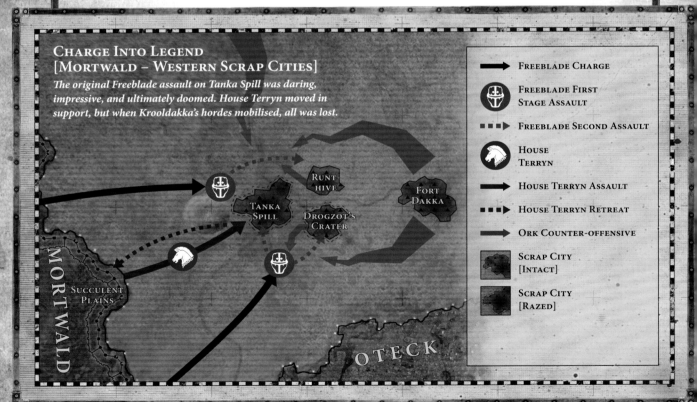

CHARGE INTO LEGEND
[MORTWALD – WESTERN SCRAP CITIES]

The original Freeblade assault on Tanka Spill was daring, impressive, and ultimately doomed. House Terryn moved in support, but when Krooldakka's hordes mobilised, all was lost.

MORTWALD

SUCCULENT PLAINS

TANKA SPILL

RUNT-HIVE

DROGZOT'S CRATER

FORT DAKKA

OTECK

→ FREEBLADE CHARGE

⊕ FREEBLADE FIRST STAGE ASSAULT

▪▪▶ FREEBLADE SECOND ASSAULT

◉ HOUSE TERRYN

→ HOUSE TERRYN ASSAULT

▪▪▶ HOUSE TERRYN RETREAT

→ ORK COUNTER-OFFENSIVE

SCRAP CITY [INTACT]

SCRAP CITY [RAZED]

The Knight Errant known as *Honour Intractable* is piloted by Taurus, Gatekeeper of House Terryn. He rarely leaves his home system – but when he does, he fights like a born hero.

Baron Darius, piloting *Intolerant*, is House Terryn's Master of Justice and its appointed executioner. He led a spearhead of his own knightly vassals on Vigilus to great effect.

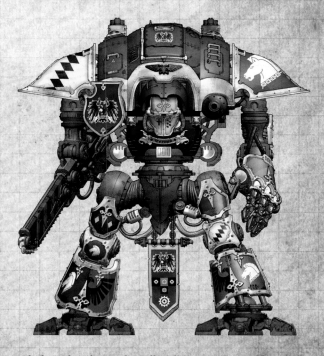

Sir Selwyn is a bladesman at heart. He took great pleasure in using his reaper chaincleaver to carve apart any Deff Dreads that he caught in Vigilus' open wastes.

Alarbus pilots the Knight Gallant known as *Honoured Vigilance*. He added another slain Titan-class foe to his tally on Vigilus with the death of the Ork walker Big Stompa.

Speedlord Krooldakka's Evil Sun was emblazoned on every vehicle of his Blitz Brigade.

Richgit Drukk was of the Bad Moons. He had access to Drogzot's crater of scrap parts.

Warhog and his fellow Blood Axes were famed for their many Dakkajets and aerial assets.

Everyone was a bit afraid of Mad Goff Murk – apart from his ally Ragzakka.

The Snakebites of Vigilus, under Ogrokk Bitespider, owned a nation of runts and squigs.

FORCES OF THE ORKS

Every one of the Ork clans, castes and sub-cultures made it to Vigilus in some form or another – and though they were at first slow to gather pace, they became unstoppable in the later stages of the war.

The Imperium, using the reprieve bought by its Bastion-class force fields during the first phase of the War of Beasts, did its best to identify and log the various greenskin forces that had battered their way onto the planet. Given that an entire armada of Ork spacecraft descended upon Vigilus at the dawn of the conflict, it is remarkable their forces were categorised at all. Yet the Imperial strategos were able to amass a rough estimation of the major Ork armies present from data amassed by convoys, evacuation craft and low-orbit reconnaissance.

Further down the line, this information was combined with field intelligence gathered from eye-witness accounts, servo-skull pict-captures, and shanty-spies that operated on and around the outskirts of each war zone. Some of these spies were able to broker deals with Blood Axe mercenaries. They did so at the expense of many Imperial lives, but their data proved sound when collated with that collected by interrogators who had acquired information from Ork captives boasting about who would soon come to avenge them. Eventually, the Aquilarian Council – and later the Vigilus Senate – was able to build up a detailed picture of the xenos foe they faced and assign the appropriate defence priorities. It was the first step in the eventual Imperial reconquest of the wastelands.

The forces that invaded the urban sprawls of Vigilus once the force fields went down were billions strong in totality. Through the sheer, shocking violence of their assaults they managed to raze massive swathes of each continent save Kaelac's Bane and Dirkden. This conquest was known as Da Great Ransakk to the Ork warlords that led the city-wrecking assaults. All the while, high-speed xenos vehicle fleets and motorised war assets circumnavigated the planet in search of battle – and fell upon the outskirts of each urban sprawl when the force fields gave out. These smoke-belching, planet-scarring mechanised hordes were known collectively as the Speedwaaagh!.

Many of the so-called Scrap Cities that dotted the wastelands shaped their specialisms about the facilities of their flagship fortress, which was simply the largest spacecraft to make planetfall without disintegrating on impact. If such a flagship fortress contained Mekaniak workshops and hangar complexes where Ork walkers were constructed, the resultant Scrap City became a hub for armies of Deff Dreads, Morkanauts and Stompas. If it was a base for Kults of Speed, it became a pit stop and workshop for the Speedwaaagh!. As the natural order of Ork-kind asserted itself, each Scrap City fell under the domain of a single war leader – though this was as often a Big Mek as a Warboss.

'Fer a while there, them force fields kept us out of the humies' cities, an' I thought this planet weren't gonna be no fun. Since then I've driven me wagon all around the planet, won a fire-eatin' race, lost three fingers, and sacked a massive fort fulla them book fings wot burn up real nice. Wot a larf!'

- Drokk da Stabba, da Black Axes

THE GREENSKIN HORDES

The combination of heavily defended fortress cities, breakneck vehicle flotillas, and earthshaking walker armies, backed up by numberless hordes of Ork infantry proved exceptionally deadly. Only the Bastion-class force fields bought Vigilus' defenders a chance to muster a cogent defence – without them, the planet's urban sprawls would likely have been reduced to cinders within a matter of months.

FORT DAKKA
FORCES OF SPEEDLORD KROOLDAKKA
Krooldakka's Blitz Brigade................. *12 Battlewagon mobs*
Ozgrog's Kult of Speed .... *54 speed mobs*
Boss Narka's Speedin' Kult................................ *17 speed mobs*
Da Oil Guzzlas .... *7 speed mobs*
Da Hubdrop Skinflintz .... *2 speed mobs*

TANKA SPILL
FORCES OF MEKBOSS BIG TANKA
Dread Mob Tanka...............................*56 Dread-class walkers*
Da Teefspitta Nobz ....*13 Knight-class walkers*
Killboss Wrekkfist's Stompa Mob .. *56 Stompa-class walkers*
Tanka's Bad Gargants .... *5 Gargant-class walkers*
Hooladakka's Rig Fleet .... *53 battle tankas*
Oddmek's Twin Skullhammerz.............*2 super-heavy tanks*
Drokburna's Speedmob..................................... *14 speed mobs*

DROGZOT'S CRATER
FORCES OF BIG MEK DROGZOT
Mekaniak Stormboyz .... *22 mob-hordes*
Richgit Drukk's Speedin' Supastarz .... *17 speed mobs*
Drogzot's Grave Raidaz ....*12 mobs*
Big Rigg's Tanka Crawlaz.................................*53 battle tankas*
Duffa's Goff Rokkers...*1 kill mob*

RUNTHIVE
FORCES OF OGROKK BITESPIDER
Buglurk's Squig Breedaz.............................*2 Runtherd mobs*
Olden Runtherd Tribes ....*3 Runtherd mobs*
Badgrot Stikkas ....*94 grot mobs*
Da Dropz Krew ....*63 grot mobs*
Redkap Runt Rebelz ....*3 grot mobs*
Deff Gunnaz Big Gunz.................................*6 artillery mobs*
Da Evun Bigga Gunz......................*2 macro-artillery mobs*
Da Snakebite Stampede .... *41 Squiggoths*
Da Big Lugz .... *12 Gargantuan Squiggoths*

MEKSTOP CITY
FORCES OF BIG MEK LUGNATZ
Lugnatz' Blitza Boyz ....*8 Battlewagon mobs*
Da Kogtribe Grindaz................................... *33 scrapper mobs*
Da Skrapyard Dogz .... *12 scrapper mobs*
Kommander Grokker's Ladz fer Hire ... *12 mercenary mobs*
Grokker's Tankmurkz ....*2 mechanised mobs*
Stormboss Stampskull's Skyburna Korps ....*12 mobs*
Drokk's Rivet Krew...*1 speed mob*

++CONTINUED IN FILE XENO8.1/PI/43
Note: A rudimentary guide to Ork glyph-based linguistics appended to file 44-48, incomplete as of 34.22 post.

GORK'S LANDING
FORCES OF BIG MEK ZOGBAG
Zogbag's Killaz .... *34 Mek-led bigmobs*
Morkanaut Mekkin' Krew .... *4 Knight-class walkers*
Gorkanaut Dekkin' Mob.................*17 Knight-class walkers*
Zogbag's Krumpin Mob.................*12 Stompa-class walkers*
Mekfist Gargants...CLASSIFIED

DA WHEEL HUB
FORCES OF BIG MEK TANKSKRAPPA
Tankskrappa's Dread Mob .... *34 super-heavy walkers*
Da Wheelboss's Mekmob.................................. *2 speed mobs*
Speedsta Bosskult .... *12 speed mobs*
Murk's Squigz-on-da-Move....................*1 speed mob auxilia*
Boss Dekkit's Blitz Brigade.....................*1 Battlewagon mob*
Da Great Gargant Gorkzilla .... *1 Mega-Gargant walker*

RAKKUK'S MEKMAZE
FORCES OF BIG MEK RAKKUK
Rakkuk's Speed Freek Eleet .... *44 speed mobs*
Nakkadakk's Doom Skwadron...............*31 Flyboy sky mobs*
Warhog's Dakka-planes ....*12 Flyboy sky mobs*
Lockjaw's Blastamob ....*1 speed mob*
Boss Shokk's Shokkaboyz ....*1 speed mob*
Krogskull's Boyz..*1 kill mob*

SKUMTOWN
FORCES OF MAD GOFF MURK
Deffstomp's Goff Krushas ....*41 mobs*
Da No-mess Kill Krew..*11 mobs*
Da Black Axes ....*19 mobs*
Da Heavy Triggaz ....*8 mobs*

HURRIKANE REKK
FORCES OF BAD MEK RAGZAKKA
Da Lootin' Pillagers ....*3 Loota hordes*
Da Nikkin' Fingaz ....*2 grot hordes*
Da Swirlygig Riders...*2 Loota hordes*
Da Bigmob Burnkrew.....................................*3 Burna hordes*
Krogzak's Burnaz ....*1 kill mob*
Da Pyro-Mekaniak Speedaz...............................*1 speed mob*
Da Big Gutz .... *14 super-heavy walkers*

SPEED FREEK RACES

In the opening phases of the war, the Speed Freeks on Vigilus, unable to invade the city sprawls due to the Bastion force field networks, were dying for a proper fight. Purely for the thrill of driving fast, they made circuits around Storvhal, the Vhulian Swirl and even Kaelac's Bane – though for the latter trips they had to take plenty of squig-based firebrew to use as anti-freeze. Vast swathes of wasteland were scarred by the grinding wheels and tracks of the Speedwaaagh!, some trails so large they were visible from space. Yet the Fortwalls that connected the major false continents to one another proved to be troublesome obstacles.

Made of double rows of yards-thick ferrocrete, these Fortwalls could not simply be blasted apart by killcannons and deffguns. Each was defended by a standing garrison of Astra Militarum infantry, and the motorcade macrohighway that ran down the centre made reinforcement – and even rebuilding – a simple task for the Imperials that laboured inside the twin barriers, with supplies coming fairly easily from the hivesprawls.

When it came to racing around the continents of Vigilus, these barriers stood in the way, making a full circumnavigation of Oteck, Dontoria, Megaborealis, Hyperia and Dirkden an impossibility – or so the Speedwaaagh! warbosses believed.

In the first phase of the War of Beasts, Krooldakka cemented his reputation upon Vigilus by pulling off a feat of wagon racing that left his rivals in awe. By brokering a deal with the crazed driver Boss Shokk and his patron, the Mad Mek Gungubbinz, Krooldakka was able to solve the Fortwall problem.

As they approached the massive Fortwall, Krooldakka purposefully allowed Boss Shokk to overtake his Battlewagon – much to the amazement of his fellows – then gave Mek Gungubbinz the signal by firing a flare. A huge bubble field came into being over the vehicles at the race's front, protecting them from the firepower of the Cadians that were lined up on the wall. It was then that Boss Shokk triggered his customised racer's rear-mounted shokk drive. Augmented by Gungubbinz' warp emitters, it made a large hole in reality, a warp tunnel wide enough to fit a Battlewagon through. With a flash, Boss Shokk disappeared – only to reappear safely on the other side of the Fortwall. The glowing portal left behind him was used by the rest of the Speedwaaagh! to bypass the fortification and complete its circuit around the false continent. So was Krooldakka's Warp-kut born, and it was the first of several new race routes opened across Vigilus.

While the force fields remained active around the hivesprawls, the Speed Freeks were able to occupy their time racing circuits instead. They did so to prove the supremacy of their wagons, to show off the latest wares of their Meks, and to gamble for teef – for wagering on something as epic as the Cross-Hyperia Sickle Run was always good for a laugh. More than that, however, they raced for the sheer joy of it, and they did not stop even when the War of Beasts got fully underway.

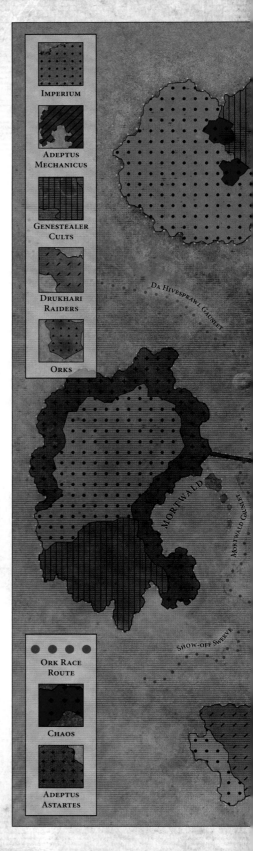

IMPERIUM

ADEPTUS MECHANICUS

GENESTEALER CULTS

DRUKHARI RAIDERS

ORKS

ORK RACE ROUTE

CHAOS

ADEPTUS ASTARTES

DA HIVESPRAWL GAUNTLET

MORTWALD

MORTWALD GAUNTLET

SHOW-OFF SWERVE

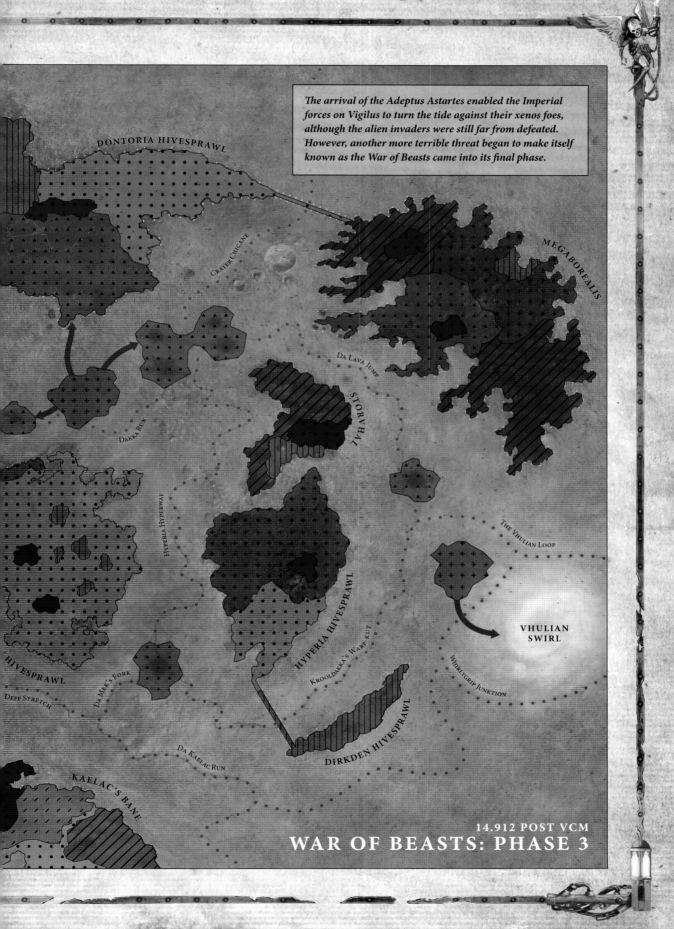

The arrival of the Adeptus Astartes enabled the Imperial forces on Vigilus to turn the tide against their xenos foes, although the alien invaders were still far from defeated. However, another more terrible threat began to make itself known as the War of Beasts came into its final phase.

DONTORIA HIVESPRAWL

CRATER CHICANE

MEGABOREALIS

DA LAVA JUMP

STORVHAL

DAKKA RUN

THE VHULIAN LOOP

HYPERIA HYPERWAY

VHULIAN SWIRL

HYPERIA HIVESPRAWL

KROOLDAKKA'S WARP-KUT

WHIRLYGRIP JUNKTION

HIVESPRAWL

DA MEK'S FORK

DEFF STRETCH

DIRKDEN HIVESPRAWL

DA KAELAC RUN

KAELAC'S BANE

14.912 POST VCM
WAR OF BEASTS: PHASE 3

FORCES OF WARLORD KROOLDAKKA, SPEEDLORD SUPREME

Krooldakka was the warlord in overall command of the Vigilus Speedwaaagh!. The first out of the fortress ships and the first to make a full circuit of the planet – by simple virtue of gunning down anyone who came close – he made himself the undisputed leader of the Kults of Speed that ruled Vigilus' wastes.

FORT DAKKA

In the overarching Ork creed of might makes right, a boss of Krooldakka's hulking stature riding in the largest Battlewagon teef could buy commanded a great deal of respect. As the Speed Freeks supposedly said – behind his back, no doubt – he may not have been the fastest, but he was the fightiest. Anyone foolish enough to approach Krooldakka's roving Blitz Brigade unbidden was taking his life into his hands. The amount of explosive firepower this fleet of gunned-up Battlewagons could lay down was enough to shatter an Imperial tank squadron at range – and this happened countless times throughout the War of Beasts.

Krooldakka had a long memory when it came to those who wronged him, an itchy trigger finger, and a ten-foot chainaxe always hungry for tough greenskin flesh to chew. Any who raced past his growling monstrosity of a Battlewagon – known as the *Planet Grinda* and driven by Krooldakka himself – to get to the finish line in a race, or the battle line in a war zone, were treated to a withering hail of big shoota bullets or a few shots from the killcannon. If they evaded that onslaught, they were crushed under the *Planet Grinda*'s wheels, or later hunted down at Fort Dakka and given a lethal beating for their trouble. Almost all the Orks of Vigilus learned not to gainsay Krooldakka when he claimed to be first into battle. Those who maintained they were the fastest often found their mates suddenly had other things to do as a hulking shadow lengthened over them.

Some Orks earned Krooldakka's respect by committing truly spectacular acts of violence. He allowed the maniacal Ozgrog and the viciously tempered Boss Narka to compete for the position of second in command, each driving the other to ever-greater stunts and feats of battle in a rivalry that has lasted more than ten years. Da Oil Guzzlas, entirely comprised of Ork Nobs riding into battle on Defftrikes, Warbikes, modified Trukks and even extensively customised aircraft, acted as Krooldakka's proving ground – one who rose through the ranks may even have found himself riding in a Battlewagon at the Speedlord's side (or, technically speaking, just behind him). Almost all of Fort Dakka's speed mobs were filthy rich, either having grown a lot of teef or punched them from the mouths of the less fortunate. The exceptions ganged together into the mobs known as Da Hubdrop Skinflintz; hangers-on who existed purely because Krooldakka hadn't got round to beating them up yet.

DROGZOT'S CRATER

To the west of Fort Dakka was Drogzot's Crater. This vast crater was filled near to the brim with millions of tons of scrap amassed by the Lootas of Big Mek Drogzot. To better get from one pile of rusting riches to another, most of Drogzot's legion of Meks used rokkit packs running on the fuel from their broken flagship, the *Fistful of Spannas*. That same fuel ran in the tanks of Richgit Drukk's mob the Speedin' Supastarz, the Big Mek's pride and joy. Considering the exceptional quality of their rokkit

fuel turbo-boostas, and their snazzy paint jobs, if any on Vigilus could be considered the Flash Gitz of the road, it was them. The Speedin' Supastarz were kept running by the twin assets of Big Rigg's Tanka Crawlaz, who provided fuel on the move, and Drogzot's Grave Raidaz, who stole and repurposed gubbins from the vehicle kills the Supastarz left in their wake.

TANKA SPILL

Drogzot's rival Boss Mek, Big Tanka, prioritised raw brute strength over speed and style, hoping to impress Speedlord Krooldakka with sheer might. His city, Tanka Spill, was devoted to the creation of massive walkers – it was this facility that assailed Mortwald. Hooladakka's Rig Fleet boasted over fifty battle tankas; these massive war wagons had massive oil tanks that allowed them to drive for weeks on end, and refuel their super-heavy allies into the bargain. Amongst these was Oddmek, the proud owner of two looted Baneblade tanks that once bore the colours of the Vigilant Guard.

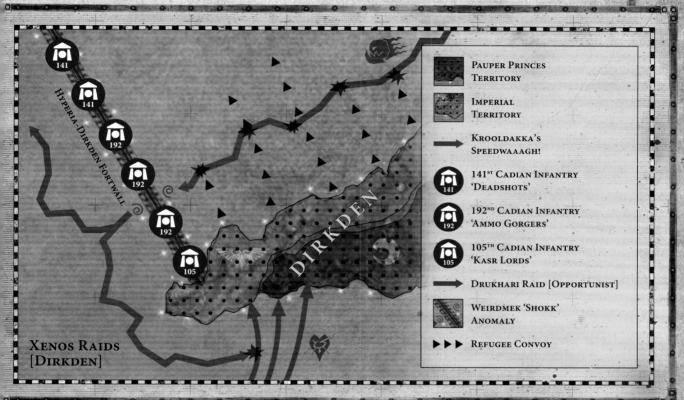

PAUPER PRINCES
TERRITORY

IMPERIAL
TERRITORY

KROOLDAKKA'S
SPEEDWAAAGH!

141 141ST CADIAN INFANTRY
'DEADSHOTS'

192 192ND CADIAN INFANTRY
'AMMO GORGERS'

105 105TH CADIAN INFANTRY
'KASR LORDS'

DRUKHARI RAID [OPPORTUNIST]

WEIRDMEK 'SHOKK'
ANOMALY

▶▶▶ REFUGEE CONVOY

XENOS RAIDS
[DIRKDEN]

RAID ON THE DIRKDEN EXODUS

The rise of the Pauper Princes led to an exodus of the loyalist citizens of Dirkden, who fled north into the wastes for the safety of Hyperia. In the third phase of the war, news had spread that all the citizens fleeing the Rescalid Underworks to the south of Dirkden had been turned back from the Hyperia-Dirkden Fortwall. It was rumoured that the Cadians and Crimson Fists there had opened fire to restore order. There was much truth in these assertions, for when it was revealed that agents of the cult were concealing themselves among the military as well as the citizenry, the Commissariat became merciless in their exterminations. No Dirkdenite would pass across the Fortwall. However, with the heartlands of Dirkden overwhelmed by cult forces and Genestealers running at will through the streets, the situation had already reached boiling point. As a direct result, dozens of mechanised refugee columns and convoys made up of military

vehicles and civilian transports left the northern perimeter of Dirkden and drove off parallel to the now closed Fortwall. The Dirkden Exodus – once a steady trickle – became a series of fast-flowing rivers.

Word reached Krooldakka via his aerial spies in Nakkadakk's Doom Skwadron. His Speedwaaagh! made a fast about-turn from its raids on the north of Hyperia. Roaring down from Hurrikane Rekk toward the northern sprawl of Dirkden, he bullied his way to the front of the Speedwaaagh! once more. If his plan worked, he could give his lads a good fight and a fast race in one go. Krooldakka's timing was sound, and his guttural laugh boomed out across the wastes as he closed in on his prey.

Though the convoy's Vigilant Guard escort reacted swiftly to the far-off trail of smoke thrown up by the encroaching Speedwaaagh!, though they took a

staggered echelon formation in good order, and though many Guardsmen were further motivated by the fact that they were defending close family members, they simply did not have enough in the way of guns to hold back the rampaging Orks.

Many of the leading vehicles of the Speedwaaagh! were blown to smithereens by long-ranged fire, and many thousands of refugees were bought time enough to make a break for Hyperia. Then Krooldakka's spearheads slashed through the militarised refugee columns like a scythe through stalks of wheat. His Blitz Brigade hardly slowed as it smashed through the Chimeras and Tauroxes sent to stop him, and he sped on without pausing for a single trophy. When the Fortwall loomed in the middle distance, he did not hesitate, but instead had his Meks open their shokk attack tunnel. The Speedwaaagh! sped straight through the wall and out the other side.

FORCES OF MAD GOFF MURK

Mad Goff Murk was the lord of an empire of dust. The fact that the dust was made from the bones of his enemies was enough for Murk, for he existed not to raise statues, to create war effigies or even to make a legend of himself from the war for Vigilus. He existed only to destroy.

The Goffs have always been known for thinking with their fists and head-butting to death anything that gets on their nerves. Yet even amongst the Goffs, Murk was a figure of fear. His red eyes glimmered with such all-consuming hatred that some amongst the Weirdboyz muttered that he had not made it out of the storms of Gork's Grin without bringing something horrible with him.

SKUMTOWN

Murk was lord of the shambolic Scrap City he insisted on calling Warboss Murk's Strong Boss Fort of Guns and Killing Axes. Everyone else simply called it Skumtown.

Naturally, they did this out of earshot, for those who used the term to Murk's face soon found their own torn off and flapping from his trophy racks.

Skumtown was little more than the bare bones of a hundred wrecked ships, their empty hulls and fuselages strewn about at random like a scrap metal elephant's graveyard, the wind howling through the abandoned shanties and tribal huts. Murk's disdain for any kind of creativity save weapon-smithing made his domain the poorest on Vigilus, save perhaps Runthive. Those who visited Murk – and few did, for he

had a habit of alienating his allies – did not comment on the shabby nature of his city, for to do so was an act of suicide; what Murk lacked in imagination he made up for in sheer psychopathic rage.

It was Murk that followed Krogskull's Boyz across the fallen spire of Megaborealis, and his Goff Krushas, No-mess Kill Krew and Black Axes that assailed the Stygian Spires as they were being overrun by Genestealers. His Loota allies, Da Heavy Triggaz, lent Murk the firepower he needed to level any threats his massed green-and-black tides of infantry could not cut down.

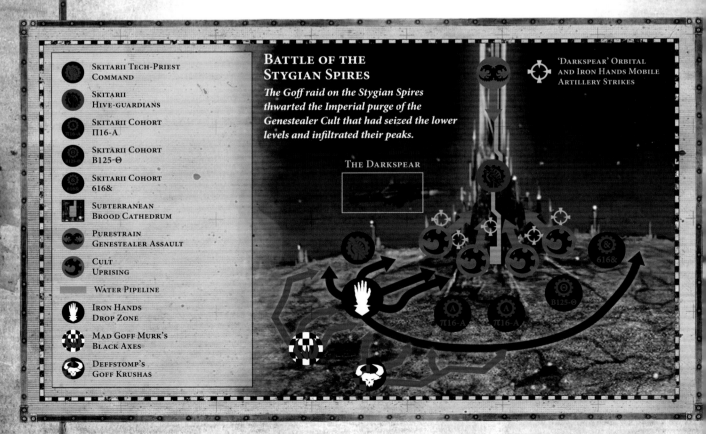

Legend

- Skitarii Tech-Priest Command
- Skitarii Hive-guardians
- Skitarii Cohort Π16-A
- Skitarii Cohort B125-Θ
- Skitarii Cohort 616&
- Subterranean Brood Cathedrum
- Purestrain Genestealer Assault
- Cult Uprising
- Water Pipeline
- Iron Hands Drop Zone
- Mad Goff Murk's Black Axes
- Deffstomp's Goff Krushas

BATTLE OF THE STYGIAN SPIRES

The Goff raid on the Stygian Spires thwarted the Imperial purge of the Genestealer Cult that had seized the lower levels and infiltrated their peaks.

THE DARKSPEAR

'DARKSPEAR' ORBITAL AND IRON HANDS MOBILE ARTILLERY STRIKES

NORTHERN SCRAP CITY CLUSTER

DA WHEEL
HUB

GORK'S
LANDING

RAKKUK'S
MEKMAZE

*A thriving war economy
sprang up across the
four northernmost Scrap
Cities. Looted wargear and
metal was traded, stolen,
set on fire and hurled
in anger between the
clans and tribes. Though
Mad Goff Murk claimed
independence, in truth all
answered to Krooldakka.*

SKUMTOWN

STORVHAL

WESTERN SCRAP CITY CLUSTER

RUNTHIVE

FORT
DAKKA

TANKA
SPILL

DROGZOT'S
CRATER

*Fort Dakka was effectively the capital city of the Ork settlements upon
Vigilus, being the base of Krooldakka's Speedwaaagh! and having the
largest more-or-less intact spaceship towering high in its midst. It was
the target of several Space Marine raids over the course of the war,
though Krooldakka's banner still flew from its highest point.*

Zogbag, a gifted Big Mek, hailed from the Deathskulls clan. He had a knack for big walkers.

Big Tanka copied a lot of Zogbag's designs, but used his own glyph to show originality.

The Speedsta Bosskult was a band of Nobs that loved nothing more than a running battle.

The air corps of the Ork war effort bore the dubious camouflage of the Blood Axes.

Da Heavy Triggaz were Goffs, but their skills at looting rivalled those of any Deathskull.

FORCES OF BIG MEK ZOGBAG

Big Mek Zogbag was a vital part of Krooldakka's war machine. It was he that created many of the technological advancements that kept the Speedwaaagh! going even against the Adeptus Astartes.

GORK'S LANDING

It was said amongst Krooldakka's supporters that the Mekaniak genius Zogbag, boss of Gork's Landing, was far more interested in making new war machines than he was in using them. Perhaps there was some truth in that, for Zogbag was a gifted Mek – though being a greenskin, he was also more than happy to stomp his enemies into a paste whenever and however he could. It was he that created the first giant war effigies on Vigilus, an act that spawned hundreds of imitations. His designs ultimately led to the creation of the Dread mobs that assailed the hivesprawls during the War of Beasts, such as those that smashed through the defences of Dontoria Hivesprawl without breaking stride. Though Krooldakka was loath to admit it, this act led to the Big Mek being almost as well-respected as the Supreme Speedlord himself.

DA WHEEL HUB

Big Mek Tankskrappa, an old apprentice of Zogbag, crashed to Vigilus in the gigantic Ork macrohauler known as *Big Tugga*. An avowed wagon specialist, Tankskrappa built his vehicular constructions with ruggedness and durability in mind, even if none of them were close to being aesthetically pleasing. A fair number of his wheeled creations he built in transit to Vigilus, and it is a testament to his skills that the best of them rode out of the crash site intact and formed the vanguard of the Speedwaaagh! elements that went straight for Megaborealis and Dontoria. The re-purposed warship *Big Tugga* became the focal point of

the Scrap City known as Da Wheel Hub ever after.

Any Speed Freek worth his salt had his vehicle tinkered with and upgraded by Tankskrappa's well-paid Mekaniak work crews. The Big Mek's partners in high-octane crime – the ageing petrol-head known as Da Wheelboss and the steel-armed Mekbreaka Drakk of the Speedsta Bosskult – were the only ones that could rival Tankskrappa's creations.

During his tenure as master of Da Wheel Hub, Tankskrappa turned his talents to the creation of ever-larger walkers – inspired by Zogbag's enormous war effigies, the Mekaniak built a vast Dread mob of his own that incorporated nearly three dozen super-heavy class walkers. During the last years of the War of Beasts, he and his fellow Big Meks worked together to create the largest and shootiest of all tributes to Gork and Mork – the Great Gargant Gorkzilla. They hoped that should that monstrosity ever shake the surface of Vigilus with its tread, even the Titans of Megaborealis would be hard pressed to slay it.

'Zogbag's mad as Mad Goff Murk, everyone knows dat. But he got the rest of da ladz workin' as well as racin', and that's no mean feat. He's got vision, has Zogbag. You can see it when you look at the Gargants wot he built. Or you can see it when he's finkin, cos sparks come flyin' outta the side of his bonce.'

- Mogga da Mouth, Runtherd

Legend:
- **HOUSE TERRYN PREFECTURE**
- **FLANKING ADAMANTIUM LANCE**
- **BOMBARDMENT PHALANX**
- ▪▪▪▶ **INITIAL ROUTE OF APPROACH**
- ➤ **HOUSE TERRYN CHARGE**
- **BIG MEK LUGNATZ' GARGANT FAKTORIES**
- **STORMBOSS STAMPSKULL'S GOFF ORKS**
- ➤ **SPEED FREEK ATTACK ROUTE**
- **STOMPA MOB TELLYPORTA ATTACK**

RAID ON MEKSTOP CITY

Mekstop City was vital to the southern Ork invasion. House Terryn's assault upon it ended in disaster when Big Mek Lugnatz teleported his Stompa Mobs directly into the fray.

RAKKUK'S MEKMAZE

Rakkuk's Mekmaze was a labyrinth of Ork shanty towns; though many tried to drive into its inner reaches in the hope of finding the best hauls of loot, very few would-be contenders drove back out again without having had something stolen from them. Right in the heart of the Mekmaze was the true treasure of the Scrap City, and that which lifted it above even Tanka Spill and Gork's Landing in prominence – a quartet of airstrips. These carefully maintained assets Rakkuk kept sacrosanct from the rampant industry that sprouted from the beached-whale-like hulks of his invasion fleet. The airstrips played host to Nakkadakk's Doom Skwadron, Warhog's Dakka-planes and Rakkuk's own Flyboyz, part of his larger Speed Freek Eleet. Though Rakkuk did not realise it, Nakkadakk was in the employ of Krooldakka himself, and would secede in a moment if given the nod.

The three aerial tribes together formed the largest Ork air force upon Vigilus several times over. Though they may have been outmatched by the skill of the Imperial pilots that fought them for aerial supremacy across the planet's smog-churned skies, they were repaired, rebuilt and bolstered with every passing week, whilst the pilots of the fighters and bombers of the Imperial war effort felt the loss of every plane downed.

HURRIKANE REKK AND THE STYGIAN SPIRES

The pyromaniac Bad Mek Ragzakka crashed his flagship *Bosstoof* dangerously close to the Vhulian Swirl. When the Swirl grew in size over the third phase of the war, its gale-force winds began to tug at the ramshackle fortress-town that had sprung up around Ragzakka's ship. It was a sign that the Weirdboyz interpreted as swiftly encroaching doom.

Only by allying with Mad Goff Murk did Ragzakka escape being relegated to a footnote in the planet's history. By concentrating their attacks on Megaborealis, Ragzakka and his flame-obsessed mobs drove a path across the continent, pushing back Skitarii legions and Genestealer Cultists alike. Only the Iron Hands were able to stop them from sacking the Stygian Spires – and even then the hive fell to a clutch of Genestealer Cultists soon after.

STOMPA MOBS

The creation of massive walking war effigies is an almost automatic process in Ork society, stemming from their unbridled ambition to conquer all before them in the names of the greenskin gods, Gork and Mork. Those on Vigilus during the War of Beasts were superlative examples of their kind.

Big Mek Zogbag rose to a position of influence early in the war for Vigilus, and in doing so inspired a new kind of Waaagh!. He claimed to be inspired by visions of giant, stompy effigies being spat onto the planet's surface by the warp storm that the Orks called Gork's Grin, and the Imperium the Cicatrix Maledictum. His imagination electrified by his premonitions of the Ork gods stomping all over the humies' cityscapes, he built giant walkers festooned with destructive weaponry.

These were at first the single-pilot war engines known as Gorkanauts and Morkanauts, and were sold to the highest bidder to pay for the war materiel he needed for the next phase. After building several dozen of these, Zogbag admitted to himself that they simply were not grand enough. It was not long before Zogbag became more ambitious. He turned his hand to Stompas, and when he had amassed enough Meks willing to help him fulfil his vision, even larger machines of war. Whilst the greenskins found themselves stymied in the early stages of the war, he had no shortage of helpers.

'These xenos walkers aren't simply war engines, gentlemen. These are graven idols, effigies of barbarous gods given life by primitive engines. To destroy them is to destroy the deities of the Ork race! Forwards!'

- Last words of Sir Thrund of Terryn

It was Zogbag that built the first Gargants upon the wastelands of Vigilus. Towering, barrel-bellied monstrosities with giant artillery pieces for arms, building-wrecking fists and gut cannons that could blast enormous chain-linked bolas into the ranks of the enemy, these machines sparked a renaissance of inventiveness across the planet. Known as the Mekfist Gargants, these ramshackle constructions were experimental and in some cases highly rudimentary – though as word about them spread they had a galvanising effect on his fellow Meks.

Where Zogbag was the trailblazer of the Vigilus war effigy, Mekboss Big Tanka was the one to take his designs and bring them to a pinnacle of destructiveness. In conjunction with the Bad Dok known as Hooladakka, he fashioned a massive Dread mob of over fifty walkers, each with a grot or Ork wired into the hot-seat. In some cases these seats were indeed hot, being situated directly over the engine, which saw the Killa Kanz

Where this glyph rose above a Mek's workshop, a new walker would soon be unleashed.

 Mek
Clever, technology, mechanical

 Blitz
Invasion, devastate

 Nob
Nobility, authority, high rank

 Gubbinz
Engine, workings

 Gargant
Titan, large robot

 Kannon
Big gun, artillery, cannon

Deff Dreads, Killa Kans, Stompas, Gorkanauts, Morkanauts and Gargants bear many of the same glyphs to proclaim their sheer killiness. Like its speakers, the Ork language is robust, but without much vocabulary.

and Deff Dreads march on their target, the Deinos Trench Line, at great speed in search of the relief of boundless killing.

This collaboration was just the start, for with the creation of even larger war effigies, Da Teefspitta Nobz were given the destructive war machines they thought they deserved, a force potent enough to win Big Tanka a permanent alliance with the Speedboss Supreme. Next to be created was a giant Kan Factory specialising in the creation of Stompas, for by this point word had spread that Big Tanka had a gift for mass production. With so many Speed Freeks roaring off to the front lines, every foot-slogging Ork north of Oteck Hivesprawl was dying for a Dread or Stompa in which to ride to battle.

The Stompa Mobs that lumbered out from Tanka Spill drove much of the greenskin conquest of western Vigilus in the second phase of the War of Beasts. When the Big Mek turned his hand to the creation of Gargants inspired by those made by Zogbag, Big Tanka found himself rising to the top of the Mek food chain. Though he took heavy casualties from the Freeblade Knights that surged out of Mortwald to assail his stronghold, his connections with the other three western Scrap Cities left him with might enough to engage and ultimately defeat the combined force of Imperial Knights and Titans sent to destroy his industry.

Meanwhile, Zogbag continued to blaze a trail of rampant construction. Though Big Tanka's creations surpassed his in number, and though Bad Mek Ragzakka of Hurrikane Rekk proved a far more capable and inventive looter of Imperial war machines, Zogbag never gave up on his vision. Working night and day by the light of his welding torch, he did not cease in his labours, and made

up for his disinterest in matters of quality with sheer numbers. It was Zogbag's dream to unleash a massive horde of Ork walkers on his enemies that would conquer not only Vigilus, but Neo-vellum and nearby Omis-Prion into the bargain. Only Gork (and possibly Mork) knew whether this was an impossible dream, for in greenskin society, a strongly held belief can soon become reality.

THE SQUIGGOTHS OF RUNTHIVE

Where there's Orks there's squigs, as the old Runtherd expression goes, and Vigilus was no exception. Only a few days after making planetfall, the elder Snakebite Warboss known as Ogrokk Bitespider saw a niche in the planet's ecosystem, and began to exploit it. His cyboar outriders had thundered out of their pens to sniff out the major Ork encampments across the planet, and found that the vast majority of Orks were already on the warpath. With most obsessing about the Speedwaaagh! or the war effigies of Da Ransakk, no-one was looking at making a name for himself as runt-master. Though it was held as a relatively lowly role in Ork society, Ogrokk knew the path of the Runtherd could lead to much greater things – and amongst those greater things were the titanic beasts known as Squiggoths.

Ogrokk sent word through his grot mobs, and before long messengers scurried out to the four corners of the planet, stowing

aboard Evil Sunz vehicles and squeezing into the gunnery pods of the Ork air forces to ensure they spread as far and as fast as possible. Soon the word was out – the grots would have a city of their own, and it would be called Runthive. There they would be able to thrive away from the gnarled fists and hobnailed boots of their oppressors – provided they did as Ogrokk told them.

As soon as that message became widespread, tens of thousands of grots snuck off to join Ogrokk and the rest of the Snakebites at Runthive. They helped tend the squigs that Buglurk's Squig Breedaz specialised in raising from the drops, ensuring the biggest and fiercest specimens were constantly well-fed (sometimes literally in person). Together, these runts banded into tribes of their own. The largest of these were the Badgrot Stikkas, Da Dropz Krew, and the Deff Gunnaz – the crews of Ogrokk's rusting but plentiful

artillery. These all formed identities and even sported colours of their own. Some even rebelled against the Olden Runtherds that wielded the whip to ensure they stayed productive – the Redkap Runt Rebelz began their careers as infamous rabble-rousers, but ended them as Squiggoth fodder.

As the lesser classes of snotling, grot and squig thrived in the shanties of Runthive, the Squiggoths became ever larger and more numerous. By the third phase of the war, Ogrokk's pride and joy, a dozen Gargantuan Squiggoths known as Da Big Lugz, had grown so large they could overturn Imperial battle tanks with a flick of their tusks. Famously bad-tempered and devastatingly flatulent, these massive armoured beasts were goaded into a stampeding charge against the southern edge of Dontoria, flattening an entire district and causing immeasurable damage before wandering off to feed.

FORCES OF THE GENESTEALER CULTS

The Genestealer Cult of Vigilus was well established across the planet, with a presence that numbered in the tens of millions – all tracing their lineage to the same Patriarch, Grandsire Wurm.

A fully mature Genestealer Cult is huge; it can number in the millions or even billions, perhaps more if it covers several worlds. The Cult of the Pauper Princes originated on Chancer's Vale, but took its fervent creed to the stars – it spread to the sentinel world of Vigilus early in its journey, and fifteen other planets besides.

In the nomenclature of the Ordo Xenos, the original occurrence of a system- or sector-spanning cult like the Pauper Princes is known as the genesis infestation. Later infestations often use the same heraldic colours as the genesis infestation to show their wider allegiance to the cult.

These identifiers may be adapted so that the cultists fit in with the dress conventions and social norms of their home world. The Pauper Princes' later infestations, apart from being less numerous, differed little from the first; with their own Patriarch biologically descended from that of the genesis infestation, the cultists of later infestations all had much the same colouration of chitin and flesh. Any small differences in markings and temperament were incidental, for these minor dynasties were cut from the same cloth as their forebears. On Vigilus, armbands and tattoos were used as a unifying insignia, but usually kept hidden from sight.

All the cultists in a given population centre are known as a gene-sect. Some planets are only populous enough to support one gene-sect, but amongst the teeming throngs of Vigilus, several co-existed. Though each gene-sect may differentiate itself with markings and subtleties of colouration, they all ultimately hail from the original Patriarch of the cult, and usually work together seamlessly, especially in times of war.

'We were not ready for this war, not entirely. The last pieces of our glorious uprising had yet to be put in place. But by the glory of the Star Children, we shall win it nonetheless.'

- Hisser Verglorian, Nexos of the Flock Beneath.

GENESTEALER CULTS

The life cycle of a Genestealer Cult is erratic, for they adapt as circumstances dictate, lurking in the shadows when necessary and expanding to fill every niche whenever the opportunity arises. On Vigilus they had so many places to hide that nearly every settlement had its own gene-sect or brood cycle, with many infiltrated Astra Militarum regiments in support.

MEGABOREALIS GENESIS SECT

Clergy of Piston's Hollow.............................. 1 sub-sect
Guardians of the Brood Cathedrum .... 1 sub-sect
Lurkers in the Oil .... 1 sub-sect
The Sumpswimmers...................................... 4 claws
Sons of Azmadiah.. 2 claws
The Dynasty Beneath .... 4 brood cycles
Nameless Creepers*................................ 2 brood cycles
Lineage of Ghent*.................................. 1 brood cycle
Heralds of the Bladed Cog*....................... 2 brood cycles
Claws of Magnar Tertius........................... 2 brood cycles
The Devoted Sons (Yorl Krauss)................... 3 brood cycles
The Writhing Wyrm .... 3 brood cycles

These cultists did not hail from Vigilus, but were greeted with open arms as a delegation from beyond. Though they held a different Patriarch as their master, they evinced the same attitudes and ultimate goals as those born of Megaborealis stock.

THE DIRKDEN GENE-SECT

The Grand Throng of Horga Threnst..................... 1 sub-sect
The Flock Beneath .... 1 sub-sect
The Halfbrothers... 1 sub-sect
Guardian Childer of the Non-Hive..................... 1 sub-sect
• New Brood Brothers (Undervigilants)....... 2 regiments
• The Lost Generation .... 3 regiments
• Achillan Seekers .... 1 regiment
The Untold Grandchilder .... 2 brood cycles
The Doting Daughters .... 2 claws
Rescalid Sewerlings .... 3 claws
The Shadowed Coil...................................... 3 claws
The Subskein Skitterlings................................ 3 claws

THE BRETHREN DONTORIAN

Dontorian Ur-Dynasty..................................... 1 sub-sect
• Cultist Astra Militarum*....................... 12 regiments
Lake Dontor Underlings................................ 1 sub-sect
Children of the Great Choke............................ 1 sub-sect
Vostoyev Subsprawlers............................ 6 brood cycles
Grodholev Subsprawlers........................... 6 brood cycles
Pravdus Truthsayers................................ 1 brood cycle
Litmus Dock Worker's Union 282..................... 2 claws
Missionary Point Recidivists............................. 1 claw
Guardia Periphery Ex-Proctors .... 2 claws
Deltarian Broodsurgers .... 4 claws
Munitorium Delverkin .... 2 claws
Hallordwight Ghouls.................................... 2 claws

So many and varied were the regiments and battalions converted to the Genestealer Cult cause that they are lumped into the same category.

OTECK GENE-SECT

Greigan Hollow 12th Reserve...................... 4 brood cycles
Oteck Vigilid 9th Militarum .... 2 regiments
Agamemnus Hollow 2nd Reserve.................. 6 brood cycles
Mysandren Hollow 18th Reserve .... 2 brood cycles
Mogadon Neophyte Cavalcade.......................... 2 claws
Ostaveer Remainder .... 2 claws
Turingsbane Data Recovery Squadron .... 8 claws
Domastran Juvesect...................................... 2 claws
Siltid River Patrol .... 9 claws
Symphall District Enigmas.............................. 9 claws
The Thirsting Wyrm (Greigan)........................... 1 claw

++**Continued in file 149f/vigil-post**++

MORTWALD GENE-SECT

The Floraquarian Sect.............................. 1 sub-sect
Electros Undercrawlers............................. 1 sub-sect
Childer Ejecta... 1 sub-sect
Djodrolev Ever-faithful.............................. 1 sub-sect
Immortalis Spireguard (somnolent cell) .... 6 brood cycles
Rejuvenis Youthstealers .... 1 brood cycle
The Ageless Wyrm .... 2 claws
Cactacean Sappers.. 1 claw
Trenchcrawlers....................................... 10 claws
Biosanctic Aberrants.................................... 1 claw

HYPERIA CULT ELEMENTS

Glatchian Grandchilder............................ 2 brood cycles
Magentine Stainclaws.............................. 3 brood cycles
Dubchec Cleanser Corps........................... 5 brood cycles
Industrial Enclave 15/BZ................................ 1 claw
Van Gollick Tarmacadians .... 12 claws (mechanised)
Fortwall Infiltrators .... 10 claws
Dust-dock Scour Detail .... 2 claws
Macro-yard Worker Detail 742........................... 1 claw

STORVHAL CULT ELEMENTS

Hekatorian Burnskins................................... 2 sub-sects
Colossid Caldera-Crawlers .... 2 brood cycles
Phaestos Mountaineers .... 5 brood cycles
Spawn of Mother Magma................................. 1 claw

The symbol of the Pauper Princes is a variation on the wyrm-form device – its multiple limbs hint at the belief that with sufficient numbers the lowly throng will always triumph over the courts and palaces of the influential.

The infestation upon Vigilus was so well-established it lived through several full brood cycles in a number of areas, the cult expanding with almost exponential growth in the substrata and abandoned zones of the hivesprawls and founding new gene-sects in each urban area. Mortwald Hivesprawl had a different gene-sect to the geothermic continent of Storvhal, and to the capital Hyperia, and so on.

Each gene-sect has its own war leaders, including a Magus, Primus, and other specialists

if it has reached a fourth and subsequent generation. On Vigilus, the cult's first Magus, Velleron of Megaborealis, was in psychic communication with the Magus of Dontoria Hivesprawl, Brothermagus Darrague. So close were they in thought and deed that they and their fellow Maguses occasionally requisitioned transit lifters and banded together to fight in the same place at the same time if they deemed it necessary.

Each Vigilus gene-sect, usually several hundred members strong at least, was further subdivided

into claws. These were the equivalents of strike forces in Imperial nomenclature, and usually numbered between fifty and a hundred warriors. Each Magus and Primus had several claws at his disposal, ranging from the Neophyte gangs of Hyperia that were able to pass for human, to the monstrous groups of Aberrants and Metamorph Hybrids of Oteck Hivesprawl that were unmistakeably alien, and hence kept out of sight until the time of war was upon them.

Claws usually have at least one leader figure. Upon Vigilus it was the Claw of the Thirsting Wyrm that put into motion the poisoning of Greigan Hollow. That claw was led by the Iconward Gilgas Vendella, though the Abominant, Bregg the Anointed, was a totem of leadership in his own right – especially amongst his fellow Aberrants.

Once the original gene-sect of Megaborealis reached the point where it could spare the resources to bud off, it sent out several Purestrain Genestealers – or in the case of those sent to Dirkden, an entire brood – on missions of infiltration. Later generations instead sent out entire armies of xenos monstrosities from the fifth generation, using hidden tunnels, disused aqua pipelines and algae-slicked crawl-ways to operate unseen. These new vectors of infection started new gene-sects at the heart of the largest population centres, spreading the cult's influence ever further.

According to Imperial records, Vigilus had only one Patriarch, but there were those who attributed Grandsire Wurm's ability to seemingly cross the planet in a disturbingly short amount of time to the theory that at least one other Patriarch existed. There was a hypothesis amongst these doom-mongers that should an infestation's outrider organisms find a population centre so rich in life that it has the equivalent of a small planetary populace unto itself, as is the case in the largest of Imperial hives, the Purestrain Genestealer sent out to colonise it may become a new Patriarch in its own right.

If this is the case, it is extremely unlikely to happen on a small planet made up of contiguous land masses, due to the psychic backlash that could result. But provided the sites are sufficiently removed it could theoretically occur. On a planet as overpopulated as Vigilus, there may indeed have been two Patriarchs, one on either side of the planet and perpetually divided by the vast oceans of wasteland in between each hivesprawl. Others posited the theory that the moon Neo-vellum, where evidence of cult activity was uncovered, had its own Patriarch – and that beast had been deliberately shipped to Vigilus to act as a double for Grandsire Wurm should he be slain in battle.

Despite the first gene-sect of Vigilus rising in Megaborealis, Dirkden Hivesprawl was unquestionably the most thoroughly infested of all the planet's false continents. By the time Marneus Calgar arrived on the planet, it was beyond redemption, its streets infested with Genestealers and their cultist worshippers to such a degree that only rearguard actions and evacuations had any real affect.

The Tempestus Scions known as Drop Force Praesidion distinguished themselves many times over the course of Dirkden's evacuation, escorting Chimeras that carried high-ranking Imperial nobles to safe zones and fighting with efficiency and unyielding determination to defy the cult wherever it sought to decapitate the Imperial command structure.

After leading the efforts of the Tempestus Scions assigned to Dirkden and ensuring the successful evacuation of dozens of noble families, Tempestor-Prime Vandred was slain towards the end of the third phase of the war. After the Hyperia-Dirkden Fortwall was declared permanently closed mid-mission, Tempestor Prime Vandred engaged a brood of Genestealer Cultists in close quarters combat to buy his charges time to escape, and was torn to pieces by the claws of xenos hybrids as a result. His sacrifice ensured the family his team was escorting reached the new evacuation point, albeit on foot as their transport was disabled. The bloodline of the Ashenid royal family was saved – though given the disastrous history of Ashenid Non-Hive, the value of that accomplishment is still up for debate.

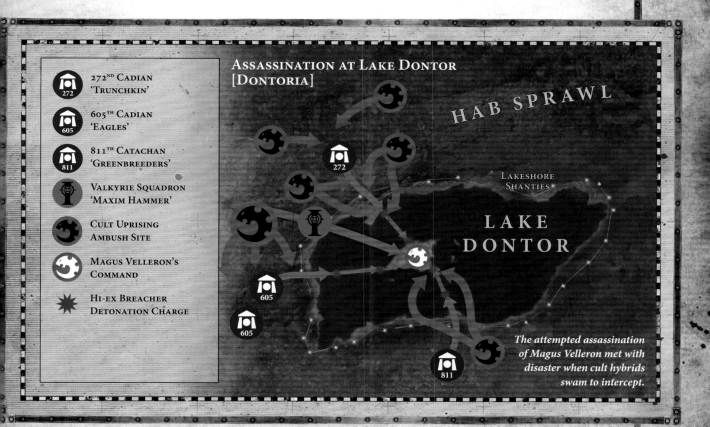

ASSASSINATION AT LAKE DONTOR [DONTORIA]

272 — 272ND CADIAN 'TRUNCHKIN'

605 — 605TH CADIAN 'EAGLES'

811 — 811TH CATACHAN 'GREENBREEDERS'

VALKYRIE SQUADRON 'MAXIM HAMMER'

CULT UPRISING AMBUSH SITE

MAGUS VELLERON'S COMMAND

HI-EX BREACHER DETONATION CHARGE

HAB SPRAWL

LAKESHORE SHANTIES

LAKE DONTOR

The attempted assassination of Magus Velleron met with disaster when cult hybrids swam to intercept.

FORCES OF THE ASURYANI

The craftworlds of the Asuryani prolong their existences by the careful manipulation of reality – on Vigilus, what began as a simple assassination spiralled out of control into a dire vendetta.

The Cosmic Serpent is synonymous with wisdom and enlightenment, for it exists in both the material dimension and the warp simultaneously.

The first Asuryani presence upon Vigilus during the War of Beasts was a warhost of bright and vibrant warriors of Saim-Hann. After the disastrous events on the outskirts of Saint's Haven, where a small force of Aeldari was gunned down by Militarum Tempestus even as they sought parley, all that changed. They returned as a sombre, vengeful corps of ghost warriors – the spirit stones animating each construct giving the slain Aeldari a chance for revenge.

The strike force of the Spiritseer Qelanaris was the most overt Asuryani presence upon Vigilus, but there were rumours in Calgar's senate that other elements of Saim-Hann – and even other craftworlds – were active in the war. For the most part, they confined their kills to the hidden cults of Chaos worshippers that operated in secret in several locations on the planet. When Calgar sent his forces to investigate the high spires above the cloud line, he found evidence of hard-fought battles. The corpses of many Chaos worshippers had been slashed apart by razored shuriken – the calling cards of the Aeldari that had turned from enemies to allies.

HYPERIA

SAINT'S HAVEN

RING OF NOTHINGNESS

AELDARI ATTACK ON HYPERIA

Symbol	Description
	CRAFTWORLD SAIM-HANN FORCES
→	MAJOR DIVERSIONARY ATTACK
▪▪▪▶	QELANARIS VENGEANCE STRIKE
	EXTREMIS GUARD [ULTRAMARINES]
	4TH COMPANY ULTRAMARINES
V	VIGILUS SENATE [AQUILARIAN PALACE]
	MILITARUM TEMPESTUS
	47TH ANTRELL LIONS

The Spiritseer Qelanaris knew well that the Imperium would defend its most vital war council with a ring of adamantium that no conventional force could breach. In order to break the circle of defence, the Saim-Hann warlord sent several major diversionary forces across the Ring of Nothingness, avoiding the bridges that spanned that great void where the Devastators of the Ultramarines 9th Company were stationed. The Ultramarines and Militarum Tempestus scrambled to compensate – and in doing so allowed Qelanaris' own force to penetrate from the north.

FORCES OF THE DRUKHARI

The Drukhari of Commorragh are much-feared murderous raiders that appear from nowhere to snatch away the unwary. On Vigilus they emerged from a hidden webway portal on Kaelac's Bane, the frequency of their raids increasing massively when the Noctis Aeterna fell across the planet.

The Dark Eldar were a constant thorn in the side of the Imperium, and with the coming of the Noctis Aeterna, that thorn proved to be a poisoned one. Their raiding tactics, thriving upon anarchy, fear and confusion, meant they found the worlds of the Imperium Nihilus very much to their taste.

With the communications that linked one Imperial force to another disrupted to the point of falling apart completely, the Drukhari were able to lance deep into Imperial territory and escape back out again before retribution could be brought against them. The Imperial war machine, already cumbersome and sluggish in comparison to the lightning raiders of the Drukhari, were disrupted further by vox-ghosts that confused and obfuscated orders. When the Drukhari raiders used their mastery of technology to lace these already fraught communiques with the screams of those they had abducted, disorder and panic broke out even amongst the veteran regiments of the Astra Militarum.

The opening stages of the War of Beasts saw the warriors of the Drukhari Kabals strike hard and fast at the cryo-geologist miner groups that sought to syphon water from the Glacia Betus and Glacia Omicroid macroquarries. What had started as occasional predation escalated into large scale war, and within a few months of the Great Rift's appearance in the skies of Vigilus half of Kaelac's Bane was denuded of all life save that of the Drukhari.

From there they spread their invasions across the west of Dirkden and deep into the south of Oteck, their raids growing bolder and more devastating with every passing week. Yet as horrific as these raids were, the true toll the Drukhari would take upon the war effort of Vigilus would only come to light later in the war.

Much of the Dark Aeldari menace in the third stage of the War of Beasts came from the Haemonculus Covens, those connoisseurs of the diabolic that sit at the rotten heart of Dark Eldar society. Ostensibly, their covens invaded the planet's urban sprawls eager to fill their larders and laboratories with fresh specimens. Their real motives were more personal, however.

At the head of the invading force was the Coven of the Altered, who – much like the Aeldari of Saim-Hann – had unfinished business with the Imperial forces of Vigilus. The coven had finally met its match in battle against Roboute Guilliman during the Indomitus Crusade, and though its warriors had recoiled from open conflict, they had regrouped in Commorragh to make a dire plan. They tracked several elements of the Ultramarines from afar, intending to strike at the Primarch through striking at his sons – and if they were able to harness Primaris gene-tech in the process, so much the better. When they heard the warriors of Ultramar were to reinforce Vigilus, they made haste for the webway portal of Kaelac's Bane and emerged from the arctic wasteland in force.

These strike forces headed straight for the southern regions of Hyperia and Oteck, launching such harrowing and spectacular attacks that they became known and feared as Carnivals of Pain. At times it was the Wracks and Grotesques of the covens that slaughtered the panicked and rioting citizens in the streets, at others it was even stranger creations, amongst them the carthorse-sized ice mantises that had been captured from Kaelac's Bane and remade into iridescent, semi-biological Pain Engines. The horrors the Drukhari unleashed could not go unanswered by the planet's defenders – a fact the Haemonculi flesh-sculptors knew only too well. In truth, the spectacle of their assault was but a lure, and it succeeded in its aim.

The Haemonculi strike was well coordinated, not only with their Kabalite allies, but with the arrow-swift assaults of their Wych Cult allies. Several Wych Cults had been lured to Vigilus with promises of rich reward should they steal away enough Primaris Space Marines not only to showcase in their arenas, but also to feed the alchemical and biomantic experiments of the Haemonculi. Though they avoided open war where possible, the Drukhari lured, engaged and in places stole away entire squads of Ultramarines that would fetch a high price back in the Dark City.

CAMPAIGN RULES

'Come, fell terrors of the outer dark! Come dire foes, tainted xenos and heretic scum. Come you all and shatter in ruin upon the defences of Vigilus, as ocean waves break brief and meaningless upon the jagged rocks. We defy you!'

- *Unknown Imperial Preacher*

VIGILUS CAMPAIGNS

These Vigilus Campaign rules allow you to bring the thrilling narrative presented in this book to life on the tabletop. Battles won and lost take on greater importance as you fight for control of Vigilus, not only reliving the climatic moments in the narrative, but also forging your own tales of glory or crushing defeat. Will your army stand in defiance or seek to tear Vigilus asunder? This is the planet's darkest hour, and its fate is in your hands.

INTRODUCTION

Linking your games together into a campaign can add a whole new dimension to your games of Warhammer 40,000. If the idea of a campaign is daunting, fear not, for on the following pages you will find everything you need to run a thrilling campaign for you and your friends set on war-torn Vigilus.

This section starts by detailing how to organise a campaign, how to group players into teams, how to arrange battles and how campaign glory points (GPs) are awarded. On pages 120-125 you will find rules for the three different phases of the War of Beasts. It is intended that players will choose the phase of the war that either best matches their collection of Citadel Miniatures, or the phase of the war that they would most like to play. Lastly, on pages 126-127 you will find additional rules for running campaigns set on other worlds within the Imperium Nihilus.

The Vigilus Campaign is ideal for new players and veterans alike. Rather than having a rigid structure, it gives players a lot of freedom with regards to the armies they muster and the missions they fight. This allows the narrative to take centre stage in your games. Players will get the most out of a Vigilus Campaign if they embrace its narrative spirit, perhaps by basing their Warlord on a general presented in this book, or by inventing a story around their army that ties them into the unfolding story of this war-torn planet.

ORGANISING A CAMPAIGN

The first thing you must do in order to organise a campaign is to find some other players to take part in it. A Vigilus Campaign is designed to have between 4-16 players divided into equal-sized teams. If you have an odd number of players, you need not worry; there is advice offered below on how to adapt the rules for uneven teams.

You will next need to decide how long you want the campaign to last. We have found it is better to choose to fight a short campaign of six to eight weeks to keep all the players involved excited – after all, there is nothing stopping you from starting a new campaign immediately after the first has been completed!

CAMPAIGN ROUNDS

A Vigilus campaign is broken into campaign rounds. Each round follows the narrative of the Vigilus war and represents a milestone in the timeline. There are 6 campaign rounds for each phase of the War of Beasts and thus it is recommended each campaign round lasts for one week in a six-week campaign.

Each campaign round will have special rules that affect the battles played in its duration. It will also state which missions earn additional bonus campaign glory points. You will need to decide how many battles each player can participate in during a campaign round. A limited approach of allowing each player to play once or twice per campaign round ensures a level playing field; this can also help balance out uneven teams by allowing the team with fewer players to participate in more battles each campaign round. Alternatively, you might decide to allow players to participate in as many battles as possible to emulate the desperate nature of war with each team rallying to earn the most victories. This method can be as frantic as it is fun! Discuss with the players which approach is best suited to your campaign.

FIGHTING BATTLES

Once the campaign is underway the players are free to organise and fight battles as and when they wish. The players can fight any Warhammer 40,000 mission but there are extra incentives for using the missions and battlezones presented in this book. Players are also free to change Army Rosters between battles. After a battle has been fought, the players earn campaign glory points as shown on the table below. It can be a good idea to nominate one player in the campaign to record all the glory points earned by each team, or for each team to have a captain that records the glory points earned by their teammates.

DECLARING THE WINNER

Once all the campaign rounds have been completed, the campaign glory points earned by each team are tallied up and the winning team is announced. To give the campaign a memorable send-off, all players should be brought together when the winner is announced. You could even schedule the last round of battles to happen immediately before the campaign is concluded to allow for some tense and nail-biting final moments.

Finishing a campaign is a momentous achievement and it shouldn't only be the winners of the campaign who are celebrated. For example, you might want to keep a record of each player's win/loss ratio and announce the individual with the highest. You could also focus on other aspects of the hobby – for example, you could include bonus awards for the 'coolest army', the 'best-painted Warlord' and the 'most sporting opponent', all voted for by the players.

CAMPAIGN GLORY POINTS	
CONDITION	CAMPAIGN GPS EARNED
Winning the battle	10 GPs to every winning player
Using a Vigilus battlezone (pg 154-159)	2 GPs to every player
Playing a Vigilus Crucible of War mission (pg 130-141)	1 GP to every player
Playing a Vigilus Echoes of War mission (pg 142-153)	3 GPs to every player
Fulfilling the criteria for bonus glory points in each campaign round	See the following pages

119

FIRST PHASE OF THE WAR OF BEASTS

ROUND 1

1.192 POST: PLANETFALL
Ork spacecraft slam down into the wastelands of Vigilus.

1.197 POST: THE COGS GRIND TO A HALT
The Council of Cogs squabble and fight over how to deal with the Ork incursions.

1.462 POST: THE GREEN KLAW CLOSES
Supreme Warlord Krooldakka rallies the Ork hordes and invades the hivesprawls.

SPECIAL RULES
In this campaign round the following special rules apply:

Rampaging Greentide: Add 1" to Advance moves and Charge moves made by ORK units.

Resolute Yet Arrogant: Add 1 to the Leadership characteristic of IMPERIUM units. However, if a player's army is Battle-forged and includes units from more than one of the following factions, they must subtract 1 from their total number of Command Points: ADEPTA SORORITAS, ADEPTUS MECHANICUS, ASTRA MILITARUM.

BONUS GPs
Players earn 5 bonus GPs each time they participate in one of the following missions:

- **Storm the Lines** (pg 134)
- **Data Recovery** (pg 140)
- **Patrol** (*Warhammer 40,000* rulebook)

ROUND 2

1.580 POST: CONVOYS AND RUNNING BATTLES
Swarms of Speed Freeks fall upon armoured convoys carrying precious resources across the planet. The Astra Militarum respond, their tank companies engaging in desperate running battles.

1.792 POST: THE FLESH-RAIDS
Drawn like bladesharks to blooded water, Drukhari prey upon isolated explorers in Kaelac's Bane, before venturing further afield to raid the southern reaches of Dirkden and Oteck Hivesprawls.

SPECIAL RULES
In this campaign round the following special rules apply:

Tank Hunters: Add 1 to wound rolls for attacks made by VEHICLES that target enemy VEHICLES.

Prey on the Weak: DRUKHARI units that have the Power From Pain ability treat the current battle round as being 1 higher than it actually is when determining what bonuses they gain.

BONUS GPs
Players earn 5 bonus GPs each time they participate in one of the following missions:

- **Convoy** (pg 130)
- **Hold Your Gains** (pg 132)
- **Running Battle** (pg 138)

ROUND 3

1.823 POST: RISE OF THE PAUPER PRINCES
A long-hidden Genestealer Cult rises up from beneath the planet's hivesprawls, battling defending Imperials and invading Orks alike.

1.909 POST: HIDDEN AGENDAS, SELFISH SOULS
Communication between hivesprawls breaks down and each looks to its own defences.

SPECIAL RULES
In this campaign round the following special rules apply:

Rise from the Shadows: Add 1 to hit rolls for shooting attacks made by GENESTEALER CULT units that target the closest enemy unit.

Growing Dissonance: IMPERIUM units cannot use abilities that affect the keyword IMPERIUM (for example, a Vexilus Praetor's Custodes Vexilla ability).

BONUS GPs
Players earn 5 bonus GPs each time they participate in one of the following missions:

- **Behead the Viper** (pg 148)
- **Hold Your Gains** (pg 132)
- **Ambush!** (*Warhammer 40,000* rulebook)

ROUND 4

1.918 POST: DOOM FROM WITHIN

The Adeptus Mechanicus forces in Megaborealis battle against the Genestealer Cult uprising. The promethium-soaked Seeping Delta is ignited in an effort to hold back the rampaging Orks outside.

1.921 POST: A SPIRE TOPPLES IN MEGABOREALIS

Long-range fire from Ork artillery topples a spire in Megaborealis, which crashes through the force field perimeter and allows hordes of Orks to invade the hivesprawl.

2.021 POST: THE DARKNESS

Vigilus is thrown into disarray as the Noctis Aeterna dawns, causing the Bastion-class force fields to fail.

SPECIAL RULES

In this campaign round the following special rules apply:

Bitter Enemies: Add 1 to hit rolls for attacks made by ADEPTUS MECHANICUS units that target GENESTEALER CULT units, and add 1 to hit rolls for attacks made by GENESTEALER CULT units that target ADEPTUS MECHANICUS units.

Null Tide: Units cannot use invulnerable saves.

BONUS GPs

Players earn 5 bonus GPs each time they participate in one of the following missions:

- **The Delta Aflame** (pg 142)
- **Convoy** (pg 130)
- **Storm the Lines** (pg 134)

ROUND 5

2.029 POST: TENTATIVE COUNTER-ATTACKS

Mechanised Astra Militarum companies slow the advance of the Speedwaaagh! across the Vigilus wastes.

2.034 POST: ON THE PATH TO WAR

En route to Vigilus, contingents of the Space Wolves and other Chapters pass planets under heavy Chaos attack.

2.230 POST: A SICKNESS IN DONTORIA

In Dontoria Hivesprawl, a vessel makes an unauthorised docking. Emerging from within, the Death Guard fight their way deep into the hivesprawl. Within the week, the deadly Gellerpox has spread through the hive.

SPECIAL RULES

In this campaign round the following special rules apply:

Swift Retaliation: Re-roll wound rolls of 1 for attacks made by ASTRA MILITARUM VEHICLES.

Deadly Contagion: At the start of the first battle round, but before the first turn begins, each player rolls a D6 for each of their INFANTRY units that is on the battlefield. On a 1, subtract 1 from that unit's Toughness characteristic. NURGLE units are not affected.

BONUS GPs

Players earn 5 bonus GPs each time they participate in one of the following missions:

- **Running Battle** (pg 138)
- **Data Recovery** (pg 140)
- **Blitz** (*Warhammer 40,000* rulebook)

ROUND 6

2.672 POST: THE SPEEDWAAAGH! ATTACKS

The Hyperia-Dirkden Fortwall is bypassed by the Speedwaaagh!, which uses a vanguard of Shokkjump Dragstas to open a warp tunnel for hundreds of vehicles to travel through.

3.084 POST: FROM THE GAUNTLET

Refugee Imperial Knights arrive from nearby Dharrovar. Each takes on a new identity as a Freeblade and swears fealty to the Aquilarian Council before diving into the battle.

3.345 POST: THE WARS OF KNOWLEDGE

As Marneus Calgar nears the Vigilus System, he sends out Vanguard forces to find out which of the nearby worlds can still be saved – and which are already beyond redemption.

SPECIAL RULES

In this campaign round the following special rules apply:

Encircled: At the start of the battle, each player receives 1 Command Point for each ORK Detachment in their army.

Oath of Fealty: Subtract 1 from the 2D6 roll to determine if Burdens apply to any FREEBLADE IMPERIAL KNIGHT units at the start of the turn.

War of Attrition: All missions use the Sustained Assault rules (pg 129). In addition, the Sustained Assault rules apply to the Defender as if they were the Attacker, as well as to the Attacker as normal. If the mission does not specify, units must be set up wholly within 6" of one of the controlling player's battlefield edges.

BONUS GPs

Players earn 5 bonus GPs each time they participate in one of the following missions:

- **Storm the Lines** (pg 134)
- **Hold Your Gains** (pg 132)
- **Blitz** (*Warhammer 40,000* rulebook)

SECOND PHASE OF THE WAR OF BEASTS

ROUND 1

3.539 POST: A DEADLY MISTAKE

Aeldari of Saim-Hann make planetfall at Hyperia Hivesprawl to eliminate Vannadan the Firebrand and his Chaos-tainted followers. However, they are met with hostile force when the Imperial forces mistake them for Drukhari raiders from Kaelac's Bane.

3.645 POST: THE ANGELS OF DEATH DESCEND

Space Marine strike forces make planetfall upon Vigilus. Within hours, they are engaged against the Ork threat in several different war zones.

4.049 POST: THE ULTRAMARINES ARRIVE

The flagship of Marneus Calgar arrives above the planetary capital, Saint's Haven. The Aquilarian Council is dissolved and the Vigilus Senate created in its place.

SPECIAL RULES

In this campaign round the following special rules apply:

Bolstered Ranks: At the start of the battle, each player receives D3 extra Command Points. Roll separately for each player.

Superior Leadership: Add 1 to the Leadership characteristic of IMPERIUM units.

BONUS GPs

Players earn 5 bonus GPs each time they participate in one of the following missions:

- **The Angels of Death Descend** (pg 144)
- **Convoy** (pg 130)
- **Meat Grinder** (*Warhammer 40,000* rulebook)

ROUND 2

4.122 POST: THE TENDRILS RUN DEEP

The Claw of the Thirsting Wyrm rises in Oteck Hivesprawl. Hunter-killer teams of Skitarii are despatched to crush the revolt and secure the Hollows.

4.123 POST: THE HUNT BELOW

Space Wolves kill packs hunt down the Genestealer hybrids poisoning the waters of Oteck Hivesprawl. However, the Deathwatch test the zone for purity and pronounce it Condemnatus, quarantining the entire area and exacerbating the planet's water shortage problem.

SPECIAL RULES

In this campaign round the following special rules apply:

Rise from the Shadows: Add 1 to hit rolls for shooting attacks made by GENESTEALER CULT units that target the closest enemy unit.

Prey on the Weak: DRUKHARI units that have the Power From Pain ability treat the current battle round as being 1 higher than it actually is when determining what bonuses they gain.

Tooth and Claw: Add 1 to charge rolls for ADEPTUS ASTARTES INFANTRY units if an enemy player has any GENESTEALER CULT units in their army.

BONUS GPs

Players earn 5 bonus GPs each time they participate in one of the following missions:

- **Extraction** (pg 136)
- **Hold Your Gains** (pg 132)
- **Patrol** (*Warhammer 40,000* rulebook)

ROUND 3

6.561 POST: BLOOD VENDETTA

Spiritseer Qelanaris leads a wraith host upon the Vigilus capital, seeking revenge against those who slaughtered his blood-bonded kin.

7.230 POST: A TERRIFYING FIND

On Nemendghast, an Ultramarines Vanguard strike force discovers the corrupted Black Legion flesh-factory known as the Forge Infernus. Though heavily outnumbered by Daemonkin warriors led by the Master of Possession Vorash Soulflayer, the Ultramarines battle-brothers launch a sabotage operation, crippling the corrupted forge. Their victory comes at great cost; of the strike force, only the Librarian Maltis escapes the planet to warn Calgar of the threat lurking at the edge of the Vigilus System, with his fellow battle-brothers recorded missing in action.

SPECIAL RULES

In this campaign round the following special rules apply:

Vengeance for the Dead: Add 1 to hit rolls for attacks made by <CRAFTWORLD> units that target IMPERIUM units.

Depleted Supplies: At the start of the battle, each player rolls a D6. On a 1 or 2 that player must subtract D3 Command Points from their total.

BONUS GPs

Players earn 5 bonus GPs each time they participate in one of the following missions:

- **Extraction** (pg 136)
- **Data Recovery** (pg 140)
- **Ambush!** (*Warhammer 40,000* rulebook)

ROUND 4

7.699 POST: THE DONTORIA FIREWALL

The Iron Hands, Necropolis Hawks and Crimson Fists purge the infected Gellerpox mutants that plague Dontoria Hivesprawl and establish a cordon around the area. However, spacecraft bearing infected mutants have already departed from Dontoria's prime spaceport, heading to other war zones in the system.

7.930 POST: ORK BOMBING RUNS

Fleets of Blitza-bommers and Wazbom Blastajets are launched from Rakkuk's Mekmaze and rain terror across the hivesprawls and supply lines. The Aeronautica Imperialis engage in deadly battles for aerial supremacy.

SPECIAL RULES

In this campaign round the following special rules apply:

Deadly Contagion: At the start of the first battle round, but before the first turn begins, each player rolls a D6 for each of their **INFANTRY** units that is on the battlefield. On a 1, subtract 1 from that unit's Toughness characteristic. **NURGLE** units are not affected.

Aerial Supremacy: Add 1 to hit rolls for attacks made by units with the Flyer Battlefield Role that target enemy **VEHICLES**.

BONUS GPs

Players earn 5 bonus GPs each time they participate in one of the following missions:

- **Convoy** (pg 130)
- **Storm the Lines** (pg 134)
- **Blitz** (*Warhammer 40,000* rulebook)

ROUND 5

8.923 POST: RACE FOR THE MANDEVILLE POINT

The Rogue Trader, Delarique du Languille, races to catch and destroy the *Illustrious Cargo*, a ship carrying Gellerpox Infected. However, she later learns that it was only one of seven infected ships to have left that day.

9.356 POST: HOPE YET

Imperial Fists, under the command of Captain Fane and accompanied by elements from a number of their successor Chapters, arrive and reinforce defence lines surrounding Mortwald.

SPECIAL RULES

In this campaign round the following special rules apply:

Bolstered Imperial Ranks: At the start of the battle, each player with any **IMPERIUM** units in their army receives D3 extra Command Points. Roll separately for each player.

War of Attrition: All missions use the Sustained Assault rules (pg 129). In addition, the Sustained Assault rules apply to the Defender as if they were the Attacker, as well as to the Attacker as normal. If the mission does not specify, units must be set up wholly within 6" of one of the controlling player's battlefield edges.

BONUS GPs

Players earn 5 bonus GPs each time they participate in one of the following missions:

- **Storm the Lines** (pg 134)
- **Data Recovery** (pg 140)
- **Blitz** (*Warhammer 40,000* rulebook)

ROUND 6

9.901 POST: A CHARGE INTO LEGEND

Freeblade Knights battle against Deff Dreads and Stompas, vowing to lay low the Ork Scrap Cities. They meet with spectacular success at Tanka Spill before the Orks counter-attack. Refusing orders to resupply, a lance of Freeblade Knights push onwards, but are brought down by two Stompa Mobs and a Blitz Brigade.

9.972 POST: AQUA METEORIS

Genestealer Cultists seize the Megaborealis tractor engines that bring ice-clad meteors from low orbit as a source of water. The glaciers of Kaelac's Bane become the last source of water available to the Imperial forces, and deadly battles break out to ensure its protection…

SPECIAL RULES

In this campaign round the following special rules apply:

Battle of Titans: Add 1 to the Attacks characteristic of **TITANIC** units.

Glory of the Four-armed Emperor: Add 1 to the Leadership characteristic of **GENESTEALER CULT** units.

BONUS GPs

Players earn 5 bonus GPs each time they participate in one of the following missions:

- **Forlorn Charge** (pg 146)
- **Convoy** (pg 130)
- **Running Battle** (pg 138)

THIRD PHASE OF THE WAR OF BEASTS

ROUND 1

12.000-13.000 POST: THE INVASION INTENSIFIES

The Ravenwing and White Scars launch assaults on the Ork Scrap Cities. The greenskins thrive on the violence, which only fuels their bellicose and warlike nature.

12.034 POST: THE SKIES BLACKEN

The skies around the Great Rift are reported to blacken and Agamemnus' psyker-prophets claim the Emperor's Tarot is turning up the same cards over and over again – the Daemonblade, crossed with the Herald of Darkness and the Knight of the Abyss.

SPECIAL RULES

In this campaign round the following special rules apply:

Escalating Violence: If one player's army includes any **ORK** units and the other player's army includes any **ADEPTUS ASTARTES** units, add 1 to the Attacks characteristic of **ORK INFANTRY** units and **ADEPTUS ASTARTES INFANTRY** units.

Null Tide: Models cannot use invulnerable saves.

BONUS GPs

Players earn 5 bonus GPs each time they participate in one of the following missions:

- **Storm the Lines** (pg 134)
- **Hold Your Gains** (pg 132)
- **Sabotage** (*Warhammer 40,000* rulebook)

ROUND 2

13.153 POST: THE SPEAR OF LIGHT

A spear of light is briefly seen in the night sky. It is recognised only by the agents of Tzeentch stationed in Storvhal as the first sign of a Chaos invasion approaching the Vigilus System.

13.991 POST: DARK SIGHTINGS

Numerous reports of bat-winged creatures haunting the highest spires of the hivesprawls coincide with stories of abductions amongst the upper strata of society. Kill teams of Astra Militarum are sent to investigate the anomalies, but none return.

SPECIAL RULES

In this campaign round the following special rules apply:

Psychic Boon: Decrease the warp charge cost of psychic powers by 1 (to a minimum of 1).

Growing Terror: Subtract 1 from the Leadership characteristic of **IMPERIUM** units.

BONUS GPs

Players earn 5 bonus GPs each time they participate in one of the following missions:

- **Patrol** (*Warhammer 40,000* rulebook)
- **Extraction** (pg 136)
- **Rescue** (*Warhammer 40,000* rulebook)

ROUND 3

14.023 POST: WAR ABOVE THE CLOUDS

Concealed by the thick pall of pollution that chokes the Vigilus skies, another war front opens. The Aeronautica Imperialis, already engaged in gruelling battles with Ork flyers, now also has to defend the hivesprawls from Chaos airborne attacks.

14.010 POST: THE INFECTION SPREADS

The Iron Hands struggle to secure their Dontoria quarantine and their heavy-handed enforcement causes the populace to panic and break out. As the plague spreads to Megaborealis and Mortwald, the Death Guard launch an ambush against the Iron Hands, with reports of daemonic entities accompanying them.

SPECIAL RULES

In this campaign round the following special rules apply:

Aerial Supremacy: Add 1 to hit rolls for attacks made by units with the Flyer Battlefield Role that target enemy **VEHICLES**.

Deadly Contagion: At the start of the first battle round, but before the first turn begins, each player rolls a D6 for each of their **INFANTRY** units that is on the battlefield. On a 1, subtract 1 from that unit's Toughness characteristic. **NURGLE** units are not affected.

BONUS GPs

Players earn 5 bonus GPs each time they participate in one of the following missions:

- **Breach of Quarantine** (pg 150)
- **Running Battle** (pg 138)
- **Ambush!** (*Warhammer 40,000* rulebook)

ROUND 4

14.111 POST: GUNFIRE IN THE BLIZZARDS

Seven Imperial armoured companies engage in desperate battles with both Drukhari raiders and Rubric Marines on the Tundric Perimeter of Kaelac's Bane.

14.193 POST: STOCKPILING AND GREED

The rulers of Mortwald seize all sterilised food and water available and stockpile it in their own strongholds. Outraged, the demagogues and preachers of the worker populace lead an insurrection on the continent's outskirts.

SPECIAL RULES

In this campaign round the following special rules apply:

Tank Hunters: Add 1 to wound rolls for attacks made by **Vehicles** that target enemy **Vehicles**.

Treacherous Conditions: When using the Battlezone: Tundric Blizzard rules (pg 155), subtract 1 (to a minimum of 1) from rolls made on the Snow Blizzards table.

Stockpiled Resources: Each player receives 1 additional Command Point for each **Astra Militarum** Detachment in their army as long as they have no **Adeptus Ministorum** models in their army.

BONUS GPs

Players earn 5 bonus GPs each time they participate in one of the following missions:

- **Hold Your Gains** (pg 132)
- **Convoy** (pg 130)
- **Storm the Lines** (pg 134)

ROUND 5

14.202 POST: DIRKDEN ABANDONED

Marneus Calgar orders the withdrawal of Imperial forces from Dirkden, leaving the xenos-tainted defenders that infest the hivesprawl to battle the Ork invaders seeking to conquer it. The Adepta Sororitas of Hyperia Hivesprawl are bolstered with reinforcements.

14.488 POST: RISE OF THE PYROCLASTS

The volcano-worshipping cults of Storvhal rise up and quickly seize a dozen critical locations. In several sites of rebellion, the banners of Tzeentch are risen high. Attempts to restore order by the Cult Mechanicus quickly come apart.

SPECIAL RULES

In this campaign round the following special rules apply:

Consolidation of Power: At the start of the battle, if the Defender has any **Imperium** units in their army, they receive D3 extra Command Points.

Glory of the Four-armed Emperor: Add 1 to the Leadership characteristic of **Genestealer Cult** units.

Get Looting, Boyz!: Improve the save characteristic of **Ork Vehicles** by 1 (eg. 4+ becomes 3+).

The Changer of Ways: If a player has a **Tzeentch Psyker** in their army, roll a D6 each time that player uses a Stratagem. On a 6, the Command Points spent on that Stratagem are refunded to that player.

BONUS GPs

Players earn 5 bonus GPs each time they participate in one of the following missions:

- **Extraction** (pg 136)
- **Data Recovery** (pg 140)
- **Blitz** (*Warhammer 40,000* rulebook)

ROUND 6

14.782 POST: THE RAPTORIAL HOST DESCENDS

Led by the Herald of the Apocalypse, Raptor warbands descend upon the upper echelons of the Vigilus hivesprawls and attack in the thousands. Entire aristocratic dynasties are eradicated overnight in a series of bloody assassinations.

14.912 POST: WAR UNENDING

Strike forces of Necropolis Hawks, Ravenwing and Ultramarines battle Chaos forces in the upper spires of every hivesprawl. Meanwhile, Ork hordes lay waste to city outskirts and Genestealer Cults continue to strike from the shadows.

The fate of Vigilus hangs in the balance.

SPECIAL RULES

In this campaign round the following special rules apply:

Bolstered Ranks: At the start of the battle, each player receives D3 extra Command Points. Roll separately for each player.

War of Attrition: All missions use the Sustained Assault rules (pg 129). In addition, the Sustained Assault rules apply to the Defender as if they were the Attacker, as well as to the Attacker as normal. If the mission does not specify, units must be set up wholly within 6" of one of the controlling player's battlefield edges.

BONUS GPs

Players earn 5 bonus GPs each time they participate in one of the following missions:

- **Carnage in the Spires** (pg 152)
- **Hold Your Gains** (pg 132)
- **Ambush!** (*Warhammer 40,000* rulebook)

CAMPAIGNS IN THE DARK IMPERIUM

All across the Imperium Nihilus, worlds are beset by terror, isolated and beleaguered defensive forces making a last stand against insurmountable daemonic hordes or fighting back vile xenos threats. For every world the Imperium wins back, another is lost to darkness.

INTRODUCTION

In this section you will find the Nihilus Events table. This is an extra layer of rules you can add to each campaign round you play in a Vigilus Campaign. Alternatively, you can use these rules to create a campaign set on another war-torn planet or sub-system within the Imperium Nihilus. This type of campaign is known as a Dark Imperium Campaign.

SETTING UP THE CAMPAIGN

When setting up a Dark Imperium Campaign, follow the guidelines on pages 118-119. Rather than choosing a phase of the War of Beasts on Vigilus to set your campaign within, you can instead use the Nihilus Events table opposite to determine the effects of each campaign round. There are three methods to do this, as follows:

THE CHAOTIC FLUX

The first method is for the rules for each campaign round to be generated randomly. To do so, roll a D6 and a D3 and consult the Nihilus Events table to determine the event and special rules that are in effect for that campaign round. It can be exciting to generate this event only when each new campaign round starts, leaving the players guessing as to what course the campaign will take.

THE ARCHITECT OF FATE

For this method, one member of the gaming group is in charge of choosing the event and special rules that take place in each campaign round. This player should be impartial and not choose results to gain their team an advantage. This method is great if your gaming group is really embracing the narrative of the campaign. The player dictating the events can take cues from the epic tales of heroism and glory that have already unfolded in the battles of the previous rounds, and might write up the story into an ongoing narrative for all the players to read.

SPOILS TO THE VICTOR

The last method is to allow the team that earned the most campaign glory points in the previous campaign round to choose the event that takes place in the next, (randomly generate the event for the first campaign round). This method adds an extra layer of tension to each campaign round as the winning team will be able to choose an event to bolster their forces (or hinder their foes).

You may want to turn this idea on its head and have the team that earned the least campaign glory points choose the event for the next campaign round, or add in a roll-off between the top and bottom team to determine who decides.

'This war, devastating as it may be, is an overture. Can you not see it in the twisting of the stars? Prepare yourselves, my learned friends. The crescendo is yet to come.'

- Marneus Calgar

NIHILUS EVENTS TABLE

D6	D3	EVENT	SPECIAL RULE
1	**1**	*The Great Rift swells with an all-enveloping darkness. Force fields flicker out in showers of sparks and sorcerous barriers fade like smoke.*	**Null Tide:** Models cannot use invulnerable saves.
	2	*Warp energy sets the skies ablaze as psykers feel the surging tides of the empyrean overflow inside them.*	**Warp Surge:** Add 1 to Psychic tests and Deny the Witch tests. In addition, add 1 to the number of mortal wounds that a model suffers from Perils of the Warp.
	3	*Waves of empyric energy wash over the planet, imbuing the psykers of the warring armies with great power.*	**Psychic Boon:** Decrease the warp charge cost of psychic powers by 1 (to a minimum of 1).
2	**1**	*The theatre of war is plunged into sub-zero temperatures as a ferocious winter cloaks vast areas in ice and blizzards.*	**Ever-winter:** All battles must use the Battlezone: Tundric Blizzard rules (pg 155).
	2	*Powerful winds kick up swirling torrents of dust that race across the planet, engulfing all in their path.*	**Gargantuan Dust Storms:** All battles must use the Battlezone: Wasteland Dust Storm rules (pg 154).
	3	*The ground trembles and splits as the planet is shaken by tectonic strife.*	**Seismic Tremors:** All battles must use the Battlezone: Warquake rules (pg 156).
3	**1**	*This stage of the war is characterised by deadly tank battles that rage across the planet.*	**Tank Hunters:** Add 1 to wound rolls for attacks made by VEHICLES that target enemy VEHICLES.
	2	*All sides vie for control of the skies, and desperate aerial dogfights erupt above every battle.*	**Aerial Supremacy:** Add 1 to hit rolls for attacks made by units with the Flyer Battlefield Role that target enemy VEHICLES.
	3	*Control of the planet's surface is critical and every side calls for fire support from low orbit to aid the fight.*	**Orbital Bombardments:** All missions use the Preliminary Bombardment rules (pg 128). In addition, the Preliminary Bombardment rules apply to the Defender as if they were the Attacker, as well as to the Attacker as normal.
4	**1**	*The warring sides are driven to destroy each other by the bitter enmity that has grown between them.*	**Bitter Hatred:** Add 1 to hit rolls for shooting attacks.
	2	*The escalating violence brings out a bloodthirsty streak on all sides, and close-quarter conflicts become especially brutal.*	**Battle Frenzy:** Add 1 to the Attacks characteristic of all units.
	3	*As the conflict drags on, all forces feel the strain of constant war.*	**Wavering Resolve:** Subtract 1 from the Leadership characteristic of all models.
5	**1**	*In the aftermath of a cataclysmic space battle, fractured remnants of sundered craft rain down in a blaze of fire.*	**Orbital Debris:** Each player rolls 3D6 at the start of each of their turns. For each 6, they can pick a different enemy unit; that unit suffers D3 mortal wounds.
	2	*The planet is swept by torrents of corrosive rainfall, hampering all forces out in the open.*	**Acid Rain:** Roll a D6 at the start of each battle round. On a 1, 2 or 3 subtract 1 from hit rolls made for shooting attacks during that battle round, and subtract 1 from Advance and charge rolls made during that battle round.
	3	*A virus outbreak sweeps through the populace of the world, taking its toll on all combatants.*	**Deadly Contagion:** At the start of the first battle round, but before the first turn begins, each player rolls a D6 for each of their INFANTRY units that is on the battlefield. On a 1, subtract 1 from that unit's Toughness characteristic. NURGLE units are not affected.
6	**1**	*In this bleak, unending conflict, a lack of supplies can mean the difference between victory and defeat.*	**Depleted Supplies:** At the start of the battle, each player rolls a D6. On a 1 or 2 that player must subtract D3 Command Points from their total.
	2	*Events on this planet have a critical effect on the wider war across the system, and all sides reroute troops and supplies to fuel the war effort.*	**Bolstered Ranks:** At the start of the battle, each player receives D3 extra Command Points. Roll separately for each player.
	3	*Victory must be secured, no matter the losses! Every side in the conflict sends legions of troops into the fray, caring not if they live or die, as long as some advantage can be won.*	**War of Attrition:** All missions use the Sustained Assault rules (pg 129). In addition, the Sustained Assault rules apply to the Defender as if they were the Attacker, as well as to the Attacker as normal. If the mission does not specify, units must be set up wholly within 6" of one of the controlling player's battlefield edges.

NARRATIVE PLAY MISSIONS

The missions presented in this book are designed to allow you to play narrative play games based on some of the events that took place during the War of Beasts on Vigilus. These missions are also ideal for playing games set on any war-ravaged planet of the Imperium Nihilus.

On the following pages you will find twelve new narrative play missions inspired by the events described in this book. The first six Crucible of War missions are designed to represent some of the challenges regularly faced by the warring armies on Vigilus, and indeed in the Imperium Nihilus at large – such as a convoy of vehicles carrying essential supplies having to fend off an opportunistic foe, or a force working behind enemy lines struggling to reach their extraction point. The last six Echoes of War missions recreate specific events from the story of Vigilus, from the Adeptus Mechanicus' scorching victory in the Seeping Delta to the last charge of the Dharrovar Knights.

These missions can be played individually or as part of a Vigilus or Dark Imperium campaign, as described on pages 118-127. To play a mission individually, you can either choose the mission that you most want to play, or roll on one of the tables below.

CRUCIBLE OF WAR	
D6	**MISSION**
1	Convoy (pg 130)
2	Hold Your Gains (pg 132)
3	Storm the Lines (pg 134)
4	Extraction (pg 136)
5	Running Battle (pg 138)
6	Data Recovery (pg 140)

ECHOES OF WAR	
D6	**MISSION**
1	The Delta Aflame (pg 142)
2	The Angels of Death Descend (pg 144)
3	Forlorn Charge (pg 146)
4	Behead the Viper (pg 148)
5	Breach of Quarantine (pg 150)
6	Carnage in the Spires (pg 152)

MISSION SPECIAL RULES

These missions use one or more additional special rules to better represent the different tactics and strategies used by attackers and defenders. Some of the more in-depth mission special rules are collected below and referenced by the missions that appear later in this section.

DAWN RAID

Cunning commanders may attack under cover of darkness to conceal their advance from the foe.

If your mission uses Dawn Raid, both players must subtract 1 from all hit rolls made in the Shooting phase during the first battle round of the game.

PRELIMINARY BOMBARDMENT

In a major offensive, the attacker will often launch a heavy bombardment prior to the main attack.

If your mission uses Preliminary Bombardment, then at the start of the first battle round, but before the first turn begins, the Attacker should roll a dice for each enemy unit that is on the battlefield (do not roll for units that are embarked inside **TRANSPORTS**). On a roll of 6, that unit has been hit by a Preliminary Bombardment; that unit suffers D6 mortal wounds. **INFANTRY** units that are hit by a Preliminary Bombardment can choose to go to ground before the damage is determined – if they do, they only suffer D3 mortal wounds, but cannot take any actions during their first turn.

RANDOM BATTLE LENGTH

War is rarely predictable, and the time available to achieve your objectives is never certain.

If your mission uses Random Battle Length, at the end of battle round 5, the player who had the first turn must roll a D6. On a roll of 3+, the game continues, otherwise the game is over. At the end of battle round 6, the player who had the second turn must roll a D6. This time the game continues on a roll of 4+, otherwise the game is over. The battle automatically ends at the end of battle round 7.

RESERVES

Reserves are forces which are not directly present at the start of an engagement but are available as reinforcements during battle.

If a mission uses Reserves, it will detail which units in your army start the game in Reserve – these units are not deployed with the rest of your army.

The mission will usually state when the units placed in Reserve arrive on the battlefield – this is typically at the end of a particular Movement phase. If the mission does not specify when units arrive, roll for each unit at the end of your second Movement phase (and at the end of each of your Movement phases thereafter) – this is called a Reserve roll. On a 3+, the unit being rolled for arrives from Reserve. Note that if a unit placed into Reserve is embarked within a **Transport**, they will arrive when their transport does, not separately (if rolling, make a single roll for the transport and the units embarked in it).

The mission will explain how and where to set up units when they arrive from Reserve – typically within a short distance of a specified edge of the battlefield.

SENTRIES

Many commanders use sentries to guard vital locations and raise the alarm if intruders are spotted.

If your mission uses Sentries, the Defender will need one extra unit to act as their Sentries. Unless otherwise stated, this unit should have the Troops Battlefield Role, contain up to 10 models and have a Power Rating of 10 or less. The Sentries' Power Rating is excluded when you are calculating the total Power Level of your army.

The mission rules will detail where Sentries are set up, but it should be noted that each Sentry model moves and acts as a separate, individual unit throughout the battle. At the start of each of the Defender's Movement phases, both players roll a dice for each Sentry model, in an order chosen by the Defender. The player who rolled the highest can move the model the distance indicated on their dice in any direction (a Sentry cannot Advance as part of this move). If the rolls are tied, the Sentry does not move.

At the start of the game, all is quiet and the alarm has yet to be sounded, but it is raised if any of the following occur:

- A model from the Attacker's army fires a ranged weapon or manifests a psychic power.
- A model from the Attacking player's army attacks a Sentry in the Fight phase but fails to kill them. Note that Sentries cannot fire Overwatch until after the alarm is raised.
- A model from the Attacking player's army is spotted by a Sentry. An enemy unit is spotted if it is within a certain range of any Sentry at the end of any Movement phase (irrespective of whether or not that unit is visible to the Sentry). The spotting range depends upon the Power Rating of the Attacker's unit, as detailed below:

POWER RATING	SPOTTED WITHIN
5 or less	3"
6-10	6"
11-19	9"
20 or more	12"

If the alarm is raised during the Attacker's turn, their turn ends after the action that raised the alarm has been completed. If the alarm is raised during the Defender's turn, the Defender immediately starts a new turn in which they can typically set up response forces or reinforcements; this will be detailed in the mission itself. In either case, the Sentries are now under full control of the Defender.

SUSTAINED ASSAULT

Occasionally, an army will possess overwhelming superiority in numbers, with wave upon wave of its troops hurling themselves forward.

If your mission uses Sustained Assault, any of the Attacker's units that are destroyed can be brought back into play later in the battle, to represent their almost limitless supply of reinforcements. At the end of each of the Attacker's Movement phases, roll a dice for each of their destroyed units, adding 2 to the result if that unit has the Troops Battlefield Role. On a 4+, immediately set up that unit within 6" of a battlefield edge – the mission will specify which.

The Attacker can also, at the end of any of their turns, remove any of their units from the battlefield that have a quarter or less of their starting number of models (or, in the case of single-model units, a quarter or less of its starting number of wounds). This unit then counts as having been destroyed for all purposes, and so can be brought back into play later as described above.

CRUCIBLE OF WAR
CONVOY

In times of war, vital supply lines become hotly contested battlefronts. The attackers seek to disrupt and destroy the enemy convoys in order to bleed their foe of resources, whilst the defenders must make sure their cargo arrives safely to further fuel the war effort.

THE ARMIES

Each player must first muster an army from their collection. A player can include any models in their army, but if their army is Battle-forged they will also be able to use the appropriate Stratagems included with this mission (see opposite). Once the armies have been chosen, the players must decide who will be the Attacker and who will be the Defender. If the Power Level of one of the armies is a third or more higher than the opposing army's Power Level, then the player whose army has the higher Power Level should be the Defender and their opponent should be the Attacker. Otherwise the players can roll off to decide.

THE CONVOY

To play this mission, the Defender will require suitable models to represent the convoy. They can nominate any **Vehicles** in their army that individually have a Power Rating of 15 or less to make up their convoy. If the Vehicles nominated are part of a unit of multiple Vehicles, then all Vehicles in that unit must be nominated. Vehicles with the Flyer Battlefield Role cannot be chosen to be part of the convoy. The combined Power Rating of the convoy must be less than one third of the Power Level of the Attacker's army.

During the game, models in the convoy cannot attempt to charge.

THE BATTLEFIELD

Create a battlefield using the deployment map below and then set up terrain. A central road runs across the board horizontally. Ruined buildings and craters are dotted around the battlefield to represent the war-torn planet.

DEPLOYMENT

After terrain has been set up, the Defender sets up all of their units wholly within their deployment zone. The Attacker's units are all set up in Reserve (pg 129); they will arrive during the battle as described below.

FIRST TURN

The Attacker has the first turn.

ATTACKER'S RESERVES

The Attacker can bring on any of their Reserve units at the end of each of their Movement phases. When a unit arrives from Reserve it must be set up wholly within 12" of either of the Attacker's battlefield edges and more than 9" from any enemy models.

ESCAPE ROUTE

Any unit in the convoy can move off the battlefield edge labelled 'Escape Route' so long as all of the models in that unit are able to make it off the board by that edge in the same phase. Any models that do so are said to have escaped, and are removed from the battlefield and take no further part in the battle.

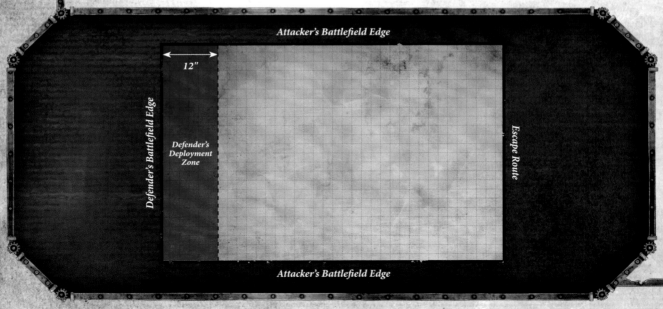

Attacker's Battlefield Edge

12"

Defender's Battlefield Edge

Defender's Deployment Zone

Escape Route

Attacker's Battlefield Edge

STRATAGEMS

In this mission, the players can use Command Points (CPs) to use the following bonus Stratagems:

1CP
OUTRIDERS
Attacker Stratagem
This force takes up a flanking position.

Use this Stratagem during deployment. Pick a unit from your army. Instead of placing it in Reserve, set it up on the battlefield wholly within 12" of any table edge and more than 9" from any enemy models. You can only use this Stratagem once per battle.

1CP
FIELD REPAIRS
Defender Stratagem
This unit performs emergency maintenance on a damaged vehicle.

Use this Stratagem at the end of your Movement phase. Pick a VEHICLE from your army within 1" of a friendly INFANTRY unit. That VEHICLE regains D6 lost wounds. You can only use this Stratagem once per turn.

1CP
SIGNAL FLARE
Attacker Stratagem
A bright light illuminates the target, directing the fire of nearby allies.

Use this Stratagem after one of your units scores a hit on an enemy unit in the Shooting phase. Until the end of that phase, re-roll hit rolls of 1 for attacks made by units in your army that target that same enemy unit.

2CP
TEMPORARY DISPLACER FIELD
Defender Stratagem
Although short-lived, this temporary field protects vehicles from incoming fire.

Use this Stratagem at the start of the Shooting phase. Until the end of that phase, subtract 1 from hit rolls for attacks that target units in your convoy.

2CP
MELTA RIG
Attacker Stratagem
This cache of explosives unleashes massive damage upon the enemy vehicle.

Use this Stratagem at the start of the Fight phase. Pick an INFANTRY unit from your army within 1" of an enemy VEHICLE. That enemy VEHICLE suffers D6 mortal wounds. You can only use this Stratagem once per turn.

1CP
BREAKOUT ACTION
Defender Stratagem
In a last-ditch effort, the convoy breaks away from the enemy line.

Use this Stratagem at the start of your Movement phase. Roll a D6 and add the result to the Move characteristic of all units in your convoy until the end of that phase. You can only use this Stratagem once per battle.

BATTLE LENGTH

The battle ends when there are no models from the convoy left on the battlefield (either because they have escaped or been destroyed).

VICTORY CONDITIONS

At the end of the battle, add up the Power Ratings of all the Defender's escaped units (see Escape Route) and compare this to the Power Level of the convoy (count the entire unit's Power Rating, even if some of its models were destroyed before the unit escaped).

If the combined Power Rating of the escaped units is equal to or greater than half the Power Level of the convoy as a whole, the Defender wins a major victory. If at least one model from the convoy escaped but the total is less than half of the convoy's Power Level, the Attacker wins a minor victory. Any other result is a major victory for the Attacker.

CRUCIBLE OF WAR
HOLD YOUR GAINS

Bitterly won strategic locations are vulnerable to counter-attack, the defeated army eager to regain their lost ground. The beleaguered victors have little time consolidate their gains before they must mount their defence and hold on until further reinforcements arrive.

THE ARMIES

Each player must first muster an army from their collection. A player can include any models in their army, but if their army is Battle-forged they will also be able to use the appropriate Stratagems included with this mission (see opposite). Once the armies have been chosen, the players must decide who will be the Attacker and who will be the Defender. If the Power Level of one of the armies is a third or more higher than the opposing army's Power Level, then the player whose army has the higher Power Level should be the Defender and their opponent should be the Attacker. Otherwise the players can roll off to decide.

THE BATTLEFIELD

Create a battlefield using the deployment map below and then set up terrain. Ruined buildings and craters are dotted around the battlefield to represent the war-torn planet. Set up a small piece of terrain in the centre of the battlefield to represent the area the Defender is trying to hold.

DEPLOYMENT

After terrain has been set up, the Defender first sets up their units wholly within their deployment zone. The units set up cannot have a combined Power Rating greater than one third of the army's Power Level. The remaining units in the Defender's army are set up in Reserve (pg 129). The Attacker then sets up all their units wholly within their deployment zones.

FIRST TURN

The Attacker has the first turn.

DEFENDER'S REINFORCEMENTS

Starting from the second battle round, at the end of their Movement phase, the Defender makes a Reserve roll for each of their units in Reserve. On a 3+ the unit arrives and can be set up anywhere on the battlefield that is wholly within 12" of one of the Defender's battlefield edges and more than 9" from any enemy models. Units automatically arrive at the end of the Defender's fourth Movement phase if they have not already done so.

BATTLE LENGTH

Use the Random Battle Length rules (pg 128) to determine how long the battle lasts.

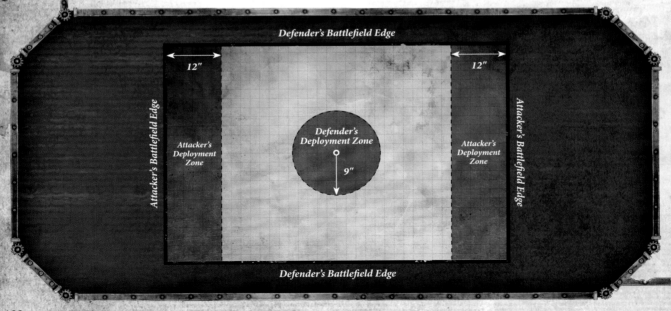

STRATAGEMS

In this mission, the players can use Command Points (CPs) to use the following bonus Stratagems:

2CP DAWN ASSAULT
Attacker Stratagem
As the last slithers of night linger, the attackers strike from the gloom.

Use this Stratagem after deployment. The Dawn Raid rules (pg 128) are in effect for the first battle round. You can only use this Stratagem once per battle.

1CP RAPID REINFORCEMENTS
Defender Stratagem
Answering the call of their beleaguered allies, this unit races into the fray.

Use this Stratagem before making a Reserve roll. The unit being rolled for automatically arrives – do not make the Reserve roll.

1CP COVER GROUND
Attacker Stratagem
Under orders to close in on the enemy, this unit moves at the double.

Use this Stratagem before a unit from your army Advances. Increase its Move characteristic by 6" until the end of the phase – do not roll a dice.

2CP DUG-IN DEFENCES
Defender Stratagem
The defenders are difficult to shift from their fortified positions on the battlefield.

Use this Stratagem after setting up one of your units. Until that unit moves (for any reason) you can add 1 to that unit's saving throws against all shooting attacks.

3CP CALL IN REINFORCEMENTS
Attacker Stratagem
Fresh troops are redeployed to this battle in a desperate attempt to seize victory.

Use this Stratagem at the end of your Movement phase. Pick a unit from your army that has been destroyed during the battle. You can set up that unit wholly within 6" of any battlefield edge and more than 9" from any enemy models, at its full starting strength.

2CP HOLD YOUR GROUND
Defender Stratagem
These stalwart warriors hold the line.

Use this Stratagem at the start of the Morale phase. Add 1 to the Leadership characteristic of all models in your army until the end of that phase.

VICTORY CONDITIONS

At the end of the battle, add up the Power Ratings of all the Attacker's units that are wholly within 12" of the centre of the battlefield and all the Defender's units that are wholly within 12" of the centre of the battlefield. The player with the higher result wins a major victory. If the score is tied the Defender wins a minor victory.

CRUCIBLE OF WAR
STORM THE LINES

The defenders are deeply fortified within their strongholds, but although they are well dug-in, they lack mobility. The attackers have brought a massive force to bear in an attempt to overwhelm the enemy through sheer numbers.

THE ARMIES

Each player must first muster an army from their collection. A player can include any models in their army, but if their army is Battle-forged they will also be able to use the appropriate Stratagems included with this mission (see opposite). Once the armies have been chosen, the players must decide who will be the Attacker and who will be the Defender. If the Power Level of one of the armies is a third or more higher than the opposing army's Power Level, then the player whose army has the higher Power Level should be the Attacker and their opponent should be the Defender. Otherwise the players can roll off to decide. The Defender receives +3 Command Points if their army includes any Fortification Network Detachments as described in the *Warhammer 40,000* rulebook.

THE BATTLEFIELD

The Defender creates the battlefield. The battlefield should be heavily fortified in the Defender's deployment zones, whilst the rest of the battlefield is left sparse to represent the no-man's land the Attackers are crossing.

DEPLOYMENT

After terrain has been set up, the Defender first sets up their units wholly within either of their deployment zones. The combined Power Rating of the units set up in the Front Line deployment zone cannot exceed one third of the Defender's army's total Power Level. The Attacker then sets up all their units wholly within their deployment zone.

FIRST TURN

The Attacker rolls a dice. On a 1, 2 or 3, the Attacker has the first turn, and on a 4, 5 or 6, the Defender has the first turn.

SUSTAINED ASSAULT

The Attacker can use the Sustained Assault rules (pg 129). Units brought back to the battlefield using these rules must be set up wholly within 6" of the Attacker's battlefield edge.

HAZARDOUS DROP ZONES

During the battle, if any of the attacker's units have abilities that allow them to be set up on the battlefield, the attacker cannot set up those units in either of the defender's deployment zones.

BATTLE LENGTH

Use the Random Battle Length rules (pg 128) to determine how long the battle lasts.

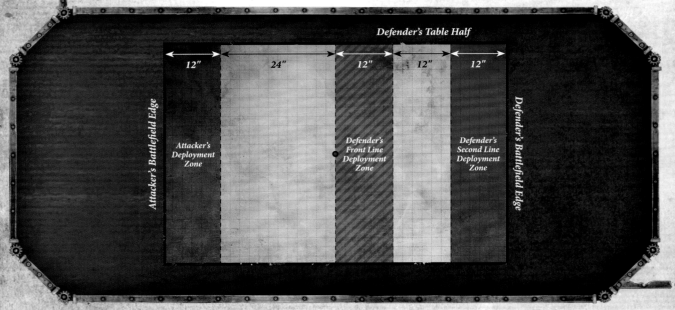

STRATAGEMS

In this mission, the players can use Command Points (CPs) to use the following bonus Stratagems:

2CP OUTFLANKING REINFORCEMENTS
Attacker Stratagem
Circling round the front line, these allies strike at the heart of the enemy position.

Use this Stratagem when you bring a unit back to the battlefield using the Sustained Assault rules. That unit can be set up anywhere wholly within 6" of any battlefield edge other than the Defender's battlefield edge.

1CP TRAPS
Defender Stratagem
Mines, razor wire and other traps can prove fatal for arriving reinforcements.

Use this Stratagem when the Attacker brings a unit back to the battlefield using the Sustained Assault rules. Roll a dice for each model in that unit. For each roll of 6, one model in that unit is slain (controlling player's choice).

1CP COVER GROUND
Attacker Stratagem
Under orders to close in on the enemy, this unit moves at the double.

Use this Stratagem before a unit from your army Advances. Increase its Move characteristic by 6" until the end of the phase – do not roll a dice.

2CP DUG-IN DEFENCES
Defender Stratagem
The defenders are difficult to shift from their fortified positions on the battlefield.

Use this Stratagem after setting up one of your units. Until that unit moves (for any reason) you can add 1 to that unit's saving throws against all shooting attacks.

2CP DAWN ASSAULT
Attacker Stratagem
As the last slithers of night linger, the attackers strike from the gloom.

Use this Stratagem after deployment. The Dawn Raid rules (pg 128) are in effect for the first battle round. You can only use this Stratagem once per battle.

2CP HOLD YOUR GROUND
Defender Stratagem
These stalwart warriors hold the line.

Use this Stratagem at the start of the Morale phase. Add 1 to the Leadership characteristic of all models in your army until the end of that phase.

VICTORY CONDITIONS

At the end of the battle, if the Attacker has any models within the Defender's Second Line Deployment Zone, they win a major victory. Otherwise, add up the Power Ratings of all the Attacker's units wholly within the Defender's Front Line Deployment Zone and all the Defender's units wholly within the Defender's Front Line Deployment Zone. The player with the higher result wins a minor victory. If the result is a tie, the Attacker wins a minor victory.

CRUCIBLE OF WAR
EXTRACTION

Deep behind enemy lines, the attacking forces have completed their objectives under the cover of darkness, but now need to reach the extraction point to be evacuated safely. The defending forces are sweeping the area and will respond with rapid retaliation as soon as the intruders are found.

THE ARMIES

Each player must first muster an army from their collection. A player can include any models in their army, but if their army is Battle-forged they will also be able to use the appropriate Stratagems included with this mission (see opposite). Once the armies have been chosen, the players must decide who will be the Attacker and who will be the Defender. If the Power Level of one of the armies is a third or more higher than the opposing army's Power Level, then the player whose army has the higher Power Level should be the Defender and their opponent should be the Attacker. Otherwise the players can roll off to decide. This mission uses the Sentries rules (pg 129). The Defender will need an additional unit to act as their Sentries.

THE BATTLEFIELD

Create a battlefield using the deployment map below and then set up terrain. Densely packed buildings represent part of a hivesprawl. At the centre of the north battlefield edge there should be an open space, or a landing pad, to represent the extraction point.

DEPLOYMENT

After terrain has been set up, the Defender sets up their unit of Sentries. At least a third of the Sentry models must be placed within 12" of the centre of the battlefield. The remainder can be placed anywhere wholly within the Defender's deployment zone, more than 6" from the Attacker's deployment zone.

The Attacker then sets up as many of their units as they wish anywhere wholly within their own deployment zone. All remaining units in both armies are placed in Reserve (pg 129); they will arrive during the battle as described below.

FIRST TURN

The Attacker has the first turn.

DAWN RAID

This mission uses the Dawn Raid rules (pg 128).

ATTACKER'S RESERVES

The Attacker can bring on any of their Reserve units at the end of each of their Movement phases. When a unit arrives from Reserve it must be set up wholly within 6" of the Attacker's battlefield edge and more than 9" from any enemy units.

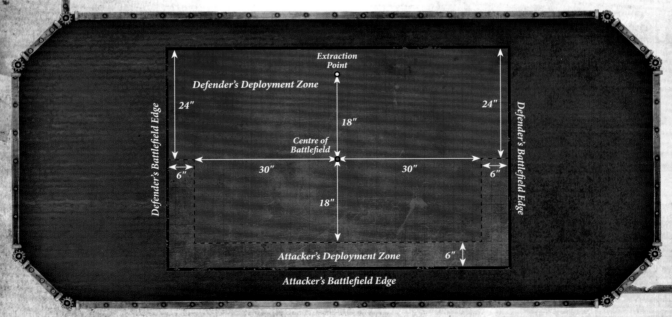

STRATAGEMS

In this mission, the players can use Command Points (CPs) to use the following bonus Stratagems:

1CP SILENCED WEAPONS

Attacker Stratagem

Suppressors attached to the muzzle allow for shots to be fired without a sound.

Use this Stratagem before one of your units makes a shooting attack. The alarm is only sounded if a model targeted by the shooting attack loses a wound but is not slain or destroyed.

2CP SENSORS

Defender Stratagem

Auspex arrays and motion scanners can be used to hunt unwanted intruders.

Use this Stratagem after you have set up your Sentries on the battlefield. Add 3" to the distance within which each Sentry model can spot a model from the Attacker's army.

1CP CAMOUFLAGE

Attacker Stratagem

This unit lies hidden, waiting to strike.

Use this Stratagem when one of your units is set up during deployment. Halve that unit's Power Rating when working out the distance at which it can be spotted by Sentries.

3CP RAPID RESPONSE

Defender Stratagem

Once the intruders are found, nearby allies redeploy to eliminate the threat.

Use this Stratagem before making a Reserve roll in the turn after the alarm is sounded. The unit automatically arrives – do not roll the dice – and can be set up wholly within 6" of any battlefield edge other than the Attacker's battlefield edge and more than 9" from any enemy units.

3CP SIGNAL BEACON

Attacker Stratagem

Upon reaching the extraction point, the signal for evacuation is triggered.

Use this Stratagem before the D6 is rolled to determine if the game ends. Add 1 to the result needed for the battle to continue.

2CP EXTRA SENTRIES

Defender Stratagem

This location is designated as high priority and is reinforced with extra guards.

Use this Stratagem before setting up your unit of Sentries. You gain a second additional unit of Sentries.

DEFENDER'S RESERVES

The Defender can bring on any of their Reserve units at the end of each of their Movement phases after the alarm has been sounded. In the first turn after the alarm has been sounded, the Defender makes a Reserve roll for each of their units in Reserve that they want to bring on to the battlefield; the unit being rolled for will only arrive on a roll of a 3+. In subsequent turns, no roll is required. Reserve units must be set up wholly within 6" of one of the Defender's battlefield edges, and more than 9" from any enemy units.

BATTLE LENGTH

Use the Random Battle Length rules (pg 128) to determine how long the battle lasts.

VICTORY CONDITIONS

At the end of the battle, add up the Power Ratings of all the Attacker's units wholly within 6" of the extraction point and then subtract the Power Rating of all the Defender's units wholly within 9" of the extraction point. If the total is one third or more of the Attacker's army's Power Level, the Attacker wins a major victory. Any other result is a major victory for the Defender.

CRUCIBLE OF WAR
RUNNING BATTLE

When two fully mechanised armies battle each other, a high-speed and furious chase often ensues as one force seeks desperately to outrun the other. While vehicles equipped for a fast pursuit will storm ahead of the pack, those slow to get off the mark will be left behind in their dust.

THE ARMIES

Each player must first muster an army from their collection. A player can include any models in their army, but this mission works especially well if players contain few, if any, units with a Move characteristic of less than 10". Additionally, if a player's army is Battle-forged they will be able to use the appropriate Stratagems included with this mission (see opposite).

Once the armies have been chosen, the players must decide who will be the Attacker and who will be the Defender. If the Power Level of one of the armies is a third or more higher than the opposing army's Power Level, then the player whose army has the higher Power Level should be the Defender and their opponent should be the Attacker. Otherwise the players can roll off to decide.

THE BATTLEFIELD

Create a battlefield using the deployment map below and then set up terrain. Craters, debris and boulders are dotted around to represent the wasteland the battle takes part in. This mission works especially well if all terrain pieces are free-standing, movable and not fixed to the battlefield.

DEPLOYMENT

After terrain has been set up, the Defender first sets up their units wholly within their deployment zone. The Attacker then sets up as many of their units as they wish wholly within their deployment zone. Any remaining units from the Attacker's army are set up in Reserve (pg 129) and will arrive during the battle as described below.

FIRST TURN

The Attacker has the first turn.

ATTACKER'S REINFORCEMENTS

Starting from the second battle round, at the end of their Movement phase, the Attacker makes a Reserve roll for each of their units in Reserve. On a 4+ the unit arrives and can be set up anywhere on the battlefield that is wholly within 6" of one of the Attacker's battlefield edges and more than 9" from any enemy models.

ROLLING TERRAIN

At the start of each battle round after the first, every model and every terrain piece is moved 6" in a straight line directly towards the Western battlefield edge. Start with models and terrain pieces closest to the Western battlefield edge. If any models or terrain pieces are moved within 1" of the Western battlefield edge, they are removed from the battle. Any such models are treated as having been destroyed for all rules purposes. Any terrain pieces that have been removed can then be placed within 6" of the Eastern battlefield edge by the Attacker. Models then act normally in the following turns.

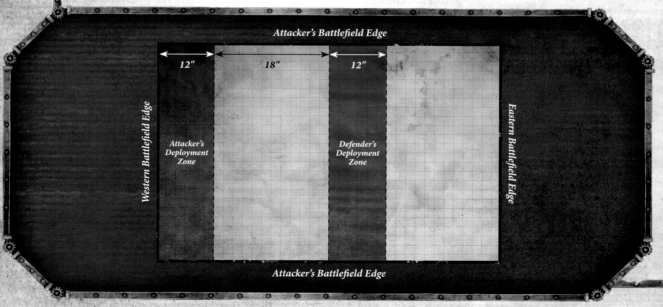

Attacker's Battlefield Edge

12"   18"   12"

Western Battlefield Edge

Attacker's Deployment Zone

Defender's Deployment Zone

Eastern Battlefield Edge

Attacker's Battlefield Edge

STRATAGEMS

In this mission, the players can use Command Points (CPs) to use the following bonus Stratagems:

OUTRIDERS
2CP

Attacker Stratagem

This force takes up a flanking position and readies for the enemy approach.

Use this Stratagem during deployment. Pick a unit from your army. Remove it from the battlefield and set it up wholly within 12" of any table edge and more than 9" from any enemy models. You can only use this Stratagem once per battle.

DESPERATE ACCELERATION
1CP

Attacker Stratagem

This vehicle's engine roars as it races across the battlefield.

Use this Stratagem at the start of your Movement phase. Pick a unit from your army and roll a D6. Add the result to that unit's Move characteristic until the end of that phase. However, at the end of that phase that unit suffers 1 mortal wound.

LAST-DITCH RAM
2CP

Attacker Stratagem

Colliding a vehicle into the enemy line is a risky tactic fraught with peril for both.

Use this Stratagem in your Charge phase. Pick a **Vehicle** unit from your army. You can re-roll charge rolls for that unit until the end of the phase. In addition, if that unit finishes a charge move this phase, pick an enemy unit within 1" and roll a D6; on a 2+ that enemy unit suffers D3 mortal wounds.

MINE
1CP

Defender Stratagem

Deployed mines can wreak havoc upon enemy armoured battle groups.

Use this Stratagem at the start of your Movement phase. Place a token within 1" of a **Vehicle** from your army to represent the mine. If a unit finishes a move within 1" of the mine, roll a D6. On a 2+ it detonates and that unit suffers D6 mortal wounds. On a 1 the mine is a dud; remove it from play. At the start of each battle round beginning with the second, move any tokens 6" towards the Western battlefield edge in the same manner as models and terrain.

DESPERATE ACCELERATION
1CP

Defender Stratagem

This vehicle's engine roars as it races across the battlefield.

Use this Stratagem at the start of your Movement phase. Pick a unit from your army and roll a D6. Add the result to that unit's Move characteristic until the end of that phase. However, at the end of that phase that unit suffers 1 mortal wound.

SMOKE SCREEN
3CP

Defender Stratagem

Smoke launchers are deployed en masse, buying a few moments of protection.

Use this Stratagem at the start of the Attacker's Shooting phase. Subtract 1 from hit rolls for attacks that target units from your army until the end of the phase. You can only use this Stratagem once per battle.

BATTLE LENGTH

Use the Random Battle Length rules (pg 128) to determine how long the battle lasts.

VICTORY CONDITIONS

At the end of the battle, add up the total Power Rating of units from the Defender's army that were destroyed. If the total is less than a third of the Defender's army's Power Level the Defender wins a major victory. If the total is greater than half the Defender's army's Power Level the Attacker wins a major victory. Any other result is a minor victory for the Defender.

CRUCIBLE OF WAR
DATA RECOVERY

Vital data regarding the war is sent in scriptorum canisters from the planet's moon. This ancient technology has degraded over the millennia and there is no way to predict exactly where the canisters will land on the planet. The defenders must swiftly recover them before the attackers can salvage them.

THE ARMIES

Each player must first muster an army from their collection. A player can include any models in their army, but if their army is Battle-forged they will also be able to use the appropriate Stratagems included with this mission (see opposite). Once the armies have been chosen, the players must decide who will be the Attacker and who will be the Defender. If the Power Level of one of the armies is a third or more higher than the opposing army's Power Level, then the player whose army has the higher Power Level should be the Attacker and their opponent should be the Defender. Otherwise the players can roll off to decide.

THE BATTLEFIELD

Create a battlefield using the deployment map below and then set up terrain. This battle could take place anywhere from debris-strewn wastelands to a cramped hivesprawl interior. This mission works especially well if no terrain pieces are set up on areas where the canisters can arrive (see below).

DEPLOYMENT

After terrain has been set up, the Defender first sets up their units wholly within their deployment zone. The Attacker then sets up their units wholly within their deployment zone. The units set up by each player cannot have a combined Power Rating greater than one third of their army's Power Level. The remaining units in each army are set up in Reserve (pg 129).

FIRST TURN

Both players roll a D6, rolling again in the case of a tie. The player who rolls highest chooses who has the first turn.

DRAWN TO BATTLE

Starting from the second battle round, at the end of their Movement phase, each player makes a Reserve roll for each of their units in Reserve. Attacking units arrive on a 4+, while Defending units arrive on a 3+. Units automatically arrive at the end of a player's fourth Movement phase if they have not already done so. When a unit arrives from Reserve, set it up wholly within 6" of a battlefield edge and more than 9" from any enemy units.

SCRIPTORUM CANISTERS

At the start of each battle round after the first, one canister arrives on the battlefield. To determine where the canister lands, roll two D6 one at a time; the first decides where along the short battlefield edge it arrives and the second decides where along the long battlefield edge it arrives. Consult the map to see where the canister lands.

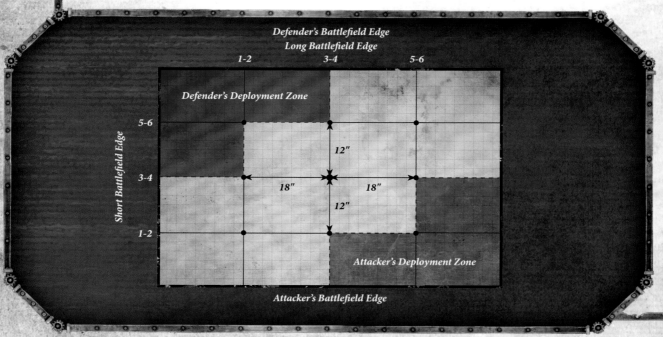

STRATAGEMS

In this mission, the players can use Command Points (CPs) to use the following bonus Stratagems:

1-3CP INFILTRATORS
Attacker Stratagem
Ordered to take forward positions, these warriors stand ready to react.

Use this Stratagem during deployment. Pick up to 3 units with the Troops Battlefield Role from your army, spending 1 CP for each unit you pick. These units can be set up anywhere on the battlefield that is wholly within 9" of the centre of the battlefield instead of within your deployment zone. You can only use this Stratagem once per battle.

2CP ENCIRCLING REINFORCEMENTS
Attacker Stratagem
Arriving from the flanks, these allies strike deep into enemy territory.

Use this Stratagem when one of your units arrives from Reserve. That unit can be set up anywhere wholly within 6" of any battlefield edge other than the Defender's battlefield edge, more than 9" from any enemy models.

2CP SIGNAL THE ATTACK
Attacker Stratagem
Once the enemy positions have been located, allies close down upon them.

Use this Stratagem at the end of your Movement phase, before making any Reserve rolls. Until the end of the turn you can add 1 to every Reserve roll you make.

1-2CP RELAY NODE
Defender Stratagem
The defenders have means to guide the arriving canisters to favourable positions.

Use this Stratagem after rolling the two D6 to determine the location of a canister. If you spend 1 CP you can re-roll one of the dice. If you spend 2 CP you can re-roll both dice.

1CP COVER GROUND
Defender Stratagem
Under orders to close in on the enemy, this unit moves at the double.

Use this Stratagem before a unit from your army Advances. Increase its Move characteristic by 6" until the end of the phase – do not roll a dice.

1CP RAPID REINFORCEMENTS
Defender Stratagem
Answering the call of their beleaguered allies, this unit races into the fray.

Use this Stratagem before making a Reserve roll. The unit being rolled for automatically arrives – do not make the Reserve roll.

Once a canister has landed it remains at that point for the duration of the battle. Players may find it helpful to use a token to indicate where a canister has landed. It is possible for multiple canisters to land at the same point during the battle.

BATTLE LENGTH
Use the Random Battle Length rules (pg 128) to determine how long the battle lasts.

VICTORY CONDITIONS
At the end of the battle, if one player has any models within 6" of a canister and there are no enemy models within 6" of it, that player captures that canister. If multiple canisters have landed at the same point, models can capture more than one canister. The player that captures the most canisters wins a major victory. If the players capture an equal number of canisters, the Attacker wins a minor victory.

THE DELTA AFLAME

As unending waves of Orks relentlessly assaulted Megaborealis, Fabricator Vosch ordered the detonation of hidden thermo-charges to ignite the promethium-rich delta and burn all to ash. The Skitarii defenders had one final order: to hunt down any Ork commanders that managed to escape the flames.

THE ARMIES

Each player must first muster an army from their collection. The Defender commands the Adeptus Mechanicus defence force of Megaborealis. The Attacker commands the hordes of attacking Orks. A player can include any models in their army, but if their army is Battle-forged they will also be able to use the appropriate Stratagems included with this mission (see opposite).

THE BATTLEFIELD

The Defender creates the battlefield. The battlefield should be heavily fortified in the Defender's deployment zone to mark the perimeter of Megaborealis, whilst the Attacker's deployment zone is left sparse to represent the no-man's land they are crossing.

DEPLOYMENT

After terrain has been set up, the Defender sets up their units wholly within their deployment zone. The Attacker then sets up their units wholly within their deployment zone.

PRELIMINARY BOMBARDMENT

Once both sides have been set up, the Attacker launches a Preliminary Bombardment (pg 128).

FIRST TURN

The Attacker has the first turn.

SUSTAINED ASSAULT

The Attacker can use the Sustained Assault rules (pg 129). Units brought back to the battlefield using these rules must be set up wholly within 6" of the Attacker's battlefield edge.

BREACH THE DEFENCES

At the end of the Attacker's Movement phase, any **CHARACTERS** from their army that are within 1" of the battlefield edge labelled 'Escape Route' can choose to leave the battlefield and venture into Megaborealis. If they do so the game ends immediately (see Victory Conditions below).

PROMETHIUM INFERNO

At the start of any battle round after the first, the Defender can choose to detonate the thermo-charges to ignite the promethium-soaked delta. If they do so, at the start of that battle round, roll a D6 for every unit that is on the battlefield. On a roll of 6, that unit suffers D3 mortal wounds. Repeat this process at the start of each subsequent battle round and reduce the roll needed by 1 each time (for example, in the following battle round units suffer D3 mortal wounds on the roll of a 5+, and so on).

BATTLE LENGTH

Use the Random Battle Length rules (pg 128) to determine how long the battle lasts.

VICTORY CONDITIONS

If any of the Attacker's **CHARACTERS** escape into Megaborealis (see 'Breach the Defences') the game ends immediately and the Attacker wins a major victory. Any other result is a major victory for the Defender.

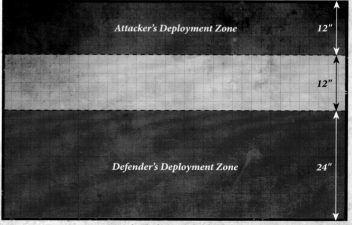

Attacker's Battlefield Edge

Attacker's Deployment Zone — 12"

— 12"

Defender's Deployment Zone — 24"

Defender's Battlefield Edge
Escape Route

STRATAGEMS

In this mission, the players can use Command Points (CPs) to use the following bonus Stratagems:

1CP — UNRELENTING DAKKA!
Attacker Stratagem
The Ork artillery batteries fire a massive salvo from behind their lines.

Use this Stratagem before rolling to see if a unit is hit by your Preliminary Bombardment. Roll 3D6 instead of 1. If you roll any 6s, that unit has been hit by 1 Preliminary Bombardment.

1CP — THE OMNISSIAH'S IMPERATIVE
Defender Stratagem
Righteous psalms to the Omnissiah blast from every vox unit in the army as new orders are rapidly rolled out. Stirring into action, the Skitarii strike swiftly at their xenos foes.

Use this Stratagem after both sides have deployed, but before the first turn begins. The Defender rolls a D6; on a 6, they get the first turn instead.

1CP — LIGHT 'EM UP, BOYZ!
Attacker Stratagem
The promethium-soaked mud-flats make it extremely hazardous to use flame-based weaponry, but for this unit of Burna Boyz, it's just too tempting…

Use this Stratagem at the start of your Shooting phase. Pick a unit of **Burna Boyz** from your army. Double the number of attacks that unit makes with its burnas this phase. However, at the end of the phase, roll a D6 for each model in the unit. For each roll of 1, that unit suffers 1 mortal wound.

1CP — NOOSPHERIC WARNINGS
Defender Stratagem
Intercepted trajectory data of the xenos artillery fire is released into the noosphere along with preventative dispersal subroutines.

Use this Stratagem when one of your **Infantry** units is hit by a Preliminary Bombardment, but before the damage is determined. Halve the number of mortal wounds (rounding up) suffered by that unit.

2CP — MIDNIGHT KRUMPIN'
Attacker Stratagem
The Ork Warlord is particularly cunning, opting to launch his attack under the cover of darkness.

Use this Stratagem after deployment. The Dawn Raid rules (pg 128) are in effect for the first battle round. You can only use this Stratagem once per battle.

3CP — ELECTROMAGNETIC DISRUPTION
Defender Stratagem
A powerful blast of electromagnetic energy is released across the battlefield, scrambling the diagnostics and sensor arrays of enemy vehicles.

Use this Stratagem at the start of the battle round. Halve the Move characteristic of enemy **Vehicle** units until the end of that battle round. This Stratagem can only be used once per battle.

MISSION VETERANS

In this mission, each player can upgrade one of the units in their army to be a mission veteran. If one player takes a mission veteran but the other does not have a suitable model, the player without the mission veteran gains 1 additional Command Point at the start of the battle.

DA ACE OF RAKKUK'S MEKMAZE
Attacker Mission Veteran Stratagem
The self-styled Ace of Rakkuk's Mekmaze led over a dozen raids into Megaborealis before he was finally shot down by an Onager Icarus array.

Pick a **Dakkajet** unit in your army to be Da Ace of Rakkuk's Mekmaze. Add 1 to wound rolls for shooting attacks made by this unit that target enemy **Vehicles**.

DECIMA GROUPING IX-12
Defender Mission Veteran Stratagem
The maniple of Ruststalkers designated Decima Grouping IX-12 were fitted with thermo-ablative plating and deployed into the flaming delta to take down the surviving Ork commanders before they could escape into the city.

Pick a unit of **Sicarian Ruststalkers** in your army to be Decima Grouping IX-12. Add 1 to the Damage characteristic of this unit's transonic blades for attacks that target enemy **Characters**. In addition, this unit is not affected by this mission's Promethium Inferno rule.

THE ANGELS OF DEATH DESCEND

When the Adeptus Astartes arrived on Vigilus, the War of Beasts was well underway. The planet's beleaguered defenders were reinforced in key positions by the Space Marine strike forces, whose presence helped push back the tides of Orks crashing against the outskirts of the hivesprawls.

THE ARMIES

This mission can be played between two players, but works especially well with two teams of multiple players. The Defender side controls the Adepta Sororitas, Astra Militarum and the relief force of Adeptus Astartes. The Attacker side controls the amassed Ork forces and should ideally contain lots of **Vehicles** to represent the Speedwaaagh! vanguard. A player can include any models in their army, but if their army is Battle-forged they will also be able to use the appropriate Stratagems included with this mission (see opposite).

THE BATTLEFIELD

The Defender side creates the battlefield. The battlefield should be heavily fortified in the Defender's deployment zone to mark the perimeter of a hivesprawl, whilst the Attacker's deployment zone is left sparse with a few craters to represent the no-man's land they are crossing.

There are 3 critical points on the map that the Attacker side will seek to control. These should be marked with objective markers.

DEPLOYMENT

After terrain has been set up, the Defender side sets up their units wholly within their deployment zone. Any **Adeptus Astartes** units in the Defender side's army must be placed in Reserve (pg 129); they will arrive during the battle as described below.

The Attacker side then sets up their units wholly within their deployment zone. Any units in the Attacker side's army with the **Vehicle** keyword can instead be set up wholly within the Attacker's vanguard deployment zone.

PRELIMINARY BOMBARDMENT

Once both sides have been set up, the Attacker side launches a Preliminary Bombardment (pg 128).

FIRST TURN

The Attacker has the first turn.

SMOG SCREEN

In the first battle round, subtract 1 from hit rolls for attacks that target units from the Attacker side's army.

ANGELS OF DEATH

Starting from the second battle round, at the end of their Movement phase, the Defender side makes a Reserve roll for each of their units in Reserve. The units arrive on the battlefield on a 3+. Each unit must be set up wholly within 6" of a battlefield edge other than the Attacker's battlefield edge and more than 9" from any enemy models. If the unit can **Fly** it can instead be set up anywhere on the battlefield more than 9" from any enemy models. In addition, units with abilities such as 'Teleport Strike' that allow them to arrive elsewhere may use these. Units automatically arrive at the end of the Defender's fourth Movement phase if they have not already done so.

BATTLE LENGTH

Use the Random Battle Length rules (pg 128) to determine how long the battle lasts.

VICTORY CONDITIONS

At the end of the battle, if the Attacker side controls 1 of the critical points they win a minor victory. If the Attacker side controls 2 or more critical points they win a major victory. Any other result is a major victory for the Defender side. A side controls a critical point if they have more models within 9" of the centre of it than the opposing side.

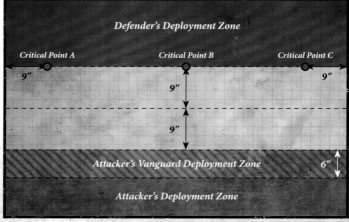

Defender's Battlefield Edge

Defender's Deployment Zone

Critical Point A   *Critical Point B*   *Critical Point C*

9"   9"   9"

9"

Attacker's Vanguard Deployment Zone   6"

Attacker's Deployment Zone

Attacker's Battlefield Edge

STRATAGEMS

In this mission, the players can use Command Points (CPs) to use the following bonus Stratagems:

1CP UNRELENTING DAKKA!
Attacker Stratagem

The Ork artillery batteries fire a massive salvo from behind their lines.

Use this Stratagem before rolling to see if a unit is hit by your Preliminary Bombardment. Roll 3D6 instead of 1. If you roll any 6s, that unit has been hit by 1 Preliminary Bombardment.

1CP NO QUARTER TO THE XENOS!
Defender Stratagem

The front line looks like it will buckle under the weight of the unrelenting Ork hordes. The command is given to rain down a barrage of righteous fire upon the enemy and reclaim what has been lost.

Use this Stratagem at the start of your Shooting phase. Pick an enemy unit within 6" of a critical point. Units from your army can re-roll hit rolls for attacks that target that unit until the end of the phase.

2CP MORE REVVIN'!
Attacker Stratagem

The Ork Warlord bellows the order for the Speedwaaagh! to spit out as much smog and kick up as much dust as possible. The vehicles rev their engines and circle the Ork advance.

Use this Stratagem at the start of the second battle round. The Smog Screen rule stays in effect during the second battle round.

2CP HYPERIA WILL NOT FALL
Defender Stratagem

A commander rises up on a fortification rampart and delivers a fiery speech that rouses all nearby to fight on no matter the odds they face.

Use this Stratagem at the start of the Morale phase. Pick a CHARACTER from your army. Until the end of that phase friendly units within 9" of that CHARACTER automatically pass Morale tests.

2CP MIDNIGHT KRUMPIN'
Attacker Stratagem

The Ork Warlord is particularly cunning, opting to launch his attack under the cover of darkness.

Use this Stratagem after deployment. The Dawn Raid rules (pg 128) are in effect for the first battle round. You can only use this Stratagem once per battle.

1CP RAPID REINFORCEMENTS
Defender Stratagem

The superior intel of the Adeptus Astartes allows them to deploy where they are most needed to help bolster the defence of Hyperia and fight back the marauding Orks.

Use this Stratagem before making a Reserve roll. The unit being rolled for automatically arrives – do not make the Reserve roll.

MISSION VETERANS

In this mission, each player can upgrade one of the units in their army to be a mission veteran. If one player takes a mission veteran but the other does not have a suitable model, the player without the mission veteran gains 1 additional Command Point at the start of the battle.

 ## TINY GORK
Attacker Mission Veteran Stratagem

Revered by the Boyz that followed it into battle, this Stompa was named 'Tiny Gork', as the path of destruction it carved was nothing short of the rampage of Gork himself.

Pick a STOMPA in your army to be Tiny Gork. At the start of each of your turns, roll a D6; on a 2+ use the top row of the model's damage table, regardless of how many wounds it has remaining. This ends immediately if the model is reduced to 0 wounds.

 ## THE STEEL HUNTERS
Defender Mission Veteran Stratagem

This legendary group of Leman Russ Battle Tanks made a defiant last stand in front of the Hyperian city gates. Though they were eventually destroyed to the last, they held their nerve till the end and cut swathes of destruction into the oncoming Ork hordes.

Pick a unit of LEMAN RUSS BATTLE TANKS in your army to be the Steel Hunters. Re-roll hit rolls of 1 for shooting attacks made by this unit.

ECHOES OF WAR
FORLORN CHARGE

On the perimeter of Mortwald, a spear of Freeblade Knights disobeyed refuelling orders, instead vowing to lay waste to the colossal Ork workshops and the stream of war machines they were producing. As they approached the Scrap Cities, the Stompa Mobs standing guard eagerly awaited the fight to come.

THE ARMIES

Each player must first muster an army from their collection. The Defender commands the Stompa Mobs and Blitz Brigades that protect the Scrap City. The Attacker commands the Imperial Knights and accompanying Freeblades. A player can include any models in their army, but if their army is Battle-forged they will also be able to use the appropriate Stratagems included with this mission (see opposite). The Defender receives +3 Command Points if their army includes any Fortification Network Detachments as described in the *Warhammer 40,000* rulebook.

THE BATTLEFIELD

The Defender creates the battlefield, which should have plenty of barricades and obstacles to represent the Ork Scrap City.

DEPLOYMENT

After terrain has been set up, the Defender sets up their units wholly within their deployment zone. The Attacker then sets up their units wholly within their deployment zone.

FIRST TURN

The Attacker has the first turn.

BATTLE LENGTH

Use the Random Battle Length rules (pg 128) to determine how long the battle lasts.

VICTORY CONDITIONS

If there are no **Buildings**, **Stompas**, **Gorkanauts** and **Morkanauts** on the battlefield, the game immediately ends and the Attacker wins a major victory. Otherwise, when the battle ends, count the number of each of the above on the battlefield and the number that have been destroyed during the battle. If the amount destroyed during the battle equals or exceeds the amount remaining on the battlefield, the Attacker wins a minor victory. Any other result is a major victory to the Defender.

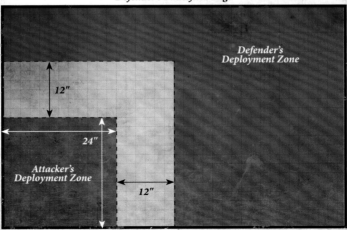

Defender's Battlefield Edge

Defender's Deployment Zone

12"

24"

Attacker's Deployment Zone

12"

Attacker's Battlefield Edge

STRATAGEMS

In this mission, the players can use Command Points (CPs) to use the following bonus Stratagems:

3CP — NEGATIVE, WE WILL NOT RETREAT
Attacker Stratagem
Despite receiving orders to retreat, the Imperial Knights charged headlong into their foe's battle lines.

Use this Stratagem at the start of your Charge phase. Until the end of that phase, **IMPERIAL KNIGHTS** from your army can attempt to charge even if they Advanced in the same turn.

1CP — MACHINE SPIRIT, GUIDE MY AIM
Attacker Stratagem
The pilot of this Imperial Knight unleashes a volley of fire with deadly accuracy.

Use this Stratagem at the start of your Shooting phase. Pick an **IMPERIAL KNIGHT** unit from your army. Add 1 to hit rolls and wound rolls for attacks made by that unit until the end of that phase.

2CP — VENGEANCE FOR OUR FALLEN BROTHER
Attacker Stratagem
As one Freeblade is brought down by the Orks, another vows to avenge it, and carves a bloody path through the xenos hordes.

Use this Stratagem after an **IMPERIAL KNIGHT** from your army is destroyed. Before removing the model, pick another friendly **IMPERIAL KNIGHT** within 6" of the destroyed model. That **IMPERIAL KNIGHT** can make a shooting attack as if it were the Shooting Phase, or be chosen to fight as if it were the Fight phase. Once its attacks have been resolved, remove the destroyed model as normal.

1CP — LET'S SHOW 'EM!
Defender Stratagem
A Stompa wades forward into the enemy lines, an effigy of Gork filling all greenskins around with the ferocious spirit of the Waaagh!.

Use this Stratagem after a **STOMPA** from your army has made a charge move. Add 1 to charge rolls made for friendly units within 12" of that **STOMPA** until the end of the phase.

1CP — SEND IN DA RIGGERS!
Defender Stratagem
From the scrap piles and nearby workshops, a horde of rigger grots scamper, braving the hazards of the battlefield to fix one of the Ork war machines.

Use this Stratagem at the end of your Movement phase. Pick a **VEHICLE** from your army. That model regains D3 lost wounds. A vehicle can only be repaired once each turn. Each time this Stratagem is resolved, roll a D6 and add the number of times this Stratagem has been used. On the roll of a 7+ this Stratagem cannot be used again in this battle.

1CP — THEY AIN'T SO TOUGH!
Defender Stratagem
As a defeated Imperial Knight falls, the Orks around bellow a challenging war cry.

Use this Stratagem when an enemy **IMPERIAL KNIGHT** is destroyed. The unit from your army that destroyed that unit (i.e. the unit that inflicted the final wound), and friendly units within 12" of the unit that destroyed it, do not have to take Morale tests until the end of the turn.

MISSION VETERANS

In this mission, each player can upgrade one of the units in their army to be a mission veteran. If one player takes a mission veteran but the other does not have a suitable model, the player without the mission veteran gains 1 additional Command Point at the start of the battle.

 ## MANDRAKE THE VENATOR
Attacker Mission Veteran Stratagem
A god among giants, Mandrake the Venator, Knight of Joren Vanaklimptas, led the Freeblades to repeated glory before they were eventually cut down.

Pick a **KNIGHT CASTELLAN** from your army to be Mandrake the Venator. You can re-roll damage rolls made for shooting attacks by this unit.

 ## THE BROTHERS GORK AND MORK
Defender Mission Veteran Stratagem
Known for their constant bickering, this Gorkanaut and Morkanaut put aside their differences when a bigger foe emerged, their rivalry pushing each to fight all the harder.

Pick a **GORKANAUT** and a **MORKANAUT** from your army to be the Brothers Gork and Mork. If these two units are within 6" of each other at the start of the Charge phase, add 2 to their charge rolls until the end of that phase.

ECHOES OF WAR
BEHEAD THE VIPER

When the insidious plotting of the Genestealer Cultists of Dirkden came to fruition, within the hivesprawl madness and violence reigned. The ruling nobles were rushed to a safe zone in armoured transports, but long had the Pauper Princes of Dirkden prepared for this day, and they were lying in wait…

THE ARMIES

Each player must first muster an army from their collection. The Defender commands the personal escort of Dirkden's ruling nobles. The Attacker commands the Genestealer Cultists lying in ambush. A player can include any models in their army, but if their army is Battle-forged they will also be able to use the appropriate Stratagems included with this mission (see opposite).

THE ESCORT

To play this mission, the Defender will require a suitable model to represent the armoured transport that carries the ruling nobles. The Defender picks one **TRANSPORT** model from their army to become the Escort. The **TRANSPORT** picked cannot have a Power Rating greater than 8 and cannot be able to **FLY**.

No units can be embarked upon the Escort before or during the battle.

THE BATTLEFIELD

Create a battlefield using the deployment map below and then set up terrain. The battlefield should be a densely populated city with roads that allow the Escort to get across. In the south-east corner is a safe zone with walls and fortifications.

DEPLOYMENT

After terrain has been set up, the Defender first separates their army into two groups. The first group must contain the Escort and any other units with a combined Power Rating not exceeding a third of the army's overall Power Level. The Escort is deployed within the Escort Deployment Zone and the rest of

this group are deployed wholly within 9" of the Escort. The rest of the army is then deployed wholly within the Garrison Deployment Zone (including the safe zone).

Any units in the Attacker's army that have the Cult Ambush ability must be set up in ambush instead of on the battlefield (see *Codex: Genestealer Cults*). Any other units must be set up in Reserve. Units set up in Reserve arrive during the battle as described below.

FIRST TURN

The Defender has the first turn.

ATTACKER'S RESERVES

Any of the Attacker's units in Reserve can arrive at the end of any of the Attacker's Movement phases. These units must be set up wholly within 12" of either of the Attacker's battlefield edges and more than 9" from any enemy models. Any of the Attacker's units that are set up in ambush arrive on the battlefield as described in the Cult Ambush ability.

IMMOBILISING THE ESCORT

If the Escort is reduced to 0 wounds, it is not destroyed (and cannot explode). Instead it is said to be immobilised. Whilst the Escort is immobilised, it cannot be targeted by attacks and is treated as a friendly model by units from both player's armies. In addition, it cannot move or make any attacks. If the Escort regains any wounds, it can move and attack (and be attacked) as normal.

BATTLE LENGTH

Use the Random Battle Length rules (pg 128) to determine how long the battle lasts.

VICTORY CONDITIONS

If the Escort is wholly within the safe zone at the end of a turn, the game immediately ends and the Defender wins a major victory. Otherwise, when the battle ends, count the number of models both players have within 9" of the Escort. The player with the most models wins a major victory. In the case of a tie, the Attacker wins a minor victory.

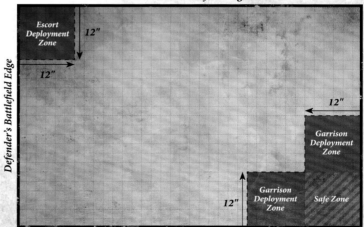

STRATAGEMS

In this mission, the players can use Command Points (CPs) to use the following bonus Stratagems:

2CP — RIGGED EXPLOSIVES
Attacker Stratagem
As the armoured escort moves through the narrow streets, an adjacent building erupts in an explosion.

Use this Stratagem at the start of your Shooting phase. Pick a terrain piece and roll a D6 for each unit within 3"; on a 4+ that unit suffers D3 mortal wounds.

2CP — HOUSEHOLD SERVITOR
Defender Stratagem
This noble has brought along his personal servitor, equipped with a host of augmentation upgrades that can repair the escort on the move.

Use this Stratagem at the end of your Movement phase. The Escort unit regains D3 lost wounds.

2CP — HAYWIRE EMITTER
Attacker Stratagem
Sourced off-world, this coveted device emits a burst of electromagnetic energy, wreaking havoc on sensor arrays.

Use this Stratagem at the end of your Movement phase. Pick a unit of **Neophyte Hybrids** from your army. Halve the Move characteristic of all enemy **Vehicle** units within 8" of that unit until the start of your next turn.

3CP — TEMPORARY REFRACTOR FIELD
Defender Stratagem
Sourced from Megaborealis, this portable device emits a temporary refractor field that can shield against even the strongest of attacks.

Use this Stratagem at the start of the Shooting phase. Until the end of that phase, the Escort has a 4+ invulnerable save. You can only use this Stratagem once per battle.

2CP — DIVERTED RESOURCES
Attacker Stratagem
More warriors join the fight to thwart the ruling nobles' escape.

Use this Stratagem at the start your turn. Pick an **Infantry** unit from your army that has been destroyed. You can set up that unit again on the battlefield, wholly within 6" of either of the Attacker's battlefield edges and more than 9" from any enemy models, at its full starting strength.

3CP — EMERGENCY ESCORT TRANSFER
Defender Stratagem
The ruling nobles of Dirkden are evacuated from their armoured transport and hastily embarked into a new vehicle.

Use this Stratagem at the end your Movement phase. If the Escort is within 1" of another friendly **Transport** unit with a Power Rating of 8 or less, that cannot **Fly**, and that does not have a unit embarked, that **Transport** becomes the Escort and the original Escort becomes a normal model. You can only use this Stratagem once per battle.

MISSION VETERANS

In this mission, each player can upgrade one of the units in their army to be a mission veteran. If one player takes a mission veteran but the other does not have a suitable model, the player without the mission veteran gains 1 additional Command Point at the start of the battle.

 GOLIATH TRUCK ZETA IV-Q
Attacker Mission Veteran Stratagem
So durable was this Goliath Truck that its crew thought the Patriarch had bestowed his blessing upon it. During the mission it proved critical in blocking escape routes.

Pick a **Goliath Truck** from your army to be Goliath Truck Zeta IV-Q. This unit's Rugged Construction ability ignores wounds on a 5 or a 6.

 DROP FORCE PRAESIDION
Defender Mission Veteran Stratagem
Assigned directly to the ruling nobles and their protection, Drop Force Praesidion fought with honour until the last to defend the armoured transport from the vile Genestealer Cultists.

Pick a unit of **Tempestus Scions** from your army to be Drop Force Praesidion. This unit automatically passes Morale tests while it is within 6" of the Escort. In addition, you can re-roll hit rolls of 1 for this unit while it is within 6" of the Escort.

14

ECHOES OF WAR
BREACH OF QUARANTINE

The quarantine set up in Dontoria by the Iron Hands to contain the Gellerpox outbreak was not to last. The civilians trapped inside attempted to force their way out, prompting the Space Marines to respond aggressively. Meanwhile, the veil of realspace began to erode, allowing Nurgle Daemons to burst through.

THE ARMIES

Each player must first muster an army from their collection. The Defender commands the Iron Hands quarantine force. The Attacker commands the pox-riddled populace, the contingent of Death Guard and the warp-born Daemons of Nurgle. A player can include any models in their army, but if their army is Battle-forged they will also be able to use the appropriate Stratagems included with this mission (see opposite).

THE BATTLEFIELD

The Defender creates the battlefield. Each of their deployment zones should be heavily fortified to mark the perimeter of the quarantined zone, whilst the centre is left clear save for a few barricades, obstacles and craters.

DEPLOYMENT

After terrain has been set up, the Attacker sets up their units wholly within their deployment zone. The Defender then sets up their units wholly within their deployment zones.

FIRST TURN

The Attacker has the first turn.

ESCAPE ROUTE

Any unit in the Attacker's army can move off a battlefield edge labelled 'Escape Route' so long as all of the models in that unit are able to make it off the board by that edge in the same phase. Any models that do so are said to have escaped, and are removed from the battlefield and take no further part in the battle.

BATTLE LENGTH

Use the Random Battle Length rules (pg 128) to determine how long the battle lasts.

VICTORY CONDITIONS

At the end of the battle, add up the Power Ratings of all the Attacker's escaped units (see Escape Route) and compare this to the Power Level of their army (count the entire unit's Power Rating, even if some of its models were destroyed before the unit escaped). If the combined Power Rating of the escaped units is one third or more of the army's Power Level, the Attacker wins a major victory. Any other result is a major victory for the Defender.

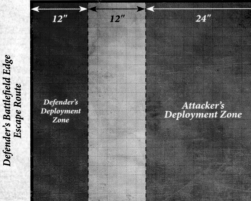

Attacker's Battlefield Edge

| 12" | 12" | 24" | 12" | 12" |

Defender's Battlefield Edge / Escape Route

Defender's Deployment Zone

Attacker's Deployment Zone

Defender's Deployment Zone

Defender's Battlefield Edge / Escape Route

Attacker's Battlefield Edge

STRATAGEMS

In this mission, the players can use Command Points (CPs) to use the following bonus Stratagems:

REALITY TEARS
2CP

Attacker Stratagem

The veil between realspace and the warp tears wide like a gaping wound and out pour the Daemons of Nurgle.

Use this Stratagem at the end of your Movement phase. Pick a **NURGLE DAEMON** unit from your army that was destroyed earlier in the battle. Set up this unit anywhere on the battlefield more than 9" from any enemy models.

WE GIVE OUR LIVES FOR THE EMPEROR
1CP

Defender Stratagem

With righteous zeal and reckless abandon, these warriors hurl themselves into the enemy lines without thought for their own safety.

Use this Stratagem at the start of the Fight phase. Pick a unit from your army. Add 1 to hit rolls and wound rolls for attacks made by that unit until the end of that phase. However, your opponent can add 1 to hit rolls and wounds rolls for attacks that target the unit you picked.

REPULSIVE DELUGE
1CP

Attacker Stratagem

The servants of Nurgle explode with vile fluids that corrode armour and sear the flesh of any caught in the entropic downpour.

Use this Stratagem after a unit from your army has been destroyed, before removing the last model from the battlefield. Roll a D6 for each enemy unit within 7" of that model. For each roll of 3+ the unit being rolled for suffers D3 mortal wounds. Once this Stratagem has been resolved remove the last model from the destroyed unit as normal.

PURGE THE UNCLEAN
1CP

Defender Stratagem

Flamer in hand, this Space Marine steps forward to unleash a righteous inferno upon the enemy.

Use this Stratagem before a unit from your army attacks in the Shooting phase. Add 1 to wound rolls made for that unit's flame weapons. For the purposes of this Stratagem, a flame weapon is any weapon profile whose name includes the word 'flame' (e.g. flamer, heavy flamer, flamestorm cannon, flamestorm gauntlet.)

THE FRENZIED POPULACE
1CP

Attacker Stratagem

Driven mad by the foul plague that has infected them, the common people are driven to attack those they once called comrades with unnatural vigour.

Use this Stratagem at the start of the Fight phase. Pick a unit of **POXWALKERS** from your army. Add 1 to the Attacks characteristic of that unit until the end of the phase.

THUNDERHAWK STRAFING RUN
3CP

Defender Stratagem

A sound of thunder roars from above before the battlefield ignites in a series of devastating detonations.

Use this Stratagem in your Shooting phase. Pick up to three enemy units within 12" of each other and roll a D6 for each. Add 1 to the result for every 10 models in the unit being rolled for. On a 5, the unit being rolled for suffers D3 mortal wounds. On a 6+ the unit being rolled for suffers D6 mortal wounds.

MISSION VETERANS

In this mission, each player can upgrade one of the units in their army to be a mission veteran. If one player takes a mission veteran but the other does not have a suitable model, the player without the mission veteran gains 1 additional Command Point at the start of the battle.

THE PUTRID BROTHERHOOD

Attacker Mission Veteran Stratagem

Veterans of the Long War, and members of the Seven Pillared warrior lodge, the Putrid Brotherhood were spreading the vile diseases of Grandfather Nurgle for over ten millennia before they set foot on Vigilus.

Pick a unit of **PLAGUE MARINES** from your army to be the Putrid Brotherhood. Add 1 to wound rolls for shooting attacks made by this unit that target enemy **VEHICLES**.

SCOUT SQUAD SICARON

Defender Mission Veteran Stratagem

Under the leadership of Sergeant Idonis, the unflinching aim of Scout Squad Sicaron neutralised half a dozen critical enemy targets without loss of civilian life.

Pick a unit of **ADEPTUS ASTARTES SCOUTS** from your army to be Scout Squad Sicaron. You can re-roll hit rolls for shooting attacks made with sniper rifles by this unit that target enemy **CHARACTERS**.

15

ECHOES OF WAR
CARNAGE IN THE SPIRES

Under the command of Haarken Worldclaimer, Black Legion Raptor warbands unleashed a war of terror upon the unsuspecting nobles of Hyperia's spires. Inceptor close support companies and squads of Assault Marines rushed to the defence, supported by Stormhawk Interceptors and Stormraven Gunships.

THE ARMIES

Each player must first muster an army from their collection. The Defender commands the Adeptus Astartes. The Attacker commands the swarms of Chaos Space Marine Raptors and their allies. A player can include any models in their army, but this mission works especially well if every unit can **FLY**. If their army is Battle-forged they will also be able to use the appropriate Stratagems included with this mission (see opposite).

BATTLEZONE

Use the rules from Battlezone: Spirescape (pg 158) to reflect the dizzying heights in which this battle is taking place.

THE BATTLEFIELD

Create a battlefield using the deployment map below and then set up terrain. There should be clusters of buildings with spaces no greater than 9" between them. Ideally these buildings should contain lots of flat areas. The Defender's deployment zone should be densely populated with buildings and, at the centre of the Defender's battlefield edge, an objective marker should be placed onto a flat area of a terrain piece to mark the entrance to the spire the Chaos Space Marine Raptors seek to infiltrate.

DEPLOYMENT

After terrain has been set up, the Defender sets up as many of their units as they wish wholly within their deployment zone. The Attacker then sets up as many of their units as they wish wholly within their deployment zone. Any remaining units are placed in Reserve (pg 129); they will arrive during the battle as described below.

FIRST TURN

The Attacker has the first turn.

ARRIVING RESERVES

Players can set up any Reserve units from their army on the battlefield at the end of each of their Movement phases. To do so, the player picks a Reserve unit from their army and makes a Reserve roll. On a 3+, the unit being rolled for can be set up anywhere on the battlefield more than 9" from any enemy models. Any units that have not arrived by the fourth battle round arrive automatically that battle round.

THE SPIRE

The Attacker's **INFANTRY** units can enter the spire if, at the start of their Movement phase, they are within 1" of the objective representing the spire entrance. If one or more of the Attacker's units does so, the game ends immediately (see Victory Conditions below).

BATTLE LENGTH

Use the Random Battle Length rules (pg 128) to determine how long the battle lasts.

VICTORY CONDITIONS

If any of the Attacker's **INFANTRY** units gain access to the spire (see 'The Spire'), the game ends immediately and the Attacker wins a major victory. Any other result is a major victory to the Defender.

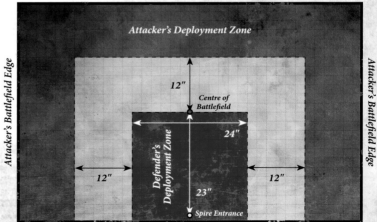

STRATAGEMS

In this mission, the players can use Command Points (CPs) to use the following bonus Stratagems:

2CP — NIGHT TERRORS
Attacker Stratagem

Under the veil of darkness the circling Raptors began their decent.

Use this Stratagem after both sides have deployed. The Dawn Raid rules (pg 128) are used in this mission.

1CP — SIGNAL THE ATTACK
Attacker Stratagem

From his Daemon-tainted vox array, the Herald of the Apocalypse orders the Raptors to begin their assault.

Use this Stratagem at the end of your Movement phase, before making any Reserve rolls. Until the end of the turn you can add 1 to every Reserve roll you make.

1CP — ATTACK FROM ABOVE
Attacker Stratagem

Diving down from above, this unit of Raptors falls unseen onto the enemy, striking before a single warning shot has been fired.

Use this Stratagem at the start of your Charge phase. Pick a unit of **RAPTORS** from your army that were set up on the battlefield for the first time this turn. You can re-roll charge rolls for that unit until the end of that phase.

3CP — STRUCTURAL DETONATION
Defender Stratagem

This building has been rigged to explode by the defenders, in the hope that the explosion will deal their foes a blow.

Use this Stratagem at the start of your Shooting phase. Pick a terrain piece no larger than 10" x 10" x 10". The terrain piece with the objective representing the spire entrance on it cannot be chosen. Roll a D6 for each model on that terrain piece; on a 6+ that model's unit suffers 1 mortal wound. In addition, at the start of your following turn, remove that terrain piece from the battlefield. Any models on that terrain piece when it is removed are immediately destroyed.

2CP — COUNTER-ASSAULT
Defender Stratagem

Rather than lie in wait for the Chaos forces to ascend, the commander issues the order to strike the enemy swiftly.

Use this Stratagem after both sides have deployed, but before the first turn begins. The Defender rolls a dice – on a 6, they get the first turn instead.

1CP — STRIKE DOWN THE HERETIC!
Defender Stratagem

This jump pack squad charges head-first into the enemy, ready to unleash vengeance upon them.

Use this Stratagem at the start of your Charge phase. Pick a **JUMP PACK** unit from your army. Add 1 to charge rolls for that unit until the end of the phase. In addition, add 1 to wound rolls for that unit until the end of the following Fight phase if it made a charge move in the same turn.

MISSION VETERANS

In this mission, each player can upgrade one of the units in their army to be a mission veteran. If one player takes a mission veteran but the other does not have a suitable model, the player without the mission veteran gains 1 additional Command Point at the start of the battle.

RHABUS THE VICIOUS
Attacker Mission Veteran Stratagem

A Heldrake infamous for preying on Valkyries and other light ships of the Imperial Navy, the name Rhabus the Vicious was uttered with terror by the Imperial pilots stationed on Vigilus.

Pick a **HELDRAKE** unit from your army to be Rhabus the Vicious. Add 1 to the Damage characteristic of shooting attacks made by this unit that target enemy **VEHICLES** that can **FLY**.

INCEPTOR SQUAD ACCIPITOR
Defender Mission Veteran Stratagem

Even as Haarken Worldclaimer and his Raptors rushed in on all sides, Inceptor Squad Accipitor held the spire entrance with grim resolve, their guns roaring until the very last.

Pick an **INCEPTOR SQUAD** from your army to be Inceptor Squad Accipitor. If this unit fires Overwatch, a roll of a 4, 5 or 6 is needed for a successful hit roll.

BATTLEZONES

The War of Beasts on Vigilus raged so fiercely that no quarter was saved from bloodshed. To lead an army to victory there required both strategic acumen and quick tactical thinking, as battles in such hostile conditions were often as threatening to a force's warriors as the enemy they faced.

In this section you will find six exciting new battlezones to use in your games of Warhammer 40,000. From deadly tundric blizzards to Genestealer-infested hivesprawls, each battlezone offers new tactical challenges to enrich your games, and introduces new rules to represent many varied battle environments. Some modify the core rules, for example by altering the range of weapons. Some provide new rules for phenomena like dust storms, volcanic eruptions and earthquakes. Some grant additional abilities and Stratagems to certain units.

These rules are designed to reflect some of the environments fought in on Vigilus during the War of Beasts, but they are entirely optional and, so long as you and your opponent agree, they can be used in any Warhammer 40,000 game, set anywhere.

Agree which, if any, battlezone rules will be used when you are setting up the battlefield, before deployment.

BATTLEZONE: WASTELAND DUST STORM

Between the hivesprawls of Vigilus stretched vast wastelands. To be caught in the fury of the vicious dust storms that prowled these wastes was a battle in itself. At their most ferocious, they could rip aircraft out of the sky and strip flesh from bone in a matter of seconds.

The Stormfront: At the start of the first battle round, the player taking the first turn nominates one of the long battlefield edges to be North. In clockwise order, the other battlefield edges become East, South and West. Note that if a mission deployment map specifies that a battlefield edge corresponds to a compass point, use the map instead of nominating edges. Then, the player rolls a D6 and consults the table below to determine which battlefield edge the storm emerges from. For the first battle round, units wholly within 12" of that battlefield edge are considered to be within the storm.

D6	BATTLEFIELD EDGE
1	North
2-3	East
4-5	West
6	South

Ebb and Flow: At the start of each battle round after the first, roll a D6. On a 3+ the range of the storm increases by 6". On a 1 or 2, the range of the storm reduces by 6" (to a minimum of 6"). Any units wholly within the range of the storm are considered to be within the storm.

Caught in the Storm Surge: At the start of your Movement phase, any VEHICLE units from your army that are within the storm and have the Flyer Battlefield Role suffer D3 mortal wounds. For each other unit in your army that is within the storm, roll a D6; on a 4+ that unit suffers 1 mortal wound.

Blinded by Dust: Subtract 1 from hit rolls for shooting attacks made by units within the storm. In addition, subtract 1 from hit rolls for shooting attacks made by units outside the storm that target units within the storm.

Shrouded by the Storm: Units within the storm count as being in cover.

BATTLEZONE: TUNDRIC BLIZZARD

In the sub-zero wastes of Kaelac's Bane, the battle was often with the environment as much as it was with the foe. Visibility was compromised by blinding blizzards, vehicles were slowed as they ploughed through snowdrifts, and deadly predators stalked the tundra to tear apart any warriors that crossed their path.

Snow Blizzards: At the start of each battle round, the player taking the first turn rolls a D6 and consults the table below:

D6	RESULT
1	**Hazardous Conditions:** For this battle round, all ranged weapons with a range of 12" or more are treated as having a range of 12". In addition, roll a D6 for each unit that is a **VEHICLE** and can **FLY**. On a 1 that unit suffers D3 mortal wounds.
2-3	**Low Visibility:** For this battle round, subtract 1 from hit rolls for shooting attacks that target an enemy unit that is more than 12" away from the firing model.
4-5	**Obscured Visibility:** For this battle round, subtract 1 from hit rolls for shooting attacks that target an enemy unit that is more than 24" away from the firing model.
6	**Clear Visibility:** No effect.

Sub-zero Temperatures: In your Movement phase, roll a D6 for each **VEHICLE** unit in your army. On a 1, halve that unit's Move characteristic until the end of the phase. Units that can **FLY** are not affected.

Apex Predators: At the start of each player's turn, they can pick an enemy **INFANTRY** unit that is more than 6" from any other unit on the battlefield and see if it is attacked by an apex predator. Roll a D6; if the result is a 6 it is attacked – roll on the table below:

D6	RESULT
1	**Attacked, but Unscathed:** The unit cannot shoot any of its weapons in the following shooting phase.
2	**Taste for Blood:** For the remainder of the battle, if the unit is picked again to see if it is attacked by an apex predator, it is attacked on a 4+ rather than a 6. If this result is rolled again for this unit, re-roll until you generate a different result.
3	**Fearsome Strike:** The unit suffers 1 mortal wound.
4	**Deadly Assault:** The unit suffers D3 mortal wounds.
5	**Savage Rampage:** The unit suffers D6 mortal wounds.
6	**Dragged into the Darkness:** The player whose turn is taking place picks a model from the unit. That model is slain.

BATTLEZONE: WARQUAKE

The relentless mining operations of the Adeptus Mechanicus' colossal bore-hives caused violent tremors and earthquakes to spread across the planet. The seismic upheaval caused by these works presented additional challenges for warring sides meeting in battle.

Fracture Points: At the start of the battle, before armies are deployed, players take it in turns to place 6 fracture points on the battlefield, numbered 1-6, starting with the player taking the first turn. Each fracture point must be placed more than 6" from any battlefield edge and more than 6" from any other fracture point. These can be marked with tokens.

In this example, the player rolls a 3 and a 4 on the two D6. A 1mm straight line is drawn through the centre of the two corresponding fracture points and continued on the same trajectory to the battlefield edges to create the fault line.

At the start of each battle round, the player taking the first turn rolls two D6, re-rolling if the result is a double. The two results determine the two fracture points a fault line runs through. Draw a straight line 1mm wide that goes through the centre of each fracture point until it reaches the battlefield edges (see example) – this represents the fault line.

If the fault line passes through any models, that model's unit is said to be intersected by the fault line.

Once the fault line has been determined, the player taking the first turn rolls a D6 and consults the table on the right to determine what rules are in effect for that battle round.

D6	RESULT
1	**Distant Tremors:** For this battle round, subtract 1 from hit rolls for shooting attacks made by units intersected by the fault line. In addition, each time a unit that does not have the **FLY** keyword moves over the fault line during that battle round, roll a D6; on a 4+ that unit suffers 1 mortal wound.
2-3	**Aftershocks:** For this battle round, apply the effects of the Distant Tremors result. In addition, roll a D6 for each **BUILDING** intersected by the fault line. On a 2+ that **BUILDING** and any units embarked within it suffer D6 mortal wounds (roll separately for each unit).
4-5	**Tectonic Displacement:** For this battle round, apply the effects of the Distant Tremors result and the Aftershocks result. In addition, roll a D6 for each unit intersected by the fault line that is not a **BUILDING** and does not have the **FLY** keyword. On a 2+ that unit suffers D3 mortal wounds.
6	**Seismic Upheaval:** For this battle round, apply the effects of the Distant Tremors result and the Aftershocks result. In addition, roll a D6 for each unit intersected by the fault line that is not a **BUILDING** and does not have the **FLY** keyword. On a 2+ that unit suffers D6 mortal wounds.

BATTLEZONE: GEOTHERMAL ERUPTION

Storvhal was a site of vast volcanic energy, its eruptions harnessed by the Adeptus Mechanicus to fuel their mining efforts. However, the volatility of the region could never truly be controlled, and as opposing forces vied to capitalise on its power, they also strived to avoid its deadly effects.

Encroaching Lava: At the start of the battle, before armies are deployed, determine which battlefield edge the wall of encroaching lava will move in from. This is the lava starting edge. Players roll off and the winner nominates a battlefield edge. The battlefield edge selected must be neither the Attacker's sole battlefield edge, nor the Defender's sole battlefield edge. It also cannot be a battlefield edge that units can move off during the battle (e.g. the battlefield edge titled 'Escape Route' in the Convoy mission, pg 130).

Once the lava starting edge has been determined, 9 lava counters are set up within 1" of that battlefield edge, equidistant from each other, as shown on the diagram, below left.

At the start of each battle round, the lava moves further onto the battlefield. The players roll off and then alternate moving the lava counters, starting with the winner of the roll off. When it is a player's turn to move a lava counter, they first roll a D6 and then choose a lava counter to move. They then move that counter a number of inches equal to the dice roll in a straight line directly towards the opposite battlefield edge, as shown on the diagram, below right. Each lava counter can only be moved once per battle round.

Engulfed in Molten Magma: Once all lava counters have been moved, the lava front is established. Draw a straight line, 1mm wide, from the centre of each lava counter to the centre of the next lava counter.

If a model is on the side of the lava front closer to the lava starting edge, it is said to be behind the lava front. Models either partially or wholly behind the lava front at the start of each battle round are immediately destroyed. This includes **BUILDINGS**, **TRANSPORTS** and any units embarked within them. Units with the **FLY** keyword and units embarked within a **TRANSPORT** that has the **FLY** keyword are not affected.

Any model that does not have the **FLY** keyword that moves through or finishes its move behind the lava front is also immediately destroyed.

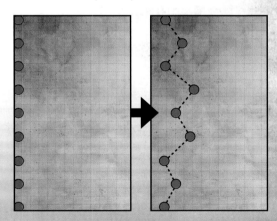

Left, the starting positions of the lava counters; right, their positions after they have been moved at the start of the first battle round. The dotted line indicates the lava front.

BATTLEZONE: SPIRESCAPE

Above the thick clouds of pollution covering Vigilus' hivesprawls, the spires of shrines and buildings reached high into the sky. At such dizzying heights, battle was perilous. While winged combatants had the advantage, the slightest error in judgement saw them plummet down to crash into the hive below.

Battle Above the Clouds: When using this battlezone, the ground level of the battlefield represents the depths of the hivesprawl below. Units cannot move across the ground level of the battlefield unless they can **FLY**. Any units without the **FLY** keyword that are set up on or moved across the ground level are immediately destroyed. In addition, if any models with the **JUMP PACK** keyword are set up on, or end a move on, the ground level of the battlefield, they are immediately destroyed.

Spire Plateaus: To allow more units that cannot **FLY** to take part in a battle using this battlezone, you and your opponent can agree before the battle to mark out certain areas as spire plateaus. These areas are not subject to the 'Battle Above the Clouds' ability above and are instead treated as normal areas of the battlefield. We recommend choosing two 24" squares to be spire plateaus, each adjacent to a different player's battlefield edge. Two example layouts are shown below.

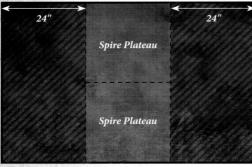
The Bridge

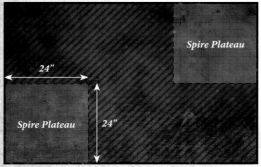
Battle of Two Spires

STRATAGEMS

When using this battlezone, you and your opponent can both use Command Points (CPs) to use the following Stratagems:

1CP — TURBO JUMP
Stratagem

At such high altitudes, jump pack troops can make daring leaps from building to building by overcharging their jets.

Use this Stratagem in your Movement phase. Pick a **JUMP PACK** unit from your army. You can double the Move characteristic of all models in that unit until the end of that phase. However, that unit cannot Advance this phase and cannot charge later this turn.

1CP — DUCK AND DIVE
Stratagem

Aerial dogfights at this altitude are fraught affairs. Pilots with an enemy on their tail can use the clouds below or the spires above to their advantage as they dip down low or pull up high to outmanoeuvre their pursuer.

Use this Stratagem at the start of your Movement phase. Pick a unit from your army with the Flyer Battlefield Role that is on the battlefield. Remove that unit from the battlefield and set it up out of sight. At the end of your following Movement phase, set the unit up anywhere on the battlefield that is more than 9" from any enemy models.

HINTS & TIPS

When using this battlezone, you can set up a thematic-looking battlefield in a number of ways. You can place cotton wool between the buildings to create the effect of spires piercing the smog and standing tall amongst the clouds. A simpler method would be to cover the battlefield in a white or black sheet to simulate clouds at day or night.

BATTLEZONE: GENESTEALER INFESTATION

From the darkened macro-ducts of Oteck to the subterranean mining cities of Megaborealis, the insidious Genestealer Cult spread its infestation far and wide across Vigilus. It was all too easy for unsuspecting armies to stumble into a nest of xenos atrocities, their only warning the strange blips on their sensors.

Sensor Blips: At the start of the first battle round, starting with the player taking the first turn, players alternate placing sensor blips on the battlefield, one at a time, until six have been placed. You can use tokens or counters to represent each sensor blip. Sensor blips must be placed within 6" of the centre of the battlefield and more than 1" from any other sensor blip.

At the start of each battle round after the first, players roll off for each sensor blip on the battlefield one at a time. The winner of each roll-off can move that sensor blip a number of inches equal to their dice result rolled during the roll-off.

If a sensor blip ends a move within 6" of a player's unit, or a player moves a unit that ends its move within 6" of a sensor blip, the sensor blip is revealed. Set up a Genestealer Infestation unit containing 2D6 models, using the Genestealer Infestation datasheet below. Set the unit up wholly within 3" of the sensor blip before removing the blip. The player who last moved that sensor blip chooses where to place the Genestealer Infestation unit.

Genestealer Infestation units are treated as enemy units by all players and Genestealer Infestation units treat all units except other Genestealer Infestation units as enemy units. Once the Genestealer Infestation unit has been set up, the unit immediately makes a charge move towards the closest enemy unit. Resolve the charge sequence as normal (including Overwatch).

Burst from the Shadows: At the end of each battle round, any Genestealer Infestation units on the battlefield have a turn that consists of only a Movement phase and a Charge phase. In their Movement phase, each Genestealer Infestation unit will move and Advance as far as possible towards the closest enemy unit. If they are within 12" of any enemy unit in their Charge phase they will attempt to charge the closest unit.

Predatory Instincts: In each Fight phase, each Genestealer Infestation model will pile in towards the closest enemy model and target the closest enemy unit with all of its attacks. If two units are equally close, randomly pick one to be their target. Genestealer Infestation units fight before all other units (including those that have charged in that turn). Players pick Genestealer Infestation units that are eligible to fight, one at a time, starting with the player whose turn is taking place. If any sequencing issues arise, the players roll-off and the winner decides the order in which the rules in question are resolved.

4 POWER

GENESTEALER INFESTATION

NAME	M	WS	BS	S	T	W	A	Ld	Sv
Genestealer	8"	3+	4+	4	4	1	3	9	5+

This unit contains 2D6 Genestealers (see above). Each model is armed with rending claws.

WEAPON	RANGE	TYPE	S	AP	D	ABILITIES
Rending claws	Melee	Melee	User	-1	1	Each time you make a wound roll of 6+ for this weapon, that hit is resolved with an AP of -4.

ABILITIES	**Flurry of Claws:** Genestealers have 4 Attacks instead of 3 whilst their unit has 10 or more models.	**Swift and Deadly:** Genestealers can charge even if they Advanced during their turn.
	Lightning Reflexes: Genestealers have a 5+ invulnerable save.	
FACTION KEYWORDS	**GENESTEALER INFESTATION**	
KEYWORDS	**INFANTRY, GENESTEALER INFESTATION**	

WAR ZONE RULES

From the verdant bio-domes of Mortwald to the esoteric factory systems of Megaborealis, from the palatial courtyards of Hyperia to the hostile tundra of the Wastes, the landscapes and war zones of Vigilus were exotic and varied. This section provides rules to help bring these locations to life on the tabletop.

When the War of Beasts came to Vigilus, desperate battles erupted all across its myriad landscapes. This section provides rules for how to populate a battlefield with terrain features so as to best represent the different war zones on the planet. It also offers suggestions on the types of missions and battlezones that work particularly well with these terrain features, and some ideas for generating your own narrative play games.

These rules are designed to be totally flexible; you can choose to use as many or as few as you wish in your games. As well as representing the various war zones on Vigilus, these rules can be used to represent any of the varied battlescapes of the Dark Imperium. You can either select a particular set to represent part of the story told in this book, or you can use them to reflect a setting of your own invention or from another story.

SCENERY TABLES

Each war zone presented here has its own scenery table. To use a scenery table, roll a D6 for each 2′ by 2′ section of the battlefield and consult the table to see which

terrain features should be set up. It is a good idea to alternate setting up each section with your opponent (or opponents). If you do not have suitable terrain features, you can either re-roll the dice until you find a result that matches your scenery collection or adjust the table to reflect your collection.

PERIMETER BATTLES

Many of the most cataclysmic battles fought on Vigilus took place on the outskirts of the besieged hivesprawls. To represent this, first divide the battlefield into two areas, one representing the outskirts of a hivesprawl and the other representing the wasteland beyond. Then use the war zone rules for your chosen hivesprawl for the outskirts, and the war zone rules for the Wastes for the wasteland. This strategy works especially well for large games of Apocalypse.

HYPERIA HIVESPRAWL

Hyperia Hivesprawl was the historic seat of power on Vigilus, home to many of the world's noble families. The clustered streets of the inner gothic quarters were home to towering Basilicanums and Sanctums, their fascias resplendent with embellishments dedicated to the Emperor.

You can play any battle you like using this set of rules, with any army in your collection. Below we suggest missions and battlezones from this book that work especially well with these rules. We have also included some further ideas – some of which are drawn from the events depicted in this book – to spark your imagination; you can use any of these as the basis for your games, or as inspiration for your own narratives.

MISSIONS AND BATTLEZONES

- Echoes of War: The Angels of Death Descend (pg 144)
- Echoes of War: Carnage in the Spires (pg 152)
- Crucible of War: Storm the Lines (pg 134)
- Battlezone: Spirescape (pg 158)

NARRATIVE IDEAS

- *A drop force of Tempestus Scions gets caught up in a running firefight with a cluster of Genestealer Acolytes amid the city streets.*
- *A strike force of Aeldari, accompanied by ghostly wraithbone constructs, clashes with the Adeptus Astartes guarding the governing palace.*
- *A small group of snipers concealed in the city heights pick off an invading army, one by one.*
- *An invading force must locate a vital artefact, hidden in a storage crate, and then return to the skyport for extraction before being lifted to safety.*

OPTIONAL RULE

If both players agree, the following optional rule can be used in any areas of the battlefield designated a Central Square (see right):

Enemy Snipers

This sector has become a hunting ground for enemy snipers who prey on any infantry foolish enough to step into the open.

Each time a unit finishes a move in this section of the battlefield, roll a D6. On a 6+ that unit suffers 1 mortal wound.

HYPERIA HIVESPRAWL SCENERY TABLE

D6	RESULT
1	**Central Square:** *A lone statue stands sentinel in this eerily quiet square.* This 2' square is barren save a lone Honoured Imperium statue that stands defiantly in the centre. **Optional Rule – Enemy Snipers:** This section of the battlefield is subject to the Enemy Snipers optional rule (see left).
2	**Ruined Thoroughfare:** *Once a crucial highway into the centre of the hive, scattered debris now litters this thoroughfare.* This 2' square contains 3 Sector Imperialis Ruins. A large street runs through the middle towards the centre of the battlefield.
3	**Munitorum Macro-yard:** *A forgotten storage facility resides in this district.* This 2' square is covered in Munitorum Armoured Containers.
4	**Bastion Shield Generator:** *Massive and imposing, the Bastion shield generator thrums with psychic energy.* This 2' square is dominated by a Void Shield Generator in its centre, with a few Sector Mechanicus buildings around it.
5	**Skyport:** *Spacecraft hastily depart from this skyport as battle erupts on all sides.* This 2' square has a Skyshield Landing Pad in its centre and some scattered Munitorum Armoured Containers and Galvanic Servohaulers around the edges.
6	**Gothic Quarter:** *Ornate buildings loom above crowded streets in this central district.* This 2' square contains up to 3 Sector Imperialis Basilicanums or Sector Imperialis Sanctums. If possible, the buildings should be arranged to create narrow streets no wider than 7".

MEGABOREALIS

Megaborealis was the domain of the Adeptus Mechanicus. Few aesthetic concessions were made to conceal the raw industrial workings of the hivesprawl's heart, and even fewer safety mechanisms were put in place to protect the populace from the hazardous materials that tended to leak out of exposed pipes and relays.

You can play any battle you like using this set of rules, with any army in your collection. Below we suggest missions and battlezones from this book that work especially well with these rules. We have also included some further ideas – some of which are drawn from the events depicted in this book – to spark your imagination; you can use any of these as the basis for your games, or as inspiration for your own narratives.

MISSIONS AND BATTLEZONES

- Echoes of War: The Delta Aflame (pg 142)
- Crucible of War: Data Recovery (pg 140)
- Battlezone: Warquake (pg 156)

NARRATIVE IDEAS

- *A macroclade of Skitarii lures their fleshy opponents into an area flooded with radiation, the better to finish them off quickly.*
- *Two entrenched forces battle each other over a network of plasma conduits, both knowing that just one stray shot could cause the volatile plasma inside to erupt, with deadly consequences.*
- *Massive seismic upheaval is making this hivesprawl a dangerous place to battle; at any moment the huge manufactorums may come crashing down.*

OPTIONAL RULE

If both players agree, the following optional rule can be used in any areas of the battlefield designated a Polluted Rad-zone (see right):

Hazardous Radiation

Sensor arrays flicker and rad counters click frantically. This district is a forsaken place that poisons all living creatures that dare set foot here.

At the start of each battle round after the first, roll a D6 for each unit in this battlefield section. On a 4+ that unit suffers 1 mortal wound. **Vehicles** and **Adeptus Mechanicus** units are not affected by this rule.

D6	RESULT
1	**Polluted Rad-zone:** *Manufactorums spill hazardous waste into this district.* This 2' square contains scattered Ryza-Pattern Ruins. **Optional Rule – Hazardous Radiation:** This section of the battlefield is subject to the Hazardous Radiation optional rule (see left).
2	**Plasma Relay Pipeline:** *The fluorescent glow of this plasma relay network shines bright even in the dark of night.* This 2' square has Thermic Plasma Conduits running through it.
3	**Ferratonic Incinerator:** *A thick plume of smoke writhes skyward from this Ferratonic Incinerator.* This 2' square has a Ferratonic Incinerator or Furnace in its centre, accompanied by 2 Galvanic Servohaulers.
4	**Haemotrope Reactor:** *This district is dominated by a thrumming energy reactor.* This 2' square has a Haemotrope Reactor in its centre, with Thermic Plasma Conduits running from it.
5	**Galvanic Magnavent:** *Black smoke belches forth from an array of chimneys in this sector.* This 2' square has a Galvanic Magnavent in its centre and 2 Alchomite Stacks around it.
6	**Hive Manufactorum:** *This district is an industrialised centre of activity crucial to the war effort.* This 2' square is populated with any 3 large Sector Mechanicus terrain pieces. Walkways run between them.

MEGABOREALIS SCENERY TABLE

THE WASTES

Swirling dust storms swept across the rad-wastes and ash dunes of the Vigilus wastelands. These were inhospitable places, but the vital supply lines that crossed them to deliver food, water and munitions to the hivesprawls were hotly contested.

You can play any battle you like using this set of rules, with any army in your collection. Below we suggest missions and battlezones from this book that work especially well with these rules. We have also included some further ideas – some of which are drawn from the events depicted in this book – to spark your imagination; you can use any of these as the basis for your games, or as inspiration for your own narratives.

MISSIONS AND BATTLEZONES

- Echoes of War: Forlorn Charge (pg 146)
- Crucible of War: Convoy (pg 130)
- Crucible of War: Running Battle (pg 138)
- Battlezone: Wasteland Dust Storm (pg 154)

NARRATIVE IDEAS

- An Astra Militarum armoured convoy must cross the desert wastes to deliver their vital cargo to the hivesprawls. However, a rag-tag band of Speed Freeks intends to have some fun with them first.
- Deciding to take the fight to the enemy, a brave group of defenders sallies forth from the safety of their hivesprawl to meet an invading foe in open terrain.
- An aerial battle is disrupted by a volatile dust storm passing through the area.
- A small group of warriors has got separated from the main force. Wandering lost through the desert, they come upon a ramshackle Ork scrap-fortress. Outnumbered and outgunned, can they hold out in the dunes until their comrades arrive?

D6	RESULT
THE WASTES SCENERY TABLE	
1-2	**Dust Dunes:** *A bleak and parched landscape stretches on to the horizon.* This 2' square is empty.
3-4	**Ruined Settlement:** *The ruins here are layered with thick mounds of dust. This settlement has stood ruined for centuries.* This 2' square contains 4 Sector Imperialis Ruins.
5	**Plasma Relay Pipeline:** *Through the swirling dust storms can be seen the faint blue glow of an active plasma pipeline.* This 2' square has Thermic Plasma Conduits running through it.
6	**Ruined Adeptus Mechanicus Outpost:** *This research lab shows recent signs of battle damage and now lies abandoned in the dunes.* This 2' square contains scattered Ryza-Pattern Ruins.

OTECK HIVESPRAWL

The Adeptus Arbites ruled with an iron fist over the press-ganged labourers that lived in the narrow confines of Oteck Hivesprawl's macro-districts. These cramped regions proved to be fertile breeding grounds for the Thirsting Wyrm cultists, who strove to capture the hivesprawl's vital water sources.

You can play any battle you like using this set of rules, with any army in your collection. Below we suggest missions and battlezones from this book that work especially well with these rules. We have also included some further ideas – some of which are drawn from the events depicted in this book – to spark your imagination; you can use any of these as the basis for your games, or as inspiration for your own narratives.

MISSIONS AND BATTLEZONES

- Crucible of War: Hold Your Gains (pg 132)
- Crucible of War: Extraction (pg 136)
- Battlezone: Warquake (pg 156)
- Battlezone: Genestealer Infestation (pg 159)

NARRATIVE IDEAS

- *A kill team of Space Wolves are on the trail of a brood of Genestealer Cultists, but their prey has left a series of booby traps to ensnare them.*
- *An insidious force is attempting to poison the reservoir, a vital water source for the planet. The defenders must drive them off before they are able to complete their task.*
- *A group of rebels seeks to steal water from the reservoir, but it is heavily guarded. They must take out the guards without raising the alarm in order to get away with their stash.*

OPTIONAL RULE

If both players agree, the following optional rule can be used in any areas of the battlefield designated a Demolished Hab-zone (see right):

Artillery Suppression

Nearby artillery has levelled this sector of the hivesprawl and continues to rain down into the ruined streets. Although wildly inaccurate, it makes moving through the area a hazardous undertaking.

Each time a unit in this section of the battlefield is chosen to move in the Movement phase, roll a D6. On a 1, that unit suffers D3 mortal wounds. On a 2 or 3, halve the Move characteristic of all models in that unit until the end of the phase. On a 4+, the unit can move as normal.

OTECK HIVESPRAWL SCENERY TABLE

D6	RESULT
1	**Demolished Hab-zone:** *This district has almost been completely levelled by artillery fire.* This 2' square contains 2 Sector Imperialis Ruins. **Optional Rule – Artillery Suppression:** This section of the battlefield is subject to the Artillery Suppression optional rule (see left).
2	**Ruined Hab-zone:** *Once home to thousands, this hab-zone now houses nothing but bones.* This 2' square contains 6 Sector Imperialis Ruins.
3	**Ruined Administratum:** *This Administratum building has been largely demolished.* This 2' square contains a Sector Imperialis Administratum in its centre and 2 Sector Imperialis Ruins.
4	**Ruined Basilicanum:** *Fierce fire fights in this district have left its Basilicanum destroyed.* This 2' square contains a Sector Imperialis Basilicanum in its centre and 2 Sector Imperialis Ruins.
5	**Adeptus Arbites Precinct:** *Once a symbol of oppression and control, this precinct now stands empty and silent.* This 2' square contains an Imperial Bastion and 2 Sector Imperialis Ruins.
6	**Reservoir Perimeter:** *This district guards the perimeter of a great reservoir that is heavily fortified.* This 2' square contains a Wall of Martyrs Defence Line and a Wall of Martyrs Firestorm Redoubt that run along a battlefield edge. If this 2' square is not adjacent to any battlefield edges, re-roll this result.

MORTWALD

Mortwald's landscapes were formed of a juxtaposition of verdant hyperflora forests, utopian bio-domes and miles of trenchworks and fortified defence lines. The people of Mortwald would sooner put their faith in a wall of armour than the esoteric technology of the Bastion-class force fields.

You can play any battle you like using this set of rules, with any army in your collection. Below we suggest missions and battlezones from this book that work especially well with these rules. We have also included some further ideas – some of which are drawn from the events depicted in this book – to spark your imagination; you can use any of these as the basis for your games, or as inspiration for your own narratives.

MISSIONS AND BATTLEZONES

- Crucible of War: Hold Your Gains (pg 132)
- Crucible of War: Convoy (pg 130)
- Crucible of War: Storm the Lines (pg 134)
- Battlezone: Warquake (pg 156)

NARRATIVE IDEAS

- *A platoon of Astra Militarum are ordered to stand and defend a stockpile of resources against an invading force determined to annihilate them.*
- *An invading force crashes against the fortified defence line around this hivesprawl, leading to a battle of attrition against the dug-in forces.*
- *A raiding party of Drukhari has concealed itself amongst the dense forest, waiting to launch their ambush on the first force to blunder into their sights.*

OPTIONAL RULE

If both players agree, the following optional rule can be used in any areas of the battlefield designated as Exotic Hyperflora (see right):

Dangerous Flora

This district of Mortwald is home to exotic off-world flora that prey upon the unwary.

Roll a D6 each time an **INFANTRY** unit finishes a move wholly within this battlefield section. On a 1, that unit suffers 1 mortal wound.

MORTWALD SCENERY TABLE	
D6	**RESULT**
1	**Sparse Hyperflora:** *This bio-dome has seen heavy fighting and much of its flora has been destroyed.* This 2' square contains 1 Citadel Wood.
2	**Dense Hyperflora:** *The crop-forests are growing wild in this region, as no-one is left to harvest them.* This 2' square contains 3 Citadel Woods.
3	**Exotic Hyperflora:** *Off-world plants and mutated flora have infiltrated this bio-dome.* This 2' square contains 3 pieces of Barbed Venomgorse and 5 Shardwrack Spines. **Optional Rule – Dangerous Flora:** This section of the battlefield is subject to the Dangerous Flora optional rule (see left).
4	**Supply Stockpile:** *Containers of rations and munitions are stored in this district.* This 2' square contains 3 Munitorum Armoured Containers.
5	**Fortified Defence Line:** *Trenches and gun emplacements line the perimeter of Mortwald.* This 2' square contains a Wall of Martyrs Defence Line and a Wall of Martyrs Firestorm Redoubt.
6	**Bastion Emplacement:** *This impressive redoubt stands strong against incursions.* This 2' square contains D3 Imperial Bastions with Aegis Defence Lines running between them.

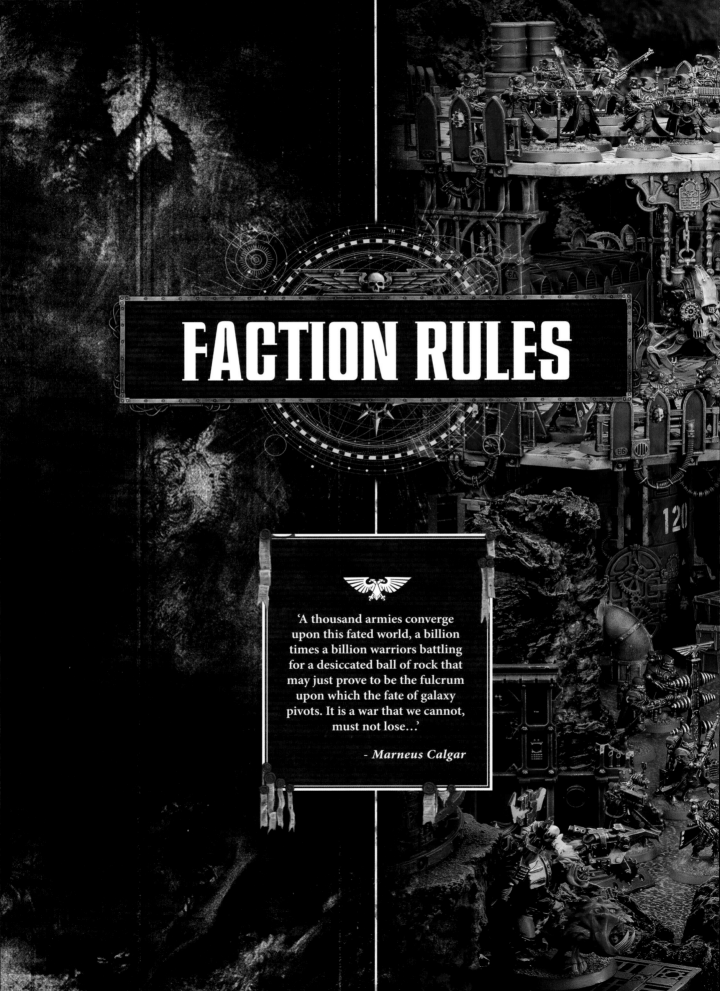

FACTION RULES

'A thousand armies converge upon this fated world, a billion times a billion warriors battling for a desiccated ball of rock that may just prove to be the fulcrum upon which the fate of galaxy pivots. It is a war that we cannot, must not lose…'

- Marneus Calgar

SPECIALIST DETACHMENTS

From the Kults of Speed that raced out of the Ork Scrap Cities when the War of Beasts first dawned, to the Victrix Honour Guard that accompanied Marneus Calgar when he made planetfall, the war on Vigilus saw many specialist fighting formations take to the battlefield. Presented here are rules to use these Specialist Detachments in all of your games of Warhammer 40,000.

SPECIALIST DETACHMENTS

This section introduces Specialist Detachments for a dozen different factions. These rules portray the many unique fighting styles of the different armies of the 41st Millennium. This section also includes new datasheets for Marneus Calgar in the Armour of Heraclus, the Victrix Honour Guard and Haarken Worldclaimer, Herald of the Apocalypse.

If your army is Battle-forged, you have access to the Specialist Detachment

Stratagems presented in this section. A Specialist Detachment Stratagem is a unique type of Stratagem used when choosing your army. This Stratagem will assign a <SPECIALIST DETACHMENT> keyword to certain units in that Detachment and will unlock Warlord Traits, Relics, Stratagems and psychic powers that those units can take.

Any Detachment from your army (except for Auxiliary Support Detachments) can be upgraded to a Specialist Detachment by using an appropriate Specialist Detachment Stratagem. A Detachment from your army can only be upgraded to a Specialist Detachment once and thus cannot have multiple Specialist Detachment Stratagems applied to it, even if they affect different units in the Detachment.

WARLORD TRAITS

If your Warlord is a **CHARACTER** and has the relevant **<SPECIALIST DETACHMENT>** keyword, you can give them a Warlord Trait from the appropriate section in this book instead of one from the *Warhammer 40,000* rulebook or a codex. Named characters such as Sammael have associated Warlord Traits in their codex and must still take that Warlord Trait if they are your Warlord.

In addition, if your army is Battle-forged, you can use the Stratagem below:

1CP

FIELD COMMANDER
Stratagem
This warrior's specialist expertise is second to none and in battle they lead those under their command with sophisticated tactics.

Use this Stratagem before the battle if you used any Specialist Detachment Stratagems when choosing your army. Choose one **CHARACTER** from your army that has gained a keyword from a Specialist Detachment Stratagem that is not your Warlord and is not a named character. You can give that character the Warlord Trait of the Specialist Detachment they are part of (note that this character is only regarded as your Warlord for the purpose of that Warlord Trait). This Stratagem can be used once for each Specialist Detachment Stratagem you have used (spend 1CP each time you use it). No two characters in your army can have the same Warlord Trait.

RELICS

Before the battle you may give a relic from this section to a **CHARACTER** from your army with the relevant **<SPECIALIST DETACHMENT>** keyword instead of a relic from a codex or *Chapter Approved*. Named characters such as Ghazghkull Thraka cannot be given relics.

Note that some relics replace one of the character's existing weapons. Where this is the case, if you are playing a matched play game or are otherwise using points values, you must still pay the cost of the weapon that is being replaced. Write down any relics your characters have on your army roster.

PSYCHIC POWERS

If you have any **PSYKERS** in your army with the relevant **<SPECIALIST DETACHMENT>** keyword, before the battle you can choose to replace one of their psychic powers with a psychic power from the appropriate section of this book (you cannot choose to replace the *Smite* psychic power).

For example, a **SPACE WOLVES** *Detachment can be upgraded to a Stalker Pack Specialist Detachment using the Specialist Detachment Stratagem found on page 183. Doing so gives the* **BATTLE LEADERS**, **BLOOD CLAWS** *and* **REIVERS** *in that Detachment the* **STALKER PACK** *keyword.*

This then allows you to give a **STALKER PACK** **CHARACTER** *the Saga of the Savage Warlord Trait and to equip a* **STALKER PACK** **CHARACTER** *with the Ironfang of Ammagrimgul relic. You can also use Command Points to use the Blood Scent and Pack Killers Stratagems in your games.*

MARNEUS CALGAR

THE LORD MACRAGGE, CHAPTER MASTER OF THE ULTRAMARINES

The Ultramarines Chapter has a long history of producing some of the Imperium's greatest heroes. Even amongst such august company, Marneus Calgar stands tall, for few figures in the last ten thousand years have commanded as much respect, and few have won so many crucial victories in the Emperor's name.

Marneus Augustus Calgar is not only a consummate warrior, but also a highly talented strategist. He is master of Ultramar, a vast swathe of space on the embattled Eastern Fringe. There, his wisdom is law, but his decisions also set the precedent for the Ultramarines and the hundreds of successor Chapters that fight for the Imperium across the galaxy. Such immense responsibility has long weighed heavily upon Calgar – though not nearly as heavily as that moment when his duty was effectively taken away.

The return of the legendary Primarch, Roboute Guilliman, had a galvanising effect on the warriors of Ultramar, and Calgar most of all. Yet the Primarch achieved in a few years more than Calgar had done in a century. Given that Guilliman is effectively a demigod, it is small wonder that Calgar's joy at his gene-sire's return was tempered by feelings of his own

irrelevancy as Guilliman first took charge of Ultramar, and then became Lord Commander of the Imperium entire.

When the Adeptus Astartes was bolstered by a great influx of Guilliman's Primaris Marines, the traditional Space Marines also feared obsolescence. It was Calgar that integrated the Space Marine Chapters with the newly assigned brethren of the Primaris Marines, both physically and spiritually.

He was the first to undergo the extremely risky surgery required to transform a traditional Space Marine into a Primaris Marine, and he died during the procedure – though after agonising minutes he, like Guilliman, was returned to life. That noble sacrifice, that martyrdom in the name of progress, showed a new way for the Space Marines of the future. Calgar donned the Armour of Heraclus, a revolutionary adaptation of the iconic Armour of Antilochus.

He launched the counter-invasion of the xenos-tainted planet of Vigilus with the veteran warriors Lethro Ados and Nemus Adranus – two of his most trusted aides from the Victrix Guard – always at his side. Already hand-picked by the Primarch to fight amongst the rarefied ranks of Macragge's finest, these heroes had the further honour of guarding the Chapter Master with their lives.

MARNEUS CALGAR
IN ARMOUR OF HERACLUS

POWER 11

NAME	M	WS	BS	S	T	W	A	Ld	Sv
Marneus Calgar in Armour of Heraclus	6"	2+	2+	4	5	8	6	9	2+

Marneus Calgar in Armour of Heraclus is a single model armed with the Gauntlets of Ultramar. Only one **MARNEUS CALGAR** may be included in your army.

WEAPON	RANGE	TYPE	S	AP	D	ABILITIES
Gauntlets of Ultramar (shooting)	24"	Rapid Fire 2	4	-1	2	-
Gauntlets of Ultramar (melee)	Melee	Melee	x2	-3	D3	-

ABILITIES	
And They Shall Know No Fear: You can re-roll failed Morale tests for this unit. **Armour of Heraclus:** Marneus Calgar has a 4+ invulnerable save. In addition, all damage suffered by Marneus Calgar is halved (rounding up). **Chapter Master:** You can re-roll failed hit rolls for friendly **ULTRAMARINES** units within 6" of Marneus Calgar.	**Master Tactician:** If your army is Battle-forged, you receive an additional 2 Command Points if Marneus Calgar is your Warlord.

FACTION KEYWORDS	IMPERIUM, ADEPTUS ASTARTES, ULTRAMARINES
KEYWORDS	CHARACTER, INFANTRY, MK X GRAVIS, PRIMARIS, CHAPTER MASTER, MARNEUS CALGAR

VICTRIX HONOUR GUARD

POWER 3

NAME	M	WS	BS	S	T	W	A	Ld	Sv
Victrix Honour Guard	6"	3+	3+	4	4	3	4	9	2+

This unit contains 2 Victrix Honour Guard. Each model is armed with a power sword, storm shield, frag grenades and krak grenades.

WEAPON	RANGE	TYPE	S	AP	D	ABILITIES
Power sword	Melee	Melee	User	-3	1	-
Frag grenade	6"	Grenade D6	3	0	1	-
Krak grenade	6"	Grenade 1	6	-1	D3	-

ABILITIES	
And They Shall Know No Fear: You can re-roll failed Morale tests for this unit. **Honour Guard of Macragge:** Roll a D6 each time a friendly **ULTRAMARINES CHARACTER** loses a wound whilst they are within 3" of this unit; on a 2+ a model from this unit can intercept that hit – that **ULTRAMARINES CHARACTER** does not lose a wound but this unit suffers a mortal wound. **Heroes of Ultramar:** This unit can perform a Heroic Intervention as if they were a **CHARACTER**.	**Storm Shield:** A model armed with a storm shield has a 3+ invulnerable save. **Calgar's Honour Guard:** If your army is Battle-forged, this unit does not take up slots in a Detachment that includes **MARNEUS CALGAR.**

FACTION KEYWORDS	IMPERIUM, ADEPTUS ASTARTES, ULTRAMARINES
KEYWORDS	INFANTRY, PRIMARIS, VICTRIX HONOUR GUARD

POINTS VALUES		
UNIT	MODELS PER UNIT	POINTS PER MODEL
Marneus Calgar	1	200*
Victrix Honour Guard	2	26**
*Includes wargear		
**Does not include wargear		

WARGEAR	
ITEM	POINTS PER ITEM
Frag grenades	0
Krak grenades	0
Power sword	4
Storm shield	5

HAARKEN WORLDCLAIMER

HERALD OF THE APOCALYPSE, PROCLAMATOR OF ABADDON'S REIGN

Before every doom, there is a portent, before every apocalypse a sign. Haarken Worldclaimer is that dark omen given form, and the otherworldly destruction he heralds is the coming of the Warmaster himself – Abaddon the Despoiler, Lord of the Black Legion.

Haarken Worldclaimer takes a heinous joy in his role as the mouthpiece of Abaddon, for it is he that proclaims the death of worlds. He does so not with some quotidian threat or hollow boast, but by driving a spear of terror and confusion deep into the heart of citizen and soldier alike. In such a fashion, he prepares the way for the coming of the Black Legion, his Raptor hosts descending on tongues of flame to bring panic and despair with each murderous onslaught.

Long ago, the Traitor Legions learned the value of fear. A planet undermined by doubt – or better yet, paralysed by it – is one already half-conquered. Worldclaimer is a scholar and collector of dark knowledge as well as a leader of men, and he knows the power of words well chosen. He has studied the Grimoire Nostromo, that vilest of treatises written in kingsblood by the Primarch Curze. He has unearthed the Clotted Scrolls,

learning well of the threats growled by Angron before he was consumed by those berzerker rages that gave his legion their reputation as Eaters of Worlds. He has even delved into the dread Book of Magnus, though it cost him a good part of his sanity to do so. In his studies, he has learned much. When he delivers his fell message – broadcast not only from his own laud hailer array but the vox-grilles and cankerous throats of a thousand acolytes – the raw and gloating hatred that drips from each syllable can shatter cohesion, cause mass surrenders, and even drive men to suicide.

Though many heralds would consider their duty done upon their lord's arrival, Haarken Worldclaimer revels in bringing destruction in person as well as from afar. His Daemon-touched relic, the Helspear, has tasted the blood of monarchs, xenos tyrants and even Chaos lords over his long service as herald to the

Despoiler, and each demoralising kill invigorates him, driving him to further acts of bloodshed. But it is not only the breasts of men and aliens into which this spear is plunged. It has become a symbolic act for Haarken, upon making planetfall, to drive his spear deep into the world's crust and roar out the fell promise that within eighty days and eighty nights, it will fall. He has yet to be proved false.

HAARKEN WORLDCLAIMER

6 POWER

NAME	M	WS	BS	S	T	W	A	Ld	Sv
Haarken Worldclaimer	12"	2+	2+	4	4	5	5	9	3+

Haarken Worldclaimer is a single model armed with the Helspear and a lightning claw. Only one **HAARKEN WORLDCLAIMER** may be included in your army.

WEAPON	RANGE	TYPE	S	AP	D	ABILITIES
Helspear	12"	Assault 1	+1	-3	D3	-
Lightning claw	Melee	Melee	User	-2	1	You can re-roll failed wound rolls for attacks made with this weapon. If a model is armed with two lightning claws, each time it fights it can make 1 additional attack with them.

ABILITIES	
Death to the False Emperor (see *Codex: Chaos Space Marines*) **Lord of the Raptors:** You can re-roll hit rolls for attacks made with melee weapons used by friendly **RAPTOR** units within 6" of this model. **Sigil of Corruption:** This model has a 4+ invulnerable save. **Herald of the Apocalypse:** Enemy units within 18" of this model must subtract 1 from their Leadership characteristic.	**Raptor Strike:** During deployment, you can set up this model in low orbit instead of placing it on the battlefield. At the end of any of your Movement phases, this model can use a Raptor strike to arrive on the battlefield – set it up anywhere on the battlefield that is more than 9" from any enemy models. **Head-claimer:** Each time an enemy **CHARACTER** is slain by an attack made by this model, add 1 to this model's Attacks characteristic.

FACTION KEYWORDS	CHAOS, HERETIC ASTARTES, BLACK LEGION
KEYWORDS	CHARACTER, INFANTRY, RAPTOR, JUMP PACK, FLY, HAARKEN WORLDCLAIMER

POINTS VALUES

UNIT	MODELS PER UNIT	POINTS PER MODEL (Including wargear)
Haarken Worldclaimer	1	115

WARLORD TRAIT

If Haarken Worldclaimer is your Warlord, he must be given the Lord of Terror Warlord Trait (see *Codex: Chaos Space Marines*).

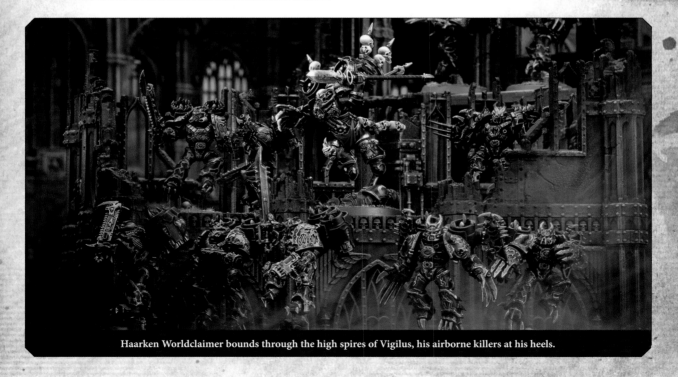

Haarken Worldclaimer bounds through the high spires of Vigilus, his airborne killers at his heels.

INDOMITUS CRUSADERS

Through the actions of brave and determined warriors, the Indomitus Crusade changed the face of the galaxy in the wake of the Great Rift. It lasted over a century, and many of the Primaris Marines that typified its forces became learned veterans of the battlefield over that time.

SPECIALIST DETACHMENT

If your army is Battle-forged, you can use the Specialist Detachment Stratagem below:

INDOMITUS CRUSADERS

1CP

Specialist Detachment Stratagem

In the wake of the Great Rift, the Indomitus Crusade battled to retake Imperial worlds plagued by the forces of Chaos.

Use this Stratagem when choosing your army. Pick a Space Marines Detachment from your army to be an Indomitus Crusaders Specialist Detachment. **Primaris Captains**, **Primaris Lieutenants**, **Primaris Ancients**, **Intercessor Squads** and **Inceptor Squads** in that Detachment gain the **Indomitus Crusader** keyword.

WARLORD TRAIT

If an **Indomitus Crusader Character** is your Warlord, you can give them the following Warlord Trait.

GREY SHIELD

During the Indomitus Crusade, this battle-brother served in a unit of Grey Shields. These strike forces were comprised of Space Marines from a range of different Chapters, allowing for a multitude of combat styles to be galvanised as one. Now, leading his own warriors into battle, this warlord is able to employ versatile strategies, switching tactics even in the thick of battle.

Once per battle, at the start of your Movement phase, if your Warlord is on the battlefield, you can choose for **Indomitus Crusader** units in the same Detachment as your Warlord to gain an additional Chapter Tactic until the start of your next turn. Pick the additional Chapter Tactic from the following: Codex Discipline, Lightning Assault, Siege Masters, Righteous Zeal, Master Artisans, Shadow Masters, The Flesh is Weak (see *Codex: Space Marines*).

Until the start of your next turn, friendly **Indomitus Crusaders** gain the benefit of that Chapter Tactic in addition to any others they already have. They are considered to have the keyword of the Chapter that Chapter Tactic belongs to for the purposes of resolving that Chapter Tactic.

RELICS OF THE INDOMITUS CRUSADE

If your army includes any Indomitus Crusaders Specialist Detachments, you can give one of the following relics to an **Indomitus Crusader Character** from your army.

RELIQUARY OF GATHALAMOR

By the time the Indomitus Crusade reached the world of Gathalamor, the Daemon hordes had already carved a bloody path across much of the planet. One of the last redoubts of the Imperium was a network of reinforced defences held valiantly by a cadre of Sisters of Silence. They were led by the stoic Knight-Centura, Ordela Grendoth, whose powerful null-field was anathema to the warp creatures that assailed the world. Gathalamor was liberated by Guilliman, but Grendoth was slain in the climactic battle. Afterwards, her bones were placed inside a reliquary which now possesses a fraction of her power.

Enemy **Psykers** must subtract 1 from Psychic tests made within 18" of the bearer. In addition, if the psychic power is not successfully manifested, roll a D6. On a 4+ the **Psyker** that attempted to manifest that psychic power suffers D3 mortal wounds.

STANDARD OF THE ULTIMA FOUNDING

This banner stood defiant when a daemonic incursion besieged Terra at the birth of the Noctis Aeterna and threatened to crush the Indomitus Crusade even before it had begun. Now, it has been planted into the soil of a hundred worlds, and inspires any veteran of the Indomitus Crusade to fight harder to rid the galaxy of the enemies of Mankind.

Primaris Ancient only. Once per battle, at the start of your Movement phase, the bearer can choose to plant this banner. If they do so, until the bearer next makes a move, friendly **Indomitus Crusader Infantry** models can re-roll hit rolls of 1 and wound rolls of 1 whilst they are within 6" of the bearer.

STRATAGEMS

If your army includes any Indomitus Crusaders Specialist Detachments, you can use Command Points (CPs) to use the following Stratagems:

LIBERATORS
1CP

Space Marines Stratagem

Liberators of countless systems and planets, vanquishers of the heretical, the daemonic and the degenerate, these warriors are a blade honed in the fires of a hundred battles.

Use this Stratagem at the start of the Fight phase. Pick an **INDOMITUS CRUSADER** unit from your army. Until the start of your next turn, each time you roll an unmodified hit roll of 6 for an attack made by a model in this unit, that attacks inflicts 2 hits on the target instead of 1.

VETERAN INTERCESSORS
1CP

Space Marines Stratagem

This squad has been noted for their exemplary service across a dozen war zones.

Use this Stratagem before the battle begins. Pick an **INDOMITUS CRUSADER INTERCESSOR SQUAD** unit from your army to be Veteran Intercessors. That unit gains the **VETERAN** keyword for the duration of the battle. In addition, add 1 to the Attacks and Leadership characteristics of that unit for the duration of the battle.

TARGET SIGHTED
1CP

Space Marines Stratagem

With pinpoint accuracy, veteran Intercessors pick out key enemy leaders, striking eye-sockets, armour joints and other weak spots with deadly volleys of fire.

Use this Stratagem at the start of your Shooting phase. Pick a **VETERAN INTERCESSORS** unit from your army. Until the end of the phase, stalker bolt rifles the models in that unit are armed with gain the following ability: 'This weapon can target a **CHARACTER** even if it is not the closest enemy unit. If you roll a wound roll of 6+ for this weapon, it inflicts a mortal wound in addition to its normal damage'.

BOLT STORM
1CP

Space Marines Stratagem

A hailstorm of bolter fire is unleashed at point-blank range. Under the sheer volume of fire, none can escape.

Use this Stratagem at the start of your Shooting phase. Pick a **VETERAN INTERCESSORS** unit from your army. Until the end of the phase, auto bolt rifles the models in that unit are armed with gain the following ability: 'When this weapon targets an enemy unit within half range, it automatically hits its target'.

RAPID FIRE
1CP

Space Marines Stratagem

The superhuman reflexes of these veteran warriors produce a devastating rate of fire.

Use this Stratagem at the start of your Shooting phase. Pick a **VETERAN INTERCESSORS** unit from your army. Until the end of the phase, bolt rifles the models in that unit are armed with change their type to Rapid Fire 2.

ULTRAMARINES VICTRIX GUARD

The Victrix Guard were hand-picked by Roboute Guilliman from the Ultramarines 1st Company to accompany him on his Indomitus Crusade. Across the many battlefields of Vigilus, elements of this veteran formation fought tirelessly at Calgar's side to earn a legacy of their own.

SPECIALIST DETACHMENT

If your army is Battle-forged, you can use the Specialist Detachment Stratagem below:

1CP — VICTRIX GUARD
Specialist Detachment Stratagem

The Victrix Guard are veteran warriors with countless centuries of combat experience between them.

Use this Stratagem when choosing your army. Pick an **ULTRAMARINES** Detachment from your army to be a Victrix Guard Specialist Detachment. **CAPTAINS, ANCIENTS, HONOUR GUARD, VICTRIX HONOUR GUARD, VANGUARD VETERAN SQUADS** and **STERNGUARD VETERAN SQUADS** in that Detachment gain the **VICTRIX GUARD** keyword.

WARLORD TRAIT

If a **VICTRIX GUARD CAPTAIN** is your Warlord, you can give them the following Warlord Trait.

WARDEN OF ULTRAMAR

The title 'Warden of Ultramar' is granted to the Captain leading the Victrix Guard. A master of combat, this indomitable and unflinching hero can swiftly spot enemy weaknesses in the heat of battle.

Once per battle, in the Fight phase, you can re-roll wound rolls for attacks made by friendly **VICTRIX GUARD** units within 6" of this Warlord.

STRATAGEMS

If your army includes any Victrix Guard Specialist Detachments, you can use Command Points (CPs) to use the following Stratagems:

1CP — FIGHT LIKE DEMIGODS
Ultramarines Stratagem

A gathering of courageous heroes, the Victrix Guard are more than capable of cutting their way through entire armies of foes.

Use this Stratagem at the start of the Fight phase. Pick a **VICTRIX GUARD** unit from your army within 6" of a friendly **VICTRIX GUARD CAPTAIN**. Add 1 to hit rolls for attacks made by that unit until the end of that phase.

3CP — STRIKE FIRST, FOR ULTRAMAR!
Ultramarines Stratagem

As the enemy close in, the Victrix Guard hold their weapons ready to deliver the first blow.

Use this Stratagem at the end of your opponent's Charge phase. Pick a **VICTRIX GUARD** unit from your army that was charged this phase, or that performed a Heroic Intervention this phase. That unit can immediately pile in and fight as if it were the Fight phase (doing so does not prevent the unit from being picked to fight in the Fight phase of that turn).

RELICS OF ULTRAMAR

If your army includes any Victrix Guard Specialist Detachments, you can give one of the following relics to a **VICTRIX GUARD CHARACTER** from your army.

SOLDIER'S BLADE

This deceptively simple sword has been a treasure of the Ultramarines since the Chapter's founding. Though it contains none of the matter-disruptive technology of a power sword, it can still carve through the thickest plates of ceramite and plasteel with ease. So perfectly forged is this monomolecular-edged blade that it has survived for millennia without ever needing to be sharpened.

Model with power sword or master-crafted power sword only. The Soldier's Blade replaces the bearer's power sword or master-crafted power sword, and has the following profile.

WEAPON	RANGE	TYPE	S	AP	D
Soldier's Blade	Melee	Melee	+1	-4	2

THE STANDARD OF MACRAGGE INVIOLATE

When the Tyrannic Wars came to the realm of Ultramar, and Hive Fleet Behemoth descended upon Macragge, it was this glorious banner that flew above the swarms of xenos beasts. To all Ultramarines, it represents the unfaltering might of their home world and their Chapter. When an Ultramarine beholds this sacred standard, he is gripped with a sense of unshakeable pride and determination, for he knows that no enemy can match the skills in battle passed down to him and his brothers by their Primarch.

ANCIENT only. Add 1 to the Leadership characteristic of friendly **ULTRAMARINES** units whilst they are within 12" of the bearer. In addition, add 1 to the Attacks characteristic of friendly **VICTRIX GUARD** units whilst they are within 6" of the bearer.

IMPERIAL FISTS SIEGEBREAKER COHORT

The Imperial Fists are renowned experts in siege warfare, stubbornly holding the enemy back for months if necessary. Should a foe manage to fight their way through to the outer rings of their defences, the Imperial Fists will collapse their own fortifications to turn them into an inescapable death-trap.

SPECIALIST DETACHMENT

If your army is Battle-forged, you can use the Specialist Detachment Stratagem below:

IMPERIAL FISTS SIEGEBREAKER COHORT
Specialist Detachment Stratagem
Countless fortifications have fallen to the concentrated fury of an Imperial Fists Siegebreaker Cohort.

Use this Stratagem when choosing your army. Pick an **IMPERIAL FISTS** Detachment from your army to be a Siegebreaker Cohort Specialist Detachment. **CAPTAINS, CENTURIONS, DREADNOUGHTS** and **VINDICATORS** in that Detachment gain the **SIEGEBREAKER COHORT** keyword.

STRATAGEMS

If your army includes any Siegebreaker Cohort Specialist Detachments, you can use Command Points (CPs) to use the following Stratagems:

STRUCTURAL DEMOLITION
Imperial Fists Stratagem
With pinpoint accuracy, enemy fortifications are reduced to rubble in moments, crushing those trapped within.

Use this Stratagem after a **BUILDING** has been destroyed by an attack made by a **SIEGEBREAKER COHORT** unit from your army. Roll 2D6 instead of 1 for each model that disembarks from that **BUILDING**. For each roll of 1, a model that disembarked (controlling player's choice) is slain.

SEISMIC DEVASTATION
Imperial Fists Stratagem
Under the ferocious barrage of attacks unleashed by the Siegebreaker Cohort, barricades collapse and even armoured vehicles are torn into flaming ruin.

Use this Stratagem at the start of the Shooting phase or Fight phase. Pick a **SIEGEBREAKER COHORT** unit from your army. Each time you roll a wound roll of a 6+ for an attack made by that unit that targets an enemy **VEHICLE** or **BUILDING** that phase, that attack inflicts a mortal wound in addition to its normal damage.

WARLORD TRAIT

If a **SIEGEBREAKER COHORT CHARACTER** is your Warlord, you can give them the following Warlord Trait.

INDOMITABLE

This warlord can never be driven back once he has set his mind to a task. He stands stoic, unrelenting, and inspires his allies to hold fast.

If your Warlord did not move in the Movement phase of this turn, friendly **IMPERIAL FISTS INFANTRY** units within 6" of your Warlord automatically pass Morale tests and receive the benefit to their saving throws for being in cover, even while they are not wholly on or within a terrain feature.

RELICS OF PHALANX

If your army includes any Siegebreaker Cohort Specialist Detachments, you can give the following relic to a **SIEGEBREAKER COHORT CHARACTER** from your army:

THE EYE OF HYPNOTH

The Eye of Hypnoth was presented to the Imperial Fists in late M39 to honour their defence of the forge world Hypnoth against Waaagh! Kromak. This device is a highly sophisticated and long-ranged auspex array; tradition dictates that it is best employed to detect hidden weaknesses in enemy armour and fortifications.

Re-roll wound rolls of 1 for shooting attacks made by friendly **SIEGEBREAKER COHORT** units within 6" of the bearer.

CRIMSON FISTS LIBERATOR STRIKE FORCE

The liberation of Rynn's World was gruelling, but those who survived became experts in fighting against the odds – and in teaching their hard-won knowledge to others. The Crimson Fists have sworn to free those Imperial worlds that are crushed under the heel of tyrants and oppressors.

SPECIALIST DETACHMENT

If your army is Battle-forged, you can use the Specialist Detachment Stratagem below:

CRIMSON FISTS LIBERATOR STRIKE FORCE
Specialist Detachment Stratagem

The daemonic siege on Rynn's World was finally lifted by the arrival of the Indomitus Crusade. The beleaguered Crimson Fists had their ranks bolstered by Primaris veterans of Rogal Dorn's heritage.

Use this Stratagem when choosing your army. Pick a **CRIMSON FISTS** Detachment from your army to be a Crimson Fists Liberator Strike Force Specialist Detachment. **PRIMARIS CHARACTERS**, **INTERCESSOR SQUADS**, **REIVER SQUADS** and **HELLBLASTER SQUADS** in that Detachment gain the **LIBERATOR STRIKE FORCE** keyword.

STRATAGEMS

If your army includes any Crimson Fists Liberator Strike Force Specialist Detachments, you can use Command Points (CPs) to use the following Stratagems:

HEROES OF RYNN'S WORLD
Crimson Fists Stratagem

The Crimson Fists strike out at threats upon beleaguered Imperial worlds, liberating them one by one as they did their home planet.

Use this Stratagem at the start of your Shooting phase. Pick a **LIBERATOR STRIKE FORCE** unit from your army. Until the end of the phase, each time you roll an unmodified hit roll of 6 for an attack made by that unit's ranged weapons, that attack inflicts 2 hits instead of 1.

PARAGONS OF DORN
Crimson Fists Stratagem

The Crimson Fists Primaris Marines are exemplars of their primogenetor, and they share his discipline under pressure. When they lay down a volley of return fire, their efficiency and speed borders on the supernatural.

Use this Stratagem at the end of an enemy Shooting phase. Pick a **LIBERATOR STRIKE FORCE** unit from your army that was targeted by one or more attacks this phase. That unit can immediately shoot as if it were your Shooting phase.

WARLORD TRAIT

If a **LIBERATOR STRIKE FORCE CHARACTER** is your Warlord, you can give them the following Warlord Trait.

EXPERT INSTRUCTOR

After the decimation of their Chapter, the surviving Crimson Fists were forced to become peerless tutors in order to quickly replenish their numbers with fresh recruits.

Re-roll hit rolls of 1 for friendly **LIBERATOR STRIKE FORCE** units within 9" of your Warlord.

RELICS OF RYNN'S WORLD

If your army includes any Crimson Fists Liberator Strike Force Specialist Detachments, you can give the following relic to a **LIBERATOR STRIKE FORCE CHARACTER** from your army.

THE VENGEFUL ARBITER

Sergeant Ricario Vicentius was a valiant warrior who served at Chapter Master Pedro Kantor's side during the Battle for Traitor's Gorge. Although he was eventually slain, it is reported he killed countless Orks despite being mortally wounded himself. After the battle, Chapter Master Kantor ordered the recovery and reissue of his bolt pistol, now named 'the Vengeful Arbiter' by his men, and it has served countless brothers from the Chapter since.

Model with bolt pistol only. The Vengeful Arbiter replaces the bearer's bolt pistol and has the following profile:

WEAPON	RANGE	TYPE	S	AP	D
The Vengeful Arbiter	12"	Pistol 2	5	-1	2

Abilities: Each time an attack made with this weapon hits, you can immediately make one additional hit roll against that target using the same weapon. These bonus hit rolls cannot themselves generate any further hit rolls.

BLACK TEMPLARS SWORD BRETHREN

The veterans of the Black Templars swear mighty oaths to uphold the honour of the Imperium in everything they do. Theirs is an especial hatred for the alien, the psyker and the heretic; they fight like legendary knights of old in their eternal crusade against the darkness.

SPECIALIST DETACHMENT

If your army is Battle-forged, you can use the Specialist Detachment Stratagem below:

SWORD BRETHREN
Specialist Detachment Stratagem

It is the ambition of every Black Templar Initiate to be elevated to the esteemed ranks of the Sword Brethren, for these warrior-knights are the elites of their Chapter.

Use this Stratagem when choosing your army. Pick a **BLACK TEMPLARS** Detachment from your army to be a Sword Brethren Specialist Detachment. **HIGH MARSHAL HELBRECHT, EMPEROR'S CHAMPION, CAPTAINS, COMPANY CHAMPIONS** and **COMPANY VETERANS** in that Detachment gain the **SWORD BRETHREN** keyword.

WARLORD TRAIT

If a **SWORD BRETHREN CHARACTER** is your Warlord, you can give them the following Warlord Trait.

MASTER SWORDSMAN

As a champion of the Feast of Blades, this warlord's skill in the art of combat is equalled by very few.

Add 1 to your Warlord's Attacks characteristic. In addition, each time you roll an unmodified hit roll of 6 for an attack made by your Warlord in the Fight phase, that attack inflicts 2 hits instead of 1.

RELICS OF THE ETERNAL CRUSADER

If your army includes any Sword Brethren Specialist Detachments, you can give the following relic to a **SWORD BRETHREN CHARACTER** from your army.

THE HOLY ORB

Created by one of the Chapter's renowned artificers, this orb is a grenade empowered by the holy wrath of the Emperor and filled in equal measure with high explosives and sacred unguents that burn the faithless with their purity.

Once per battle, in your Shooting phase, you can choose for the bearer to throw the Holy Orb instead of making a normal shooting attack. If you do so, pick a visible enemy unit within 6" of the bearer and roll a D6 for every 10 models in that unit (rounding up). For each roll of 2+ that unit suffers D3 mortal wounds.

STRATAGEMS

If your army includes any Sword Brethren Specialist Detachments, you can use Command Points (CPs) to use the following Stratagems:

UPHOLD THE HONOUR OF THE EMPEROR
Black Templars Stratagem

The Black Templars' faith in the Emperor is so strong they are able to shrug off even the most severe wounds.

Use this Stratagem at the start of the Fight phase. Pick a **SWORD BRETHREN** unit from your army. Until the end of that phase, roll a D6 each time a model in that unit loses a wound. On a 5+, that model does not lose that wound.

SUFFER NOT THE UNCLEAN TO LIVE
Black Templars Stratagem

With righteous zeal, these warriors vow to vanquish Mankind's foes in the name of the Holy Emperor.

Use this Stratagem at the start of the Fight phase. Pick a **SWORD BRETHREN** unit from your army. Add 1 to the Attacks characteristic of models in that unit for this phase. In addition, you can re-roll wound rolls for attacks made by that unit until the end of that phase.

RAVENWING ATTACK SQUADRON

The Ravenwing have a duty as hunters, watchmen, explorers and delvers into dark secrets. When they are certain their quarry is near, these Dark Angels follow their killer instincts, running the foe to ground before delivering a swift and final strike.

SPECIALIST DETACHMENT

If your army is Battle-forged, you can use the Specialist Detachment Stratagem below:

ATTACK SQUADRON
1CP

Specialist Detachment Stratagem

Dust clouds billow behind the Ravenwing Attack Squadron as it hurtles into battle. Striking swiftly, the 2nd Company huntsmen drive hard into the midst of the enemy.

Use this Stratagem when choosing your army. Pick a **DARK ANGELS** Detachment from your army to be a Ravenwing Attack Squadron Specialist Detachment. **RAVENWING** units in that Detachment gain the **ATTACK SQUADRON** keyword.

STRATAGEMS

If your army includes any Ravenwing Attack Squadron Specialist Detachments, you can use Command Points (CPs) to use the following Stratagems:

SWIFT STRIKE
2CP

Dark Angels Stratagem

In a blur of speed, the warriors of a Ravenwing Attack Squadron strike out at the enemy and then escape from their grasp before they have had time to react.

Use this Stratagem in the Fight phase after an **ATTACK SQUADRON** unit from your army has fought. That unit can immediately make a move (and Advance) as if it were your Movement phase. If there are any enemy units within 1" it can Fall Back instead.

SIGNAL THE ATTACK
1CP

Dark Angels Stratagem

As soon as one Attack Squadron has wounded its target, the others in its formation circle like vultures to complete the kill.

Use this Stratagem after an **ATTACK SQUADRON** unit from your army has attacked an enemy unit in the Shooting phase and the attack resulted in the enemy unit losing one or more wounds. Add 1 to hit rolls for attacks made by other **ATTACK SQUADRON** units from your army that target the same enemy unit this phase.

WARLORD TRAIT

If an **ATTACK SQUADRON CHARACTER** is your Warlord, you can give them the following Warlord Trait.

LIGHTNING-FAST REACTIONS

The Ravenwing are renowned for their rapid strikes and this warlord is the living embodiment of that trait. In combat, there are few who can best his speed and skill with a blade.

You can always choose your Warlord to fight first in the Fight phase, even if they didn't charge. If the enemy has units that have charged, or that have similar abilities, then alternate choosing units to fight with, starting with the player whose turn is taking place.

RELICS OF CALIBAN

If your army includes any Ravenwing Attack Squadron Specialist Detachments, you can give the following relic to an **ATTACK SQUADRON CHARACTER** in your army:

MONSTER SLAYER OF CALIBAN

This ancient weapon was traditionally bestowed upon the most honourable knight of the Order. It is said that as long as its owner stays pure of mind, this sword will strike down even the greatest of foes.

Model with power sword only. The Monster Slayer of Caliban replaces the bearer's power sword and has the following profile:

WEAPON	RANGE	TYPE	S	AP	D
Monster Slayer of Caliban	Melee	Melee	+2	-3	D3

Abilities: Add 1 to wound rolls for attacks that target an enemy **MONSTER** or enemy **VEHICLE**.

SPACE WOLVES STALKER PACK

Prowling through the smoke of corpse-strewn battlefields come the Space Wolves Stalker Packs, their eyes glinting gold in the fires of war. When they have the scent of their prey in their nostrils there is no escape, for these are hunters beyond compare, and savage on the attack.

SPECIALIST DETACHMENT

If your army is Battle-forged, you can use the Specialist Detachment Stratagem below:

STALKER PACK
1CP

Specialist Detachment Stratagem

From the shadows come Space Wolves Stalker Packs, pursuing their quarry with unwavering ferocity. Once the enemy realises they are being pursued, it is often too late to evade their fate.

Use this Stratagem when choosing your army. Pick a **SPACE WOLVES** Detachment from your army to be a Stalker Pack Specialist Detachment. **BATTLE LEADERS**, **BLOOD CLAWS** and **REIVERS** in that Detachment gain the **STALKER PACK** keyword.

STRATAGEMS

If your army includes any Stalker Pack Specialist Detachments, you can use Command Points (CPs) to use the following Stratagems:

BLOOD SCENT
2CP

Space Wolves Stratagem

Once blood has been drawn, the warriors of the Stalker Pack fall upon their enemies like savage wolves, tearing them to pieces.

Use this Stratagem in the Fight phase. Pick an enemy **INFANTRY** or **MONSTER** unit that has suffered any casualties, or has any models in it with less than their starting number of wounds. Add 1 to wound rolls for attacks made by **STALKER PACK** units from your army that target that enemy unit until the end of that phase.

PACK KILLERS
1CP

Space Wolves Stratagem

With the scent of blood in their nostrils, the Stalker Pack first tempt their foe, testing out weaknesses in the enemy lines, before descending with murderous intent.

Use this Stratagem after a **STALKER PACK** unit makes a charge move. Pick another friendly **STALKER PACK** unit within 12" of the unit that charged. Until the end of that phase, you can roll 3D6 when making Charge moves with that unit and discard the dice with the lowest score.

WARLORD TRAIT

If a **STALKER PACK CHARACTER** is your Warlord, you can give them the following Warlord Trait.

SAGA OF THE SAVAGE

Tales are told of this warrior's bestial fury. Akin to a Fenrisian Wolf alpha, he hunts down his prey before despatching them with brutal efficiency.

Add 1 to your Warlord's Attacks characteristic if they made a charge move in the same turn.

Deed of Legend: Enemy models lose at least 5 wounds as a result of attacks made by your Warlord's melee weapons in a single phase.

RELICS OF THE FANG

If your army includes any Stalker Pack Specialist Detachments, you can give the following relic to a **STALKER PACK CHARACTER** from your army.

IRONFANG OF AMMAGRIMGUL

Forged from iron mined deep within the mountain Ammagrimgul on Fenris, many songs are sung of this artificer weapon and the blood it has spilled in battle with the Emperor's foes.

Model with power axe only. The Ironfang of Ammagrimgul replaces the bearer's power axe and has the following profile:

WEAPON	RANGE	TYPE	S	AP	D
Ironfang of Ammagrimgul	Melee	Melee	+1	-2	D3

Abilities: If the wound roll for an attack made by this weapon is an unmodified 6, the target model suffers D3 mortal wounds instead of the normal damage.

CYBERNETICA COHORT

The Legio Cybernetica is one of the oldest institutions in the Adeptus Mechanicus, and it has endured for a reason. Each Kastelan Robot is a mighty idol of war – when gathered in maniples and brought to full lethality by the correct doctrina wafers, they can be unstoppable.

SPECIALIST DETACHMENT

If your army is Battle-forged, you can use the Specialist Detachment Stratagem below:

1CP — CYBERNETICA COHORT
Specialist Detachment Stratagem

Marching into battle with inhuman synchronisation come the maniples of the Legio Cybernetica, ready to wage war in their pursuit of arcane knowledge.

Use this Stratagem when choosing your army. Pick an **ADEPTUS MECHANICUS** Detachment from your army to be a Cybernetica Cohort Specialist Detachment. **TECH-PRIESTS DOMINUS**, **ENGINSEERS**, **CYBERNETICA DATASMITHS** and **KASTELAN ROBOTS** in that Detachment gain the **CYBERNETICA COHORT** keyword.

STRATAGEMS

If your army includes any Cybernetica Cohort Specialist Detachments, you can use Command Points (CPs) to use the following Stratagems:

1CP — POWER SURGE
Adeptus Mechanicus Stratagem

The datasmith delivers a burst of energy to the Kastelan Robots allowing them to cross the battlefield at an accelerated pace.

Use this Stratagem at the start of your Charge phase. Pick a unit of **CYBERNETICA COHORT KASTELAN ROBOTS** from your army within 3" of a friendly **CYBERNETICA COHORT CYBERNETICA DATASMITH**. Add 3 to charge rolls made for that unit of Kastelan Robots until the end of that phase.

1CP — STRAFING FIRE RUN
Adeptus Mechanicus Stratagem

Modifying the doctrina wafers of these Kastelan Robots grants them greater manoeuvrability and firepower – a devastating combination.

Use this Stratagem at the start of your Movement phase. Pick a unit of **CYBERNETICA COHORT KASTELAN ROBOTS** from your army that has the Aegis Protocol in effect. Until the end of that turn, treat Heavy weapons that unit is armed with as Assault weapons for all rules purposes.

WARLORD TRAIT

If a **CYBERNETICA COHORT CHARACTER** is your Warlord, you can give them the following Warlord Trait.

ADEPT OF THE LEGIO CYBERNETICA

A veteran of battle and trusted overseer of many of the Legio Cybernetica's most treasured relic robots, this warlord is especially skilled at repairing the battle damage sustained by his charges.

Once per battle, when your Warlord uses their Master of Machines ability to repair a friendly unit of **CYBERNETICA COHORT KASTELAN ROBOTS**, that unit regains D6 lost wounds instead of D3.

ARCANA MECHANICUM

If your army includes any Cybernetica Cohort Specialist Detachments, you can give the following relic to a **CYBERNETICA COHORT CHARACTER** from your army:

DOCTRINA FOREAS SERVO-SKULL

Fitted with archeotech grav-boosters, this servo-skull has been adapted to quickly dispense sanctified doctrina wafers to Kastelan Robots. This allows Datasmiths or other adepts of the Legio Cybernetica to extend their control over a wider net of robots and command greater numbers in battle.

Friendly units of **CYBERNETICA COHORT KASTELAN ROBOTS** can attempt to change their battle protocols at start of each of your Movement phases if they are within 9" of the bearer.

SERVITOR MANIPLE

A Servitor Maniple will trundle and crunch its way to war, driven by its Tech-Priest's inhuman obsession with knowledge claimed at any cost. These mindless cyborgs fight in uncanny unison, their humanity secondary to the destructive power of the weapons sutured to their limbs.

SPECIALIST DETACHMENT

If your army is Battle-forged, you can use the Specialist Detachment Stratagem below:

SERVITOR MANIPLE
Specialist Detachment Stratagem

Like a coming storm, the rhythmic whir of Kataphron tracked motive units and the ponderous crump of marching battle servitors signal the coming of a Servitor Maniple, a legion of lobotomised slaves serving only the will of the Omnissiah.

Use this Stratagem when choosing your army. Pick an **Adeptus Mechanicus** Detachment from your army to be a Servitor Maniple Specialist Detachment. **Tech-priests Dominus**, **Enginseers**, **Kataphron Breachers**, **Kataphron Destroyers** and **Servitors** in that Detachment gain the **Servitor Maniple** keyword.

STRATAGEMS

If your army includes any Servitor Maniple Specialist Detachments, you can use Command Points (CPs) to use the following Stratagems:

ENHANCED BIONICS
Adeptus Mechanicus Stratagem

These Kataphron servitors have had their bionics reinforced and augmented to offer greater protection in battle.

Use this Stratagem before the battle begins. Pick a unit of **Servitor Maniple Kataphron Breachers** or **Servitor Maniple Kataphron Destroyers** from your army. That unit has a 5+ invulnerable save for the duration of this battle.

NOOSPHERIC MINDLOCK
Adeptus Mechanicus Stratagem

The Tech-Priests that lead Servitor Maniples have advanced targeting systems hardwired into each of their Kataphron servitors that allow updated protocols to override defaults in the heat of battle.

Use this Stratagem at the start of your Shooting phase. Pick a unit of **Servitor Maniple Kataphron Breachers** or **Servitor Maniple Kataphron Destroyers** within 6" of a friendly **Servitor Maniple Tech-Priest Dominus**. Add 1 to hit rolls for attacks made by that unit until the end of the phase.

WARLORD TRAIT

If a **Servitor Maniple Character** is your Warlord, you can give them the following Warlord Trait.

MASTER OF BIOSPLICING

This Tech-Priest has no qualms about sacrificing one specimen to preserve another.

At the end of your Movement phase, you can pick a unit of **Servitors** from your army within 6" of your Warlord and a unit of **Kataphron Breachers** or **Kataphron Destroyers** from your army within 6" of your Warlord. 1 model from that unit of **Servitors** is immediately slain. A model in that unit of **Kataphron Breachers** or **Kataphron Destroyers** then regains D3 lost wounds, or, if there are no wounded models in the unit and any models in the unit have been slain, you can return one slain model to the unit with 1 wound remaining (this model is set up in unit coherency and cannot be set up within 1" of any enemy models – if it is not possible to place this model, it is not returned to the unit).

ARCANA MECHANICUM

If your army includes any Servitor Maniple Specialist Detachments, you can give the following relic to a **Servitor Maniple Character** from your army.

THE GENECOG CORPUS

This axe samples genetic data as it hacks into its foe, growing deadlier with each swing.

Model with omnissian axe only. The Genecog Corpus replaces the bearer's omnissian axe and has the following profile:

WEAPON	RANGE	TYPE	S	AP	D
The Genecog Corpus	Melee	Melee	+1	-2	2

Abilities: If the wound roll for an attack made by this weapon is an unmodified 6, the target model suffers D3 mortal wounds instead of any normal damage.

ANOINTED THRONG

The strange biological offshoots of the Genestealer Cult are misshapen, muscular, and utterly devoted to the creed. The mightiest amongst them are anointed with holy oils and the blood of their Purestrain kin, and they fight like berserk zealots in the name of their war leaders.

SPECIALIST DETACHMENT

If your army is Battle-forged, you can use the Specialist Detachment Stratagem below:

ANOINTED THRONG
1CP

Specialist Detachment Stratagem

To those of the Genestealer Cults, the Abominant is seen as a holy figure, blessed by their grandsire to lead them out of the subterranean darkness to conquer the stars.

Use this Stratagem when choosing your army. Pick a **GENESTEALER CULTS** Detachment from your army to be an Anointed Throng Specialist Detachment. **ABOMINANTS** and **ABERRANTS** in that Detachment gain the **ANOINTED THRONG** keyword.

STRATAGEMS

If your army includes any Anointed Throng Specialist Detachments, you can use Command Points (CPs) to use the following Stratagems:

DEVOTION TILL DEATH
2CP

Genestealer Cults Stratagem

These Aberrants sell their lives dearly to their foes, striking at them even after being mortally wounded themselves.

Use this Stratagem at the start of the Fight phase. Pick an **ANOINTED THRONG ABERRANT** unit from your army. Until the end of that phase, when a model from that unit is slain, that model is not removed from the battlefield as normal, but can instead immediately pile in and fight, even if it has already been chosen to fight that phase. After its attacks have been resolved, it is then removed from the battlefield.

FIGHT FOR THE ANOINTED ONE!
1CP

Genestealer Cults Stratagem

In battle, the ferocious war cry of their leader inspires the throng to heightened levels of fanaticism as they unleash zealous brutality upon their foe.

Use this Stratagem at the start of your Fight phase. Pick an **ANOINTED THRONG ABERRANT** unit within 6" of an **ANOINTED THRONG ABOMINANT**. Re-roll wound rolls of 1 for attacks made by that unit until the end of that phase.

WARLORD TRAIT

If a **ANOINTED THRONG CHARACTER** is your Warlord, you can give them the following Warlord Trait.

INSIDIOUS MINDWYRM

Birthed into corporeal existence by the Patriarch's psychic overspill, this Mindwyrm familiar manifests the most sinister and insidious aspects of its master. Holding little regard for the creature in its thrall, it uses its powerful will to drive the hapless Abominant and its followers into battle without cease.

Add 1 to charge rolls for your Warlord and friendly **ANOINTED THRONG** units that are within 6" of your Warlord when the roll is made.

SACRED RELICS OF THE CULT

If your army includes any Anointed Throng Specialist Detachments, you may give one of the following relics to an **ANOINTED THRONG CHARACTER** in your army.

BLESSED SLEDGEHAMMER

Graced by the Patriarch himself, this power sledgehammer is saturated with the psychic energy of the brood, not only making it lighter to carry, but imbuing it with terrible power.

ABOMINANT only. The Blessed Sledgehammer replaces the bearer's power sledgehammer and has the following profile:

WEAPON	RANGE	TYPE	S	AP	D
Blessed Sledgehammer	Melee	Melee	x2	-4	D6

Abilities: Damage rolls of 1 or 2 made with this weapon count as 3 instead.

DELIVERANCE BROODSURGE

When the cult wishes to secure a vital location it will send a flotilla of transports hurtling into the crucible of battle, the cramped hulls of each Goliath Truck packed with devotees of the creed. All are desperate to claim first blood in order to impress their Patriarch.

SPECIALIST DETACHMENT

If your army is Battle-forged, you can use the Specialist Detachment Stratagem below:

DELIVERANCE BROODSURGE
Specialist Detachment Stratagem

Pouring from Goliath transports comes a living tide of warriors. Surging forward with frothing fervour, the broodsurge is nigh impossible to stop.

Use this Stratagem when choosing your army. Pick a **GENESTEALER CULTS** Detachment from your army to be a Deliverance Broodsurge Specialist Detachment. **ACOLYTE ICONWARDS**, **NEOPHYTE HYBRIDS**, **ACOLYTE HYBRIDS** and **GOLIATH TRUCKS** in that Detachment gain the **DELIVERANCE BROODSURGE** keyword.

STRATAGEMS

If your army includes any Deliverance Broodsurge Specialist Detachments, you can use Command Points (CPs) to use the following Stratagems:

THE FIRST TO DRAW BLOOD
Genestealer Cults Stratagem

With impetuous fervour and passion, these warriors of the cult charge headlong into the enemy, seeking blood and glory.

Use this Stratagem at the start of your Fight phase. Pick a **DELIVERANCE BROODSURGE** unit from your army that made a charge move this turn. Add 1 to wound rolls for attacks made by that unit until the end of that phase.

RECKLESS MANOEUVRE
Genestealer Cults Stratagem

At the last moment, this fanatical driver slews their vehicle around, hurling the passengers into the fray.

Use this Stratagem at the end of your Movement phase. Pick a **DELIVERANCE BROODSURGE GOLIATH TRUCK** unit from your army. **DELIVERANCE BROODSURGE** units embarked within that **GOLIATH TRUCK** can immediately disembark if they did not embark within it this turn. If any units do so, roll a D6 for each model disembarking. For each 1, a model that disembarked (your choice) is slain. Models that disembark in this manner must be set up more than 9" from any enemy models and cannot move that phase.

WARLORD TRAIT

If a **DELIVERANCE BROODSURGE CHARACTER** is your Warlord, you can give them the following Warlord Trait:

AUGUR OF THE INSURGENT

This Warlord's presence amongst the Deliverance Broodsurge is testament to every warrior chosen that they are destined for greatness, and they waste no time in proving it to their foe.

You can re-roll Advance rolls and charge rolls for friendly **DELIVERANCE BROODSURGE** units if they are within 6" of your Warlord when the roll is made.

SACRED RELICS OF THE CULT

If your army includes any Deliverance Broodsurge Specialist Detachments, you may give one of the following relics to a **DELIVERANCE BROODSURGE CHARACTER** in your army.

VIAL OF THE GRANDSIRE'S BLOOD

Iconwards most favoured by their Patriarch are sometimes blessed with vials filled with its blood. These holy vessels are hung from the Iconward's sacred banner and fill nearby cultists with a zealous devotion to their cause. Not only symbolic in nature, each drop of blood holds considerable psychic energy that can imbue a faithful warrior with incredible strength and reflexes.

Add 1 to the Leadership characteristic of friendly **GENESTEALER CULTS** units within 6" of the bearer. In addition, once per battle, at the start of the Fight phase, you can pick a **GENESTEALER CULTS INFANTRY** model from your army within 3" of the bearer. Add 2 to that model's Attacks and Strength characteristics until the end of that phase.

WINDRIDER HOST

Fighting a Windrider Host has been likened to being hunted by the flying coatls of Mezolustrius VI. These swift Aeldari swerve and dart through the air, dealing out vicious pinpoint attacks – then, just when the survivors think their assailants have moved on, the airborne host comes around for the kill…

SPECIALIST DETACHMENT

If your army is Battle-forged, you can use the Specialist Detachment Stratagem below:

WINDRIDER HOST
1CP
Specialist Detachment Stratagem

The Windrider Host is the fury of the craftworld carried upon the storm. The speed and cunning of this airborne formation mirrors that of the Cosmic Serpent itself.

Use this Stratagem when choosing your army. Pick a Craftworld Detachment from your army to be a Windrider Host Specialist Detachment. **Autarch Skyrunners, Farseer Skyrunners, Warlock Skyrunners, Warlock Skyrunner Conclaves, Windriders** and **Vypers** in that Detachment gain the **Windrider Host** keyword.

STRATAGEMS

If your army includes any Windrider Host Specialist Detachments, you can use Command Points (CPs) to use the following Stratagems:

NIMBLE ESCAPE
2CP
Craftworlds Stratagem

After striking their quarry, the warriors of the Windrider Host pull off a daring manoeuvre to twist out of the grasp of the enemy.

Use this Stratagem in the Fight phase after a **Windrider Host** unit from your army has fought. That unit can immediately make a move (and Advance) as if it were your Movement phase. If there are any enemy units within 1" it can Fall Back instead.

TEMPEST OF BLADES
3CP
Craftworlds Stratagem

When the command to kill is given, a gale of razor-edged discs is unleashed to tear the enemy's lines to shreds.

Use this Stratagem at the start of your Shooting phase. Pick a **Windrider Host Farseer Skyrunner** unit from your army. Improve the Armour Penetration characteristic of shooting attacks made by friendly **Windrider Host** units within 6" of the unit you picked by 1 until the end of that phase (e.g. AP-1 would become AP-2).

WARLORD TRAIT

If a **Windrider Host Character** is your Warlord, you can give them the following Warlord Trait.

WILD RIDER

Making full use of the agility of their jetbikes, this Warlord leads their host back in a feint, only to turn at the last moment and rush the unprepared foe with a devastatingly swift charge.

Your Warlord, and any friendly **Windrider Host** units within 6" of your Warlord, can charge even if they Fell Back this turn.

REMNANT OF GLORY

If your army includes any Windrider Host Specialist Detachments, you may give one of the following relics to a **Windrider Host Character** in your army.

Howling Skysword of Galaleth

Legend surrounds the famed weaponsmith Galaleth, but little is known of her true origins. Her distinctive skyswords have been found scattered across a dozen maiden worlds and, despite the passing of millennia, the edge of each never dulls. The blade of this skysword vibrates as it is swung, emitting a shrieking noise that is the harbinger of doom for all who face it in battle.

Model with witchblade only. The Howling Skysword of Galaleth replaces the bearer's witchblade and has the following profile:

WEAPON	RANGE	TYPE	S	AP	D
Howling Skysword of Galaleth	Melee	Melee	User	0	3
Abilities: This weapon always wounds on a roll of 2+.					

WRAITH HOST

Where the main Asuryani assault is arrow-swift, the Wraith Host strides forward through the twilight of war, unhurried and all but impervious to the bullets and laser blasts levelled against them. When they are in striking range, the demise of the enemy is assured.

SPECIALIST DETACHMENT

If your army is Battle-forged, you can use the Specialist Detachment Stratagem below:

WRAITH HOST
Specialist Detachment Stratagem
Guided by Spiritseers, the wraith hosts of the craftworlds are the noble houses of Aeldari myth given life once more.

Use this Stratagem when choosing your army. Pick a Craftworld Detachment from your army to be a Wraith Host Specialist Detachment. **Spiritseers** and **Wraith Constructs** in that Detachment gain the **Wraith Host** keyword.

STRATAGEMS

If your army includes any Wraith Host Specialist Detachments, you can use Command Points (CPs) to use the following Stratagems:

WRATH OF THE DEAD
Craftworlds Stratagem
With cold and unforgiving fury, these wraith constructs carve a path of devastation through the enemy.

Use this Stratagem at the start of the Fight phase. Pick a **Wraith Host Wraith Construct** unit from your army. Add 1 to the Attacks characteristic of models in that unit until the end of that phase.

SPIRIT SHIELD
Craftworlds Stratagem
Diverting the defensive properties of their rune armour, this Spiritseer shrouds their precious wraith constructs from harm.

Use this Stratagem at the end of your Movement phase. Pick a **Wraith Host Wraith Construct** unit from your army that is within 6" of a friendly **Wraith Host Spiritseer**. Until the start of your next turn, that unit gains a 4+ invulnerable save but the **Spiritseer** loses the 4+ invulnerable save granted by its Rune Armour.

WARLORD TRAIT

If a **Wraith Host Character** is your Warlord, you can give them the following Warlord Trait.

REVERED BY THE DEAD

This Spiritseer shares strong ties of kinship with the wraith constructs under their command, and their ferocious determination to vanquish the enemy resonates through each towering warrior that follows them to battle.

You can re-roll charge rolls for friendly **Wraith Host Wraith Construct** units whilst they are within 6" of your Warlord.

RUNE OF BATTLE

Before the battle, a **Wraith Host Psyker** can replace a psychic power they know (excluding *Smite*) with the following psychic power:

TWILIGHT GLOOM

A thin tear between reality and the spirit world enshrouds the ghost warriors in a veil of dark shadows.

Twilight Gloom has a warp charge value of 6. If manifested, pick a friendly **Wraith Host** unit within 18" of the psyker. Until the start of your next turn, that unit receives the benefit to their saving throws for being in cover, even while they are not wholly on or within a terrain feature.

REMNANT OF GLORY

If your army includes any Wraith Host Specialist Detachments, you may give one of the following relics to a **Wraith Host Character** in your army.

WARP-SPAWN BANE

This witch staff is anathema to psykers and creatures of the warp.

Model with witch staff only. Warp-spawn Bane replaces the bearer's witch staff and has the following profile:

WEAPON	RANGE	TYPE	S	AP	D
Warp-spawn Bane	Melee	Melee	User	0	2

Abilities: This weapon always wounds on a roll of 2+. In addition, ignore invulnerable saves for attacks made by this weapon that target enemy **Psykers** or **Daemons**.

EMPEROR'S BLADE ASSAULT COMPANY

Though the Astra Militarum are not known for their mobility, there are regiments and battalions that specialise in mechanised warfare. Each rugged transport is packed with warriors ready to spring out the moment the debarkation klaxons sound, lasguns spitting death.

SPECIALIST DETACHMENT

If your army is Battle-forged, you can use the Specialist Detachment Stratagem below:

1CP EMPEROR'S BLADE ASSAULT COMPANY
Specialist Detachment Stratagem

Designed to quickly seize key strategic locations, the core of the Emperor's Blade Assault Company comprises squads of hardened troopers mounted aboard fast-moving armoured transports.

Use this Stratagem when choosing your army. Pick an **ASTRA MILITARUM** Detachment from your army to be an Emperor's Blade Specialist Detachment. **COMPANY COMMANDERS, PLATOON COMMANDERS, COMMAND SQUADS, SPECIAL WEAPON SQUADS, VETERANS, INFANTRY SQUADS, CHIMERAS** and **TAUROXES** in that Detachment gain the **EMPEROR'S BLADE** keyword.

WARLORD TRAIT

If an **EMPEROR'S BLADE CHARACTER** is your Warlord, you can give them the following Warlord Trait.

MECHANISED COMMANDER

This officer excels at leading their troops into the fray from within their Chimera transports. Their orders booming over the vehicle's vox array, they deftly deploy their forces for war.

OFFICER from your army with the Voice of Command ability only. Your Warlord can issue orders whilst embarked within an **EMPEROR'S BLADE CHIMERA** or **EMPEROR'S BLADE TAUROX** (measuring ranges from any point on the vehicle) and is treated as being within 3" of a vox-caster. When doing so, these orders can only be issued to friendly **EMPEROR'S BLADE** units.

HEIRLOOM OF CONQUEST

If your army includes any Emperor's Blade Specialist Detachments, you can give the following relic to an **EMPEROR'S BLADE CHARACTER** from your army.

THE SHIELD OF MORTWALD

This archeotech from Grand Castellan Deinos' personal collection is rumoured to date back to the Age of Strife.

The bearer has a 3+ invulnerable save, which cannot be re-rolled for any reason. The first time this invulnerable save is failed, the Shield of Mortwald ceases to function for the rest of the battle.

STRATAGEMS

If your army includes any Emperor's Blade Specialist Detachments, you can use Command Points (CPs) to use the following Stratagems:

1CP MECHANISED FIRE SUPPORT
Astra Militarum Stratagem

The transports of an Emperor's Blade Assault Company lay down supporting fire to protect infantry from close quarters attacks.

Use this Stratagem in the enemy Charge phase after an **EMPEROR'S BLADE INFANTRY** unit from your army is chosen as the target of an enemy unit's charge. Pick an **EMPEROR'S BLADE CHIMERA** or **EMPEROR'S BLADE TAUROX** from your army within 6" of the unit being charged. The vehicle picked can fire Overwatch at the charging unit even if it is not the target of the charge, and when doing so, will hit the enemy on hit rolls of 4+, regardless of modifiers.

1CP RAPID REDEPLOY
Astra Militarum Stratagem

The soldiers of an Emperor's Blade Assault Company are expertly drilled in disembarking from their transport at the last moment to secure critical points on the battlefield.

Use this Stratagem at the end of your Movement phase. An **EMPEROR'S BLADE** unit embarked within an **EMPEROR'S BLADE CHIMERA** or **EMPEROR'S BLADE TAUROX** can disembark. That unit cannot move further in this phase, but can otherwise act normally for the rest of the turn. That unit counts as having moved for any rules purposes, such as shooting Heavy weapons.

EMPEROR'S WRATH ARTILLERY COMPANY

The pounding impacts of an artillery company's devastating bombardment have been likened to the Emperor's own fury descending from the heavens. Rightly so, for their commanders are experts in turning the brute force of their charges into a true weapon of terror.

SPECIALIST DETACHMENT

If your army is Battle-forged, you can use the Specialist Detachment Stratagem below:

1CP — EMPEROR'S WRATH ARTILLERY COMPANY
Specialist Detachment Stratagem

The world fills with fire and thunder as the shells of the Emperor's Wrath Artillery Company strike home.

Use this Stratagem when choosing your army. Pick an **ASTRA MILITARUM** Detachment from your army to be an Emperor's Wrath Specialist Detachment. **COMPANY COMMANDERS**, **MASTERS OF ORDNANCE**, **BASILISKS**, **HYDRAS**, and **WYVERNS** in that Detachment gain the **EMPEROR'S WRATH** keyword.

STRATAGEMS

If your army includes any Emperor's Wrath Specialist Detachments, you can use Command Points (CPs) to use the following Stratagems:

1CP — SUPPRESSIVE FIRE
Astra Militarum Stratagem

Artillery rounds rain down from the sky. The shells are inaccurate, but serve to disrupt enemy infantry movement.

Use this Stratagem at the start of your Shooting phase. Pick an **EMPEROR'S WRATH VEHICLE** unit from your army. That unit cannot shoot this phase. Instead, it lays down suppressive fire; pick an enemy **INFANTRY** unit that is within range of at least one of its weapons. Until the start of your next turn, that enemy unit cannot fire Overwatch and halves its Move characteristic.

2CP — POUNDING BARRAGE
Astra Militarum Stratagem

Focusing on coordinates voxed in from forward spotters, the crews of each artillery piece continue to load and fire, load and fire, filling the air with a steady rain of high explosives.

Use this Stratagem at the start of your Shooting phase. Pick an **EMPEROR'S WRATH VEHICLE** unit from your army. Pick one of that unit's ranged weapons. That unit can shoot twice with that weapon this phase.

WARLORD TRAIT

If an **EMPEROR'S WRATH CHARACTER** is your Warlord, you can give them the following Warlord Trait.

LORD OF ORDNANCE

As this officer surveys the land, they shrewdly identify strategic enemy locations an artillery strike would best disrupt, succinctly directing the crews under their command on where to fire.

Each time you roll a wound roll of 6+ for an attack made by a friendly **EMPEROR'S WRATH** unit while they are within 6" of your Warlord in the Shooting phase, the Armour Penetration characteristic of that attack is improved by 1 (i.e. AP0 becomes AP-1, AP-1 becomes AP-2).

HEIRLOOM OF CONQUEST

If your army includes any Emperor's Wrath Specialist Detachments, you can give the following relic to an **EMPEROR'S WRATH CHARACTER** from your army.

AGRIPINAA-CLASS ORBITAL TRACKER

After crushing a Chaos incursion in the Agripinaa System, the surviving Astra Militarum regiments were gifted with a dozen of these sophisticated pieces of archeotech. From low orbit, these devices scan the planet's surface and relay detailed data to the troops on the ground.

In your Shooting phase, pick an **EMPEROR'S WRATH** unit from your army within 6" of the bearer. Until the end of that phase, enemy units do not receive the benefit of cover when targeted by shooting attacks made by that unit.

EMPEROR'S CONCLAVE INFANTRY COMPANY

The Emperor's Conclave is no ordinary gathering of Astra Militarum manpower, but a well-honed fighting force united in its aggressive pursuance of victory and its faith in the old Imperial Guard maxim, 'The Emperor Protects.' They give no quarter, whether at range or in melee.

SPECIALIST DETACHMENT

If your army is Battle-forged, you can use the Specialist Detachment Stratagem below:

1CP — EMPEROR'S CONCLAVE INFANTRY COMPANY
Specialist Detachment Stratagem

Regiments raised from shrine worlds and other centres of the Imperial Creed have an unshakeable faith in the Emperor.

Use this Stratagem when choosing your army. Pick an **Astra Militarum** Detachment from your army to be an Emperor's Conclave Specialist Detachment. **Company Commanders**, **Platoon Commanders**, **Command Squads**, **Infantry Squads**, **Conscripts**, **Ministorum Priests** and **Crusaders** units in that Detachment gain the **Emperor's Conclave** keyword.

WARLORD TRAIT

If an **Emperor's Conclave Character** is your Warlord, you can give them the following Warlord Trait.

FIERY DENOUNCER

This leader's damning rhetoric fills their followers with a bitter hatred for the foe that drives their every action.

Re-roll hit rolls of 1 for your Warlord and friendly **Emperor's Conclave** units within 6" of your Warlord in the Fight phase.

STRATAGEMS

If your army includes any Emperor's Conclave Specialist Detachments, you can use Command Points (CPs) to use the following Stratagems:

2CP — NO QUARTER GIVEN!
Astra Militarum Stratagem

With fervent belief, these warriors fight till their last breath.

Use this Stratagem at the start of the Fight phase. Pick an **Emperor's Conclave** unit from your army. Until the end of that phase, when a model from that unit is slain, that model is not removed from the battlefield as normal, but can instead immediately pile in and fight, even if it has already been chosen to fight that phase. After its attacks have been resolved, it is then removed from the battlefield.

1CP — SANCTIMONIOUS CHARGE
Astra Militarum Stratagem

Singing a glorious hymn to the Emperor's divine power, these soldiers fear not the alien or the heretic as they fix bayonets and charge into the fray.

Use this Stratagem after an **Emperor's Conclave Ministorum Priest** makes a charge move. Until the end of that phase, add 1 to charge rolls for other friendly **Emperor's Conclave** units while they are within 12" of that **Ministorum Priest**.

HEIRLOOM OF CONQUEST

If your army includes any Emperor's Conclave Specialist Detachments, you can give the following relic to an **Emperor's Conclave Character** from your army:

LITANIES OF THE HOLY SYNOD

To hear the psalms of this ancient Terran manuscript recanted fills the common soldier with faith and valour.

If a friendly **Emperor's Conclave** unit within 6" of the bearer takes a Morale test, roll two D6 and use the lowest result to determine the outcome of the Morale test. In addition, if the bearer is slain, before removing the model from the battlefield, pick another friendly **Emperor's Conclave** unit within 6" of the bearer. For the rest of the battle that unit does not have to take Morale tests and can add 1 to its Attacks characteristic.

EMPEROR'S FIST TANK COMPANY

One of the most iconic sights on the battlefields of the Imperium is a massed tank charge, the ground trembling beneath the tracks of dozens of armoured juggernauts. Their turret weapons roar together, the sound like a pride of godly lions roused to destructive wrath.

SPECIALIST DETACHMENT

If your army is Battle-forged, you can use the Specialist Detachment Stratagem below:

EMPEROR'S FIST TANK COMPANY
Specialist Detachment Stratagem

Designed to smash the enemy battle lines asunder, the massed might of an Emperor's Fist Tank Company is a terrifying sight, squadron after squadron of Leman Russ tanks roaring across the battlefield.

Use this Stratagem when choosing your army. Pick an **ASTRA MILITARUM** Detachment from your army to be an Emperor's Fist Specialist Detachment. **LEMAN RUSS** units in that Detachment gain the **EMPEROR'S FIST** keyword.

STRATAGEMS

If your army includes any Emperor's Fist Specialist Detachments, you can use Command Points (CPs) to use the following Stratagems:

UNYIELDING ADVANCE
Astra Militarum Stratagem

The tank crew of this Leman Russ are experts in maintaining a steady rate of fire, even when escorting convoys or racing down highly mobile foes.

Use this Stratagem at the start of your Shooting phase. Pick an **EMPEROR'S FIST** unit from your army. That unit can shoot its turret weapon twice as described in the Grinding Advance ability no matter how far it moved in the preceding Movement phase.

STEEL PHALANX
Astra Militarum Stratagem

The impetus of this phalanx's charge is such that the combined Leman Russ Battle Tanks are able to smash aside all impediments, routing infantry and overturning enemy armour with their sheer belligerence and bulk.

Use this Stratagem at the start of your Charge phase. Pick an enemy unit. Each time an **EMPEROR'S FIST** unit from your army finishes a charge move within 1" of that enemy unit, roll a D6; on a 4+ that enemy unit suffers D3 mortal wounds.

WARLORD TRAIT

If an **EMPEROR'S FIST CHARACTER** is your Warlord, you can give them the following Warlord Trait.

UNFLINCHING RESOLVE

This warlord's cool head is legendary. Even as the foe charges directly into their front lines, this warlord and his troops keep their nerve and take aim carefully, their accurate salvoes ripping through the onrushing enemy ranks and decimating their lines.

You can re-roll hit rolls when your Warlord, and friendly **EMPEROR'S FIST** units within 6" of your Warlord, fire Overwatch.

HEIRLOOM OF CONQUEST

If your army includes any Emperor's Fist Specialist Detachments, you can give the following relic to an **EMPEROR'S FIST CHARACTER** from your army.

HAMMER OF SUNDERANCE

The Hammer of Sunderance is a battle cannon with glorious reputation. It is said the blows it deals the enemy are the Emperor's wrath made manifest, and as it punches into enemy tanks and fortifications, it leaves grievous wounds and crippled armour in its wake.

Model with battle cannon only. Hammer of Sunderance replaces the bearer's battle cannon and has the following profile:

WEAPON	RANGE	TYPE	S	AP	D
Hammer of Sunderance	72"	Heavy D6	8	-2	3

TEMPESTUS DROP FORCE

The Militarum Tempestus specialise in the rapid delivery of exceptionally well-trained warriors. When such a force disembarks from a low-hovering Valkyrie it becomes all the more lethal, for their pinpoint attacks can tear out the heart of an enemy battle line in seconds.

SPECIALIST DETACHMENT

If your army is Battle-forged, you can use the Specialist Detachment Stratagem below:

1CP

TEMPESTUS DROP FORCE
Specialist Detachment Stratagem

Deployed on Vigilus to adapt to the ever-changing theatres of war, Drop Forces are highly mobile kill teams, experts in rapid redeployment from Valkyrie and neutralisation of key enemy threats in the thick of battle.

Use this Stratagem when choosing your army. Pick a **MILITARUM TEMPESTUS** Detachment from your army to be a Tempestus Drop Force Specialist Detachment. **TEMPESTOR PRIMES, TEMPESTUS SCIONS, TEMPESTUS COMMAND SQUADS** and **VALKYRIES** in that Detachment gain the **TEMPESTUS DROP FORCE** keyword.

WARLORD TRAIT

If a **TEMPESTUS DROP FORCE CHARACTER** is your Warlord, you can give them the following Warlord Trait.

GRAVE-CHUTE COMMANDO

An veteran of planning and leading airborne assaults by grav-chute, this warlord and his company are highly sought after when aerial deployment is the order of the day.

Add 1 to hit rolls for attacks made by friendly **TEMPESTUS DROP FORCE INFANTRY** units that disembarked from a friendly **TEMPESTUS DROP FORCE VALKYRIE** this turn while they are within 6" of your Warlord.

RELICS OF THE PROGENIUM

If your army includes any Tempestus Drop Force Specialist Detachments, you can give the following relic to a **TEMPESTUS DROP FORCE CHARACTER** from your army.

CYPRA MUNDI NULL-EMITTER

Forged on Cypra Mundi, this small device is granted to officers of the Schola Progenium serving as escort upon the Black Ships of the Astra Telepathica. Emitting a minor null-field, it protects the wearer from psychic attack.

If the bearer is targeted or affected by a psychic power, roll a D6; on a 2+ the psychic power has no effect on the bearer.

STRATAGEMS

If your army includes any Tempestus Drop Specialist Detachments, you can use Command Points (CPs) to use the following Stratagems:

1CP

PRECISION DROP
Astra Militarum Stratagem

These elite troops have deployed via low altitude grav-chutes into dozens of war zones.

Use this Stratagem at the start of your Movement phase. Pick a **TEMPESTUS DROP FORCE VALKYRIE** from your army. Until the end of that phase, if models embarked within that **VALKYRIE** use the Grav-chute Insertion ability to disembark, do not roll a D6 for each model to determine if any are slain. Instead, no models from that unit are slain by that ability.

1CP

AERIAL FIRE SUPPORT
Astra Militarum Stratagem

After deploying the soldiers within, Drop Force Valkyries quickly identify and eliminate enemy threats on the ground.

Use this Stratagem in the enemy Charge phase after a **TEMPESTUS DROP FORCE INFANTRY** unit from your army is chosen as the target of an enemy unit's charge. Pick a **TEMPESTUS DROP FORCE VALKYRIE** from your army within 6" of the unit being charged. That **VALKYRIE** can fire Overwatch at the charging unit even if it is not the target of the charge, and when doing so, will hit the enemy on hit rolls of 4+, regardless of modifiers.

STOMPA MOB

The greenskins roar their approval as their beloved Stompas pound across the field, sometimes even teleporting straight into the midst of the foe with cannons blazing. Up goes the bellicose and joyful chant – 'Stomp! Stomp! Stomp!' – as these fat-bellied Ork walkers trample the foe into the ground.

SPECIALIST DETACHMENT

If your army is Battle-forged, you can use the Specialist Detachment Stratagem below:

STOMPA MOB
1CP
Specialist Detachment Stratagem

Belching smoke and fire, a mob of clanking Stompas lumbers across the battlefield, crushing all in their path.

Use this Stratagem when choosing your army. Pick an **ORK** Super-heavy Detachment from your army to be a Stompa Mob Specialist Detachment. **STOMPA** units in that Detachment gain the **STOMPA MOB** keyword. In addition, you can pick one model in that Stompa Mob Specialist Detachment to gain the **CHARACTER** keyword. However, the only Warlord Trait it can be given is either Gork's One or Mork's One (see right) and the only relic it can take is Tezdrek's Stompa Power Field (see right).

WARLORD TRAIT

If a **STOMPA MOB CHARACTER** is your Warlord, you can give them one of the following Warlord Traits.

GORK'S ONE

Smashing into enemy lines and destroying all in sight with its mega-choppa, this Stompa is truly blessed by Gork.

Add 1 to hit rolls and wound rolls for attacks made by your Warlord in the Fight phase.

MORK'S ONE

Its volleys of fire striking with uncanny accuracy to blast foes apart, this Stompa is truly blessed by Mork.

Add 1 to wound rolls for shooting attacks made by your Warlord.

SHINY GUBBINZ

If your army includes any Stompa Mob Specialist Detachments, you can give the following relic to a **STOMPA MOB CHARACTER** from your army.

TEZDREK'S STOMPA POWER FIELD

This colossal power field generator produces an energy bubble powerful enough to protect a Stompa.

The bearer has a 5+ invulnerable save.

STRATAGEMS

If your army includes any Stompa Mob Specialist Detachments, you can use Command Points (CPs) to use the following Stratagems:

STOMP, STOMP, STOMP!
1CP
Orks Stratagem

The Stompa raises its huge metal foot as high as it is able before bringing it crashing down into the enemy ranks. Those caught directly beneath are flattened into puddles of gore, whilst others are flung in all directions as the ground shakes from the impact.

Use this Stratagem at the start of the Fight phase. Pick a **STOMPA MOB** unit from your army that is within 1" of any enemy units. Roll a D6 for each enemy model within 3" of that unit; on a 6+ that model's unit suffers 1 mortal wound.

STOMPA-PORTA
4CP
Orks Stratagem

Teleporting across the battlefield, this Stompa materialises with all guns blazing and leaves a path of total annihilation in its wake.

Use this Stratagem during deployment. You can set up a **STOMPA MOB** unit from your army on a tellyporta pad instead of placing it on the battlefield. Units on a tellyporta pad can teleport into battle at the end of any of your Movement phases – set them up anywhere on the battlefield that is more than 9" from any enemy models.

KULT OF SPEED

The Orks love fighting more than life itself, and some of them get a taste for doing it at breakneck speed. With a screech of tyres and a vast cloud of dust, the Kult of Speed careens straight into the enemy, the hail of bullets issued as they charge a precursor to the true carnage of their assault.

SPECIALIST DETACHMENT

If your army is Battle-forged, you can use the Specialist Detachment Stratagem below:

KULT OF SPEED
1CP
Specialist Detachment Stratagem
Orks thrive on the high-octane thrills of the Kults of Speed, large nomadic cavalcades that rampage across war zones leaving carnage in their wake.

Use this Stratagem when choosing your army. Pick an **ORK** Detachment from your army to be a Kult of Speed Specialist Detachment. **SPEED FREEKS** in that Detachment gain the **KULT OF SPEED** keyword.

STRATAGEMS

If your army includes any Kult of Speed Specialist Detachments, you can use Command Points (CPs) to use the following Stratagems:

TURBO-BOOSTAS
2CP
Orks Stratagem
These Speed Freeks have kustom-rigged blastajet engines hastily strapped onto their rides to provide a massive boost of speed.

Use this Stratagem at the start of your Movement phase. Pick a **KULT OF SPEED** unit from your army. If that unit Advances this phase, double that unit's Move characteristic instead of rolling a dice.

CHARGE THROUGH 'EM!
2CP
Orks Stratagem
At breakneck pace, these Speed Freeks slaughter their foes and burst through enemy lines to strike at critical points beyond.

Use this Stratagem before a **KULT OF SPEED** unit from your army makes a consolidation move. That unit consolidates 2D6" instead of 3".

WARLORD TRAIT

If a **KULT OF SPEED CHARACTER** is your Warlord, you can give them the following Warlord Trait.

QUICK, LADZ!

The thrilling rush of acceleration in the heat of battle fills these Orks with an insane and reckless courage. This warlord races at the head of the Kult of Speed, bellowing for his warriors to keep up the pace.

Friendly **KULT OF SPEED** units within 12" of your Warlord in the Morale phase automatically pass Morale tests if they Advanced in the same turn.

SHINY GUBBINZ

If your army includes any Kult of Speed Specialist Detachments, you can give the following relic to a **KULT OF SPEED CHARACTER** from your army:

SKARGRIM'S SNAZZTRIKE

A notorious Speedboss named Skargrim led his Kult of Speed into Gork's Grin – the name the Orks gave to the Great Rift. Finding themselves upon a strange and twisted world, the Orks under his command waged war against the daemonic inhabitants, revelling in the slaughter that followed. As the dust settled, Skargrim was nowhere to be found, but his Wartrike was recovered without a dent or scratch upon it and, surprisingly, a glossy new red paint job. Many Speedbosses have since taken Skargrim's Snazztrike for their own – and even when they fall in battle, the Snazztrike is inevitably recovered, still just as shiny.

DEFFKILLA WARTRIKE only. Add 1 to the bearer's Toughness characteristic. In addition, the bearer gains a 5+ invulnerable save.

DREAD WAAAGH!

The vision of a dozens-strong mob of Deff Dreads and Killa Kans has inspired many Meks across the galaxy. Those that make it a reality have an army of gunned-up battering rams at their behest – when the Dread Waaagh! is called, even a garrisoned hive wall can be reduced to rubble by its assault.

SPECIALIST DETACHMENT

If your army is Battle-forged, you can use the Specialist Detachment Stratagem below:

1CP

DREAD WAAAGH!
Specialist Detachment Stratagem

Coming in all shapes and sizes, the clanking monstrosities of a Dread Waaagh! are all designed with one purpose in mind – the utter destruction of their poor, unsuspecting foes.

Use this Stratagem when choosing your army. Pick an **ORK** Detachment from your army to be a Dread Waaagh! Specialist Detachment. **BIG MEKS**, **GORKANAUTS**, **MORKANAUTS**, **DEFF DREADS** and **KILLA KANS** in that Detachment gain the **DREAD WAAAGH!** keyword.

WARLORD TRAIT

If a **DREAD WAAAGH! CHARACTER** is your Warlord, you can give them the following Warlord Trait.

DREAD MEK

Fixing Dreads all day long, this Big Mek likes to think he knows a thing or two about 'em! He will often accompany his charges into the fray with spanner in hand, either to dish out some quick field repairs or to krump any enemies that stray too close.

Model with the Big Mekaniak ability only. When your Warlord uses its Big Mekaniak ability to repair a **DREAD WAAAGH!** unit, add 1 to the number of wounds regained.

STRATAGEMS

If your army includes any Dread Waaagh! Specialist Detachments, you can use Command Points (CPs) to use the following Stratagems:

2CP

KUSTOM AMMO
Orks Stratagem

This impressive payload is worth a Bad Moon's gob full of teef.

Use this Stratagem in your Shooting phase. Pick a **DREAD WAAAGH!** unit from your army. That unit can shoot twice this Shooting phase with all of its ranged weapons.

1CP

MEK CONNECTIONS
Orks Stratagem

The Big Mek of this Dread Waaagh! has a fearsome reputation. Any Mekboyz that know 'wot's best' will keep some gubbinz aside in their workshops for when his Dreads roll into town.

Use this Stratagem at the end of your Movement phase. Pick a **DREAD WAAAGH!** unit from your army that is within 1" of a **MEK WORKSHOP**. If you use the Kustom Job ability to give that unit a kustom job, it receives something 'extra speshul' on a 4+ instead of a 6+.

SHINY GUBBINZ

If your army includes any Dread Waaagh! Specialist Detachments, you can give one of the following relics to a **DREAD WAAAGH! CHARACTER** from your army.

DA SOUPED-UP SHOKKA

It is rumoured that Da Souped-up Shokka is one of only a handful of weapons made by the legendary Mekaniak, Orkimedes. This shokk attack gun has had its power cranked up in every way possible, sending its hapless ammunition through the warp with so much visceral force it can punch a Snotling-shaped hole through walls of solid ceramite.

Model with shokk attack gun only. Da Souped-up Shokka replaces the bearer's shokk attack gun and has the following profile:

WEAPON	RANGE	TYPE	S	AP	D
Da Souped-up Shokka	60"	Heavy 2D6	2D6	-5	D6

Abilities: Before firing this weapon, roll once to determine the Strength of all its shots. If the result is 11+ each successful hit inflicts D3 mortal wounds on the target in addition to any normal damage.

BLITZ BRIGADE

Speed Freek warlords who crave high-octane assaults and heavy firepower combine both aspects into the Blitz Brigade. An assemblage of the biggest, ugliest Battlewagons teef can buy, this roaring avalanche of dented metal crushes all before it.

SPECIALIST DETACHMENT

If your army is Battle-forged, you can use the Specialist Detachment Stratagem below:

BLITZ BRIGADE
1CP

Specialist Detachment Stratagem

Blitz Brigades launch devastating opening salvoes of fire, before the Battlewagons, Gunwagons and Bonebreakas ram and smash through everything in their path.

Use this Stratagem when choosing your army. Pick an **ORK** Detachment from your army to be a Blitz Brigade Specialist Detachment. **WARBOSSES**, **BATTLEWAGONS**, **GUNWAGONS** and **BONEBREAKA** units in that Detachment gain the **BLITZ BRIGADE** keyword.

WARLORD TRAIT

If a **BLITZ BRIGADE CHARACTER** is your Warlord, you can give them the following Warlord Trait.

BACK-SEAT DRIVER

This Warboss is never content to let the drivers of his Battlewagons have all the fun.

While your Warlord is embarked within a **BLITZ BRIGADE TRANSPORT**, add 1" to that transport's Move characteristic. In addition, while your Warlord is embarked within it, that transport gains the 'Ere We Go ability.

SHINY GUBBINZ

If your army includes any Blitz Brigade Specialist Detachments, you can give the following relic to a **BLITZ BRIGADE CHARACTER** from your army.

DA BLITZ SHOUTA

This looted vox-network allows a Warboss to bellow orders from his Battlewagon.

At the start of your Shooting phase, if the bearer is embarked within a **BLITZ BRIGADE BATTLEWAGON**, pick an enemy unit that is visible to that **BATTLEWAGON**. Until the end of the phase, re-roll hit rolls of 1 for attacks made by friendly **BLITZ BRIGADE** units within 6" of that **BATTLEWAGON** that target the enemy unit you picked.

STRATAGEMS

If your army includes any Blitz Brigade Specialist Detachments, you can use Command Points (CPs) to use the following Stratagems:

OPENING SALVO
1CP

Orks Stratagem

The start of the battle is often the only point the crew of a Gunwagon will take the time to aim properly. The devastating volley of fire arcs across the battlefield before hitting the enemy lines.

Use this Stratagem in your Shooting phase of the first battle round. Pick a **BLITZ BRIGADE GUNWAGON** from your army. Double the Range characteristic of that unit's weapons until the end of that phase.

KRUSH 'EM
1CP

Orks Stratagem

Bonebreakas of the Blitz Brigades are experts in crushing hapless victims beneath their spiked deff rollas.

Use this Stratagem in the Fight phase when a **BLITZ BRIGADE BONEBREAKA** from your army is chosen to fight. Roll three D6 for the Bonebreaka Ram ability and choose the highest result.

HOLD ON, BOYZ!
2CP

Orks Stratagem

The Warboss shouts at his ladz to grab onto the Battlewagon and hitch a ride across the battlefield.

Use this Stratagem during your Movement phase before you move a <CLAN> **BLITZ BRIGADE BATTLEWAGON** from your army. Pick a friendly <CLAN> **INFANTRY** unit wholly within 3" of that model and remove it from the battlefield. After that **BATTLEWAGON** has moved, set the <CLAN> **INFANTRY** unit up on the battlefield wholly within 3" of that **BATTLEWAGON**, and more than 3" from any enemy models. (Note that this infantry unit is not embarked within the Battlewagon and therefore does not count towards the number of models it can transport.) That infantry unit cannot move further this phase (but counts as having moved this turn for all rules purposes) and it cannot charge this turn.